MECHANICAL FACTORS
AND THE SKELETON

MECHANICAL FACTORS AND THE SKELETON

Edited by
IAN A F STOKES
Oxford Orthopaedic Engineering Centre
University of Oxford

John Libbey: London

This book is derived from the scientific meeting 'Mechanical Factors and the Skeleton — The effects of forces and movements on bone, joints and connective tissue' held in Oxford, April 1980, by the Oxford Orthopaedic Engineering Centre and the Biological Engineering Society.

British Library Cataloguing in Publication Data:

Mechanical factors and the skeleton.
  1. Human mechanics — Congresses
  2. Bones — Congresses
  I. Stokes, Ian A.F.
  612'.75   QP303

First published 1981 by

John Libbey & Company Limited
80-84 Bondway, London SW8 1SF

ISBN 0-86196-006-8

Printed and bound in Great Britain by
Biddles Ltd, Guildford and King's Lynn

CONTENTS

Mechanical factors in degenerations and pathological conditions of the skeleton

Preface

The biomechanics of the musculoskeletal system presents a challenge to both the practising clinician and the research worker. There are mechanical factors related to the pathogenesis, diagnosis and treatment of most, if not all, orthopaedic disorders. While the mechanisms of traumatic injury are becoming increasingly well understood, factors such as aging, which make one individual more susceptible to injury than another, are less clear. Some kind of mechanical injury process is implicated in progressive degenerative disease, and this degeneration is often accelerated as a result of permanent damage after acute injury.

These considerations are important when we attempt to design and modify our working environment and lifestyle to minimise hazards. More immediately, orthopaedic specialists are faced with the problem of diagnosing and treating the increasing number of people who complain of intolerable musculoskeletal pain or functional impairment. Observations of the movements of joints and their response to applied forces are an essential part of the diagnostic process. Subsequently, most orthopaedic treatments aim in some way to alter the mechanical function of the joints and the skeleton. Despite this, there is poor understanding of the detailed biomechanics of the skeleton and its tissues.

It was an awareness of this which prompted the Oxford Orthopaedic Engineering Centre and the Biological Engineering Society to organise a conference to examine the current state of knowledge, and of ignorance, in this field of orthopaedics and bioengineering. This book records edited contributions to that meeting in April 1980, organised in three sections to follow the pattern of the original sessions. Each section has an authoritative introduction. In the introduction to the first section, Dr Seedhom has concentrated on one aspect of the mechanics of joints, the estimation of forces in joints, and dispelled much of the mystique which surrounds this crucial part of orthopaedic biomechanics. The ten papers which follow in that section are all firmly directed towards a particular problem of joint disorder or treatment.

In the introduction to the section on biomechanics of bone and soft tissue, Dr Lanyon viewed the mechanical properties of these tissues as part of a continuous process of resorption and remodelling, the regulation of which is the key to the success or failure of their structural role. The following nine papers also concentrate on the effects of the mechanical stimulus on the growth and remodelling of connective tissues and bones, while having a wide range of clinical problems as the starting point for the studies they describe.

The third section confronts a crucial problem, namely the role of mechanical factors in the aetiology and pathogenesis of degenerative disease and other pathological change in the musculoskeletal system. There is a mechanical stimulus given to the connective tissue of the body in its remodelling processes and in its repair following damage. Failure of these mechanisms is apparently one of the major factors in the development of degenerative disease. In his introductory paper for this section, Mr Goodfellow examined the way in which synovial joints are designed to retain their shape and function, and how this may show us eventually the mechanisms of their failure. Eight papers follow this introduction, each of which deals with a clinical orthopaedic problem and describes and explores a mechanical component of it.

A better understanding of the skeleton's remodelling and repair processes, and of their mechanical stimuli, would lead to a major advance in the field of orthopaedic medicine. It was difficult for the meeting in Oxford to confront the magnitude of this challenge. However, the aim of both the meeting and this book is to bring together as much as possible of the available evidence from research. This book demonstrates that many disciplines in clinical orthopaedics and research are being brought to bear on these problems. This book, besides being a source of information, will I hope also be a source of stimulation for everyone working in these fields.

Ian A.F. Stokes

Joint forces in perspective

B.B. SEEDHOM

INTRODUCTION

The biomechanics of joints includes studies of the forces arising in joints, the mechanisms of transmission of these forces through the joints, the stresses they cause and the effects of these forces and stresses on the different joint tissues, or on materials used for diagnosis, treatment or research purposes. However, I hope it may be more useful to review here one topic from this vast field, that of joint forces.

For outsiders to the engineering field, and even for some within the field but who are non-specialists, this area is almost surrounded by mystique. It is, therefore, appropriate to outline the procedure for estimating these forces.

TECHNIQUE FOR ESTIMATION OF JOINT FORCES

In engineering applications, forces acting on a machine component may be measured directly by means of transducers or by strain-gauging the component. The forces acting on the component cause measurable changes in the physical properties of the component itself or of those of the sensing elements (dimensions or electrical resistance, for instance) and often these changes are proportional to the forces producing them.

For ethical reasons, it is normally not possible to carry out direct measurements of internal joint forces or muscle tensions by introducing transducers or strain-gauges into the human joint. There are, however, two published studies in which such direct measurements were possible, one by Rydell (1966) and the other by English & Kilvington (1978). In both cases the measurements were taken from patients who had a prosthetic hip replacement which was strain-gauged. In Rydell's experiment the strain-gauge circuit was connected to the measuring instruments by leads taken out through the surgical wound. English and his co-workers incorporated a transmitter, and so the movement of the patient was not in any way restricted when the measurements were taken.

Normally, internal forces in human joints must be calculated. The analysis of forces applied, for instance in a joint in the lower limb, is not different from that applied in a joint of an engineering structure. In fact, when an engineer calculates the forces in a human joint he deals with a mechanical model (of the joint and surrounding muscles) that is susceptible to analysis. The model is based on assumptions and approximations. These assumptions and approximations are not arbitrary and are, or should be, assessed for every joint and activity considered. For instance, a two-dimensional model of the knee may be justified in activities in which the loading on the lower limb is symmetrical as during sitting in, or rising from, a chair by a healthy individual. In such cases, 'side', or lateral forces - those acting on the body or arising in the joint due to muscle tensions - are negligible. The muscles surrounding the knee are not greatly inclined to the axes of the long bones. However, in an activity in which the loading is not symmetrical on the lower limb, for instance during walking or running, or due to a pathological condition in which an individual would lean more on one leg, and rotate the torso during rising from a chair, a three-dimensional model of the knee has to be considered. However, for the analysis of forces in the hip joint, a three-dimensional model should be considered in almost all cases. As the model of the joint is developed the various assumptions and approximations must be considered carefully.

The calculations of internal forces in an engineering structure require knowledge of the external forces acting on it (eg stationary and moving weights, wind-force), the configuration of the structure, and its dimensions. Similar data are required for calculating the forces acting in a human joint. Once the mechanical model has been decided upon, the data required for force calculations in a complex situation may be:

1. The spatial positions of the body segments.
2. Anthropometric data, which include:
   a. Masses of the body segments and the locations of their centres of mass.
   b. The radii of gyration of the various body segments.
   c. Geometries of the bone surfaces, and the position of the region of contact between them.
   d. Muscle moment arms about strategic points, and the directions of the tensions they exert.
3. The external reactions on the body, which may be between the foot and the floor, or the body and a seat or a bed, or between the hand and for instance a screwdriver.
4. Electromyographic traces which would indicate which muscles are active.

These data have to be obtained throughout one or more cycles of the activity being studied. The procedure followed then is briefly described in Fig. 1. Double differentiation of the various segments' displacements and rotations with respect to time is carried out yielding the linear and rotational accelerations of the segments. From the accelerations and segments' masses and radii of gyration the inertial forces and moments can be calculated. If these are significant we obtain a force system which comprises the components of external reactions and moments acting on the body, the gravitational forces, and the components of the inertial forces and moments. Analysis by the well-known method of sections can then follow, to obtain the internal

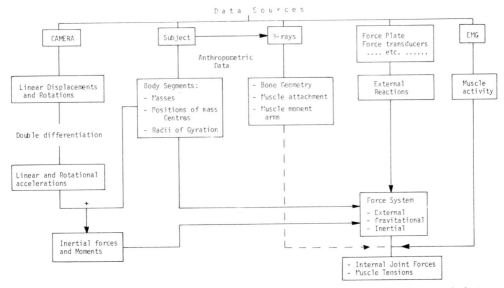

Fig. 1. *Method for estimation of in-vivo forces about a human joint*

joint forces and muscle tensions using the force system, the various anthropometric data and the electromyographic recordings.

From the above, it seems that the experimental procedure is well defined and the analysis of joint forces is unambiguous. Frequently, especially in meetings of many disciplines, objections and suspicions are raised concerning the application of the same procedures and analyses to mechanical structures, cadavers and living subjects. It can be stated that the analyses apply since everything and everyone does and shall obey Newton's laws, dead or alive!

However, the reported magnitude of forces in the same joint have risen in some cases from three or four times body weight in the late 1960s to five or seven times body weight in the late 1970s. These rises are neither due to changes in the laws nor are they due to inflation, unlike most things! There are genuine difficulties in obtaining much of the data required for the calculations, and there are uncertainties about some of the assumptions made. It is therefore relevant to discuss next the difficulties encountered and the sources of error in the results obtained.

DIFFICULTIES IN OBTAINING EXPERIMENTAL DATA, AND SOURCES OF ERROR

Anthropometric Data

a. *Mass Properties of the body segments*

Mass properties refers to the masses of the body segments, the positions of their centres of mass and their inertial properties. Experimental data have been obtained by cutting cadavers at the joints, and then measuring and weighing the parts. Simple balancing and oscillation tests have been conducted, and the linear dimensions, masses, mass centres and moments of inertia have been reported in the literature.

Almost a century ago Braune & Fischer (1890) dissected three cadavers and published the mechanical properties of the segments. For almost 70 years thereafter, there seems to have been neither the desire nor the necessity to extend their work. Spurred by the US Astronautics programme, however, Dempster (1955) carried out a study on eight cadavers, and his published data are the basis of all modern segmental models. Whitsett (1963) developed a 'mean man' model from Dempster's figures for the segmental masses and lengths. The segments are represented by simple geometrical solids, such as spheres or tapered cylinders, and their properties are used to compute their moments of inertia and, by summation, the moment of inertia of the whole body. Santschi, Dubois & Omoto (1963) carried out further work whereby they measured the mass centres and the moments of inertia of the body of each of 66 subjects in eight different body positions. Hanavan (1964) used Santschi's results as a norm against which to test segmental models. He attempted to fit a model to each of the 66 Santschi subjects by incorporating some of the subjects' anthropometric dimensions in the segmental model, thereby constructing a 'tailor-made' model. The subject's whole body mechanical properties were computed from the model. Smith (1972) developed the concept of a moment of inertia factor using the published data of Whitsett and Dempster for his calculations. An elaborate study of the inertial property distribution of the human torso was carried out by King Liu & Wickstrom (1972).

Thus most workers in the field of joint forces make use of segmental data published in two or three studies. The reason is obvious; the way in which such data can be obtained from cadavers is tedious (if not repugnant), and accurate and efficient methods for obtaining the data from living subjects have yet to be fully developed.

b. Bone Geometries and Muscle Attachments

The geometries of bones of living subjects can be determined with adequate accuracy from single or biplanar X-rays, depending on the activity considered, and so can many of the moment arms of the muscles. Seedhom & Terayama (1976) and Ellis et al. (1979) developed this method in their studies of knee forces. A two-dimensional cardboard model of the bones of the lower leg was made with the help of X-ray photographs of the subjects. The bone model was superimposed on each of the life-size projected frames of the cine film taken of the subject during the activity considered. The relevant anthropometric data were thus obtained from an almost 'tailor-made' model. This method is still time-consuming and would require modification to speed up data processing.

For the sake of speed, a simpler method is often used. The position of the contact regions between bones, moment arms of the various muscles, and directions of the acting forces along these muscles are obtained from one or two dissections and then related mathematically to, for instance, the angle of flexion of the joint considered. This latter is measured in the experiment by placing markers on the body segments at either side of the joint. This method has been developed by earlier workers such as Morrison (1968), who used a scaling factor to take account of the variations in bone geometries and moment arms from one

4

subject to another. However, this was not found to be adequate, since there is little geometrical similarity in the muscles moment arms of the knee, although a geometrical similarity has been shown to exist between the overall dimensions of the knee (Seedhom et al., 1972). The errors in force calculations due to variations in moment arms between subjects was the largest source of error in Morrison's measurement of knee forces.

Assumptions

Joint force estimations rely on simplifying assumptions about the anatomy and the muscle actions. These can have significant effect on results. For example, an assumption which has been held by many for a long period is the one concerning the tension in the patellar ligament and the quadriceps tendon. As recently as three years ago, they were assumed to be equal. Friction in synovial joints was assumed to be negligible, and the patello-femoral joint was considered as a frictionless, circular pulley. Direct measurements by Bishop & Denham (1977) and by Ellis et al. (in press) showed that the ratio of the tension in the patellar ligament to that in the quadriceps tendon changes from unity to 0.55 as the angle of the knee changes from full extension to 120° of flexion, because the 'pulley' assumption was incorrect.

Where it was considered (either by convenience or on the basis of good sense) that no antagonistic muscle action is present, electromyography may show otherwise. For instance, in an isometric extension exercise of the knee joint the hamstrings and the calf muscles may both be active (Gostling & Slater, 1979; P.T. Yang and S.H. Yeoh, unpublished). Also, it is assumed frequently that all the muscles within a group act simultaneously, and that the tensions they exert are proportional to their physiological cross-sectional areas. The first of these two assumptions is not always correct. For instance, in the case of the quadriceps femoris group, during rocking motion whilst sitting, the rectus femoris is active whilst the vasti are electrically silent.

The assumption that the line of action of the muscle is a straight one joining the centroids of its areas of origin and insertion can result in considerable error. Many muscles curve over deeper muscles or over bony surfaces. The degree of curving of a muscle will still vary from one subject to another, and also during an activity depending on the relative positions of the limb segments.

Processing of Cine Film Data

The record of a particular human activity on a cine film provides a set of displacement-time data. Whilst most points on the displacement-time graph seem to lie along a fairly well-defined curve, there is usually some scatter of points about a 'smooth' curve passing amongst them. The process of fitting a smooth curve to slightly erratic data points may be carried out in several ways. Whichever method is employed, it is difficult to specify the correct curve for the data. The choice of a best curve, despite refined computational techniques for curve fitting, remains a somewhat arbitrary procedure. Curve fitting by eye, relying on human judgement of the best curve, is for many purposes satisfactory but the process is neither repeatable nor will it produce the same results when applied by different people. The data smoothing could also be carried out by curve fitting of ordinary power functions, orthogonal polynomials (Cooke, 1971), or periodic functions (Lanczos, 1967) to the data points. The moving average could also be used, but the procedure may have severe smoothing effects (Hamming, 1962).

There are also problems in the differentiation techniques to obtain the second derivative for acceleration. The estimation of velocity and acceleration from displacement-time data is a process sensitive to errors in the data points. There are at least five different methods for obtaining the second derivative, the advantages and disadvantages of which were thoroughly discussed by Smith (1971).

Method of Analysis of Statically-Indeterminate Models

The number of unknown variables (tensions in the various muscles and tendons and ligaments, and reactions between the articulating surfaces) usually exceeds the number of equations that can be written to satisfy static equilibrium. Such a situation is known as a statically-indeterminate one.

Optimisation techniques have been used to compute the muscle and joint forces in these situations. A number of solutions have been used to resolve this problem. The simplest requires that a choice is made between two alternative muscles to produce a moment about the joint. At the other extreme, the forces in the entire musculature and ligamentous system of the limb may be manipulated by computational techniques. Optimisation criteria are set by the investigator. These are designed to rationalise the choice of muscle actions in indeterminate situations. Prior to the implementation of these criteria, e.m.g. may be used to eliminate those muscles which are inactive during the activity considered. This type of analysis was implemented by Paul (1965) in the case of hip forces. The hip joint is surrounded by 22 muscles, and by ignoring the six rotators the unknown forces were still numerous. E.m.g. studies have shown that the muscles act in groups, so Paul used this knowledge to combine the muscles into six groups. Even then, two muscle groups were still left whose actions could not be discerned by e.m.g. The optimisation criterion chose one of these two groups, namely the one which gave the lower value of joint force.

Another type of analysis which used the minimisation criterion as the over-ruling one was used by Seireg & Arvikar (1973). They developed a mathematical model of the lower limb which incorporated 29 muscles, all assumed to act in straight lines. The magnitudes of tensile forces acting along these lines were calculated subject to two constraints. Static equilibrium was required, and muscle forces, or joint forces, were minimised. Seireg & Arvikar obtained unique solutions by linear programming techniques. They found that their predictions correlated with e.m.g. studies for the activities they considered. These were standing, squatting and leaning.

DEVELOPMENTS

The quantity of data which must be handled to produce a now familiar joint force-time graph is mammoth. In order that the benefits of research in this field extend to the clinical situation, the procedure

6

for data acquisition must be efficient. Workers researching in this
area find that what calls on their ingenuity, perhaps more than any
aspect of the problem, is the task of developing fast techniques for
accurate measurements. Much development has taken place in this area in
the past decade.

The great development in computer technology has had an enormous
effect. Data representing the measured quantities, which previously
were input to the computer manually, may now be input in vast quantities
by direct interfacing of the analogue output of all of the measuring
devices to the computer memory via an analogue-to-digital converter.
This facility for fast data logging made it possible to analyse more
than one cycle of any particular activity, and to obtain data from many
subjects.

The most relevant of such developments to this review are systems for
monitoring kinetic and kinematic data from subjects 'on-line'. In such
a system the external force reactions to the lower limb, for instance,
are measured by an accurate force plate. The angles between the various
body segments are measured by electric or polarised light goniometers,
or alternatively using recent development in which reflective markers
can be placed on carefully chosen locations on the limb, and these
markers are detected and tracked by a television/computer interface.
The vertical and horizontal coordinates of each of the markers are
stored on computer disc, and appropriate software is then used to take
the raw coordinate data - from two or three cameras - and derive from it
the three-dimensional spatial coordinates of the markers. Such a system
has been developed at the Universities of Strathclyde and Dundee, and
more recently at the Oxford Orthopaedic Engineering Centre. Another
variation on this system is one which uses light-emitting diodes instead
of reflective markers, and such a system is also being used at
Strathclyde. The degree of accuracy in the force measurements is
adequate for most practical purposes. Spatial measurement has been
refined greatly and Whittle (1980) has reported that the spatial
position of markers on a moving object can be recorded to within five
millimetres or less. With such a degree of accuracy it would be
possible to use the system to detect excessive relative movement of the
femur with respect to the tibia due to antero-posterior instability.

The techniques for analysis of joint forces are now so advanced that
it is appropriate to ask whether there is a need for more refined
developments and techniques, and to point out areas of the application
of those which deserve more attention.

Great care has been taken to develop the systems, for automatic and
accurate simultaneous kinematic and kinetic measurements. It seems
feasible to include e.m.g. recording with relative ease within these
systems. This would be useful in particular for examining patients with
muscle dysfunction.

None of the above systems so far seems to take into account variations
in anthropometric data between individuals. This is certainly a very
difficult matter; it would require extra data from each individual, and
the development of much software. It might also slow down the data
processing procedure.

However, it may still be a worthwhile exercise to invest some effort
in the development of a fast method of obtaining 'tailor-made'

anthropometric models. Using such models, joint forces can be calculated with a higher degree of accuracy, which is essential for a number of cases, for instance:

a. In the case of patients who have severe joint deformities, either congenital or pathological, and who have to undergo corrective or reconstructive surgery in order to achieve a desirable distribution of the load acting on the joint.
b. In the field of prosthetic fixation: 'Is the load acting three or seven times body weight?' might become a critical question in the case of a patient with very osteoporotic bone.
c. In studying many of the fast and athletic activities, where it might not be possible to use any apparatus to monitor the external reactions (nor e.m.g. for that matter), and where one must rely only on the cine film data and the anthropometric model of the subject to calculate both inertia forces and external reactions.

There are many areas which are under-researched. Many studies which consider the problem of force distribution in pathological joints concentrate on either that joint or even the diseased compartment of it. It is important to remember that the pathology of one compartment can affect the mechanics of another compartment in the same joint, and probably affect the mechanics of the other joints in the same limb, as well as those of the other limb.

The biomechanical studies in many of the most competent centres concentrate on the painful conditions of patients rather than their prevention. Some biomechanics research should be directed also to sporting activities and sports' injury. The number of athletes is increasing, the competitiveness is becoming more intense, and the number of injuries is also increasing. It would be desirable to reduce the probability of many of today's athletes becoming the future's chronic patients. It is important to be able to give advice against injurious types of exercise. It may also be possible to give advice on sound methods of training and improving performance. For advice to become effective and more useful, it should be accompanied by evidence and accurate knowledge.

References

Bishop, R.E.D. & Denham, R.A. (1977): A note on the ratio between tensions in the quadriceps tendon and infra-patellar ligaments. Eng. Med. 6, 53.
Braune, W. & Fischer, O. (1890): Ueber der Schwerpunkt der Menschen Koerpers. Abh. Koenigl. Saechs. Gessellsch. Wissensch. 26, 561.
Cook, J.B. (1971): Development of a procedure incorporating a modified version of Forsythe's method for polynomial curve fitting. 4A. Project. Department of Computational Science, University of Leeds.
Dempster, W.T. (1955): Space requirements of the seated operator. Wright Air Development Centre report. T.R.-55-159, Wright-Patterson, A.F.B., Ohio. (A.D. Space 10203): USAF.
Ellis, M.I., Seedhom, B.B., Amis, A.A., Dowson, D. & Wright, V. (1979): Forces in the knee joint whilst rising from normal and motorised chairs. Eng. Med. 8, 33.

Ellis, M.I., Seedhom, B.B., Dowson, D., & Wright, V. (in press): The ratio of tensions in the quadriceps femoris tendon and patellar ligament. Eng. Med. 9, 195 (1980).

English, T.A. & Kilvington, M. (1978): A direct telemetric method for measuring hip load. In 'Orthopaedic engineering', ed J.D. Harris & K. Copeland, pp. 198-201. London: Biological Engineering Society.

Gostling, P. & Slater, A.N. (1979): Forces in the knee joint during isometric exercise. A final year project. Department of Mechanical Engineering, University of Leeds.

Hamming, R.W. (1962): Numerical methods for scientists and engineers. New York: McGraw Hill.

Hanavan, E.F. (1964): A mathematical model of the human body. AMRL-TR-64-102. Wright-Patterson Air Force Base, Ohio: USAF.

King Liu, Y. & Wickstrom, J.K. (1972): Estimation of the inertial property distribution of the human torso from figmented cadaveric data. In 'Prospectives in biomedical engineering', ed R.M. Kenedi, pp. 203-213. London: Macmillan.

Lanczos, C. (1967): Applied analysis. London: Pitman.

Morrison, J.B. (1967): The forces transmitted by the human knee joint during activity. PhD thesis, University of Strathclyde.

Paul, J.P. (1965): Forces at the human hip joint. PhD thesis, University of Strathclyde.

Rydell, N.W. (1966): Forces acting on the femoral head prosthesis. Acta Orthop. Scand. Suppl. 88.

Santschi, W.R., Dubois, J. & Omoto, C. (1963): Moments of inertia and centres of gravity of the living human body. AMRL-TDR-63-36, Wright-Patterson Air Force Base, Ohio: USAF.

Seedhom, B.B., Longton, E.B., Wright, V. & Dowson, D. (1972): Dimensions of the knee. Radiographic and autopsy study of sizes required for a knee prosthesis. Ann. Rheum. Dis. 31, 54.

Seedhom, B.B. & Terayama, K. (1976): New forces during the activity of getting out of chair with and without the aid of arms. Biomed. Eng. 11, 278.

Seireg, A. & Arvikar, R.J. (1973): A mathematical model for evaluation of forces in the lower extremities of the musculo-skeletal system. J. Biomech. 6, 313.

Smith, A.J. (1972): A study of forces on the body in athletic activities with particular reference to jumping. PhD thesis, University of Leeds.

Whitsett, C.E. (1963): Some dynamic response characteristics of weightless man. AMRL-TDR-63-18, Wright-Patterson Air Force Base, Ohio: USAF.

Whittle, M.W. (1980): Annual report of the Oxford Orthopaedic Engineering Centre.

2

Stress on the articular surface of the hip joint in healthy adults and patients with idiopathic osteoarthrosis of the hip joint

P. BRINCKMANN, W. FROBIN AND E. HIERHOLZER

INTRODUCTION

Arthrosis of the hip joint is a common condition and has an increasing incidence with age in persons aged over 30 years. There is a considerable number of cases of osteoarthrosis in which the etiology is not known. These cases are denoted as idiopathic coxarthrosis. At present the importance of mechanical factors in the etiology of idiopathic coxarthrosis is not clear. Therefore this paper investigates whether excessive compressive stress on the articular surface of the hip may be a primary cause of idiopathic coxarthrosis. A method of calculating the stress on the articular surface of the hip joint has been developed. The stress was calculated for the hip joints of healthy adults and of persons with idiopathic coxarthrosis. The comparison of the results obtained for these two groups will provide information about the potential importance of compressive stress with respect to the etiology of idiopathic coxarthrosis.

CALCULATION OF THE STRESS ON THE HIP JOINT

The method employed to calculate the stress on the articular surface of the hip joint depends on:

a. The geometrical configuration of the joint, ie the three-dimensional shape of the contact area of the femoral head and the acetabulum.
b. The resultant force on the joint.
c. A mechanical model of the joint, which specifies the distribution of stress on the articular surface.

The three-dimensional geometry of the contact area of the femoral head and the acetabulum was reconstructed from anterior/posterior radiograms of the hip joint. The resultant force used in the calculations was chosen to represent typical values which occur during normal physiologic activities. For this reason we employed those forces which are effective during three specific phases of the gait cycle: the stance phase of slow gait, and the two phases of maximal load which occur shortly after 'heel strike' and before 'toe off' (gait phases 1, 2 and 3).

The mechanical model of the hip joint which served for the derivation of the stress distribution consisted of a rigid sphere and a concentric spherical shell separated by a soft intermediate layer. It was assumed that friction was negligibly small. This implies that only normal stress is effective on the articular surface. It follows from this model that the compressive stress varies in proportion to the cosine of the angle between any point on the surface and the pole of the stress distribution (Greenwald & O'Connor, 1971).

The calculation of the resultant force in the stance phase of slow gait shows that the magnitude of the resultant is proportional to the body weight, W. It is assumed that the same relation (however, with different factors of proportionality) holds true in the 'heel strike' and 'toe off' phase of gait. It follows that the maximum stress B on the articular surface may be split into factors:

$$B = W \cdot B_{rel}$$

B_{rel} is called the relative stress. The relative stress depends only on the geometry of the joint, the direction of the resultant force and the geometric parameters of the musculoskeletal system, which determine the magnitude of the resultant. By comparing B and B_{rel} for the coxarthrosis patients and the healthy control group, it was possible to investigate the potential influence of body weight and geometry for the stress on articular cartilage separately.

The selection of the two groups of subjects used for this study, the consequences of the model calculation and the mathematical methods employed for calculating the stress have been described elsewhere (Brinckmann, Frobin & Hierholzer, 1980a,b). 343 hip joints of healthy adults (165 male, 178 female) and 289 hip joints of patients with idiopathic coxarthrosis (142 male, 147 female) were investigated. As body weight was not known with sufficient precision for all hip joints investigated the stress B was calculated for a slightly smaller number of cases than the relative stress B_{rel}. B was calculated for 304 healthy joints (151 male, 153 female) and 239 arthrotic joints (130 male, 109 female).

RESULTS AND DISCUSSION

Table 1 shows the results together with the parameters of the age and body weight distributions for the two groups. As can be seen, the relative stress B_{rel} showed no difference between healthy and arthrotic joints. In neither of the three gait phases was the difference in the mean values of the aggregate healthy and arthrotic group significant. Since B_{rel} depends only on the geometry of the joints and the relevant part of the musculoskeletal system it can be inferred that joints with idiopathic coxarthrosis with respect to the geometry 'at large' do not differ from normal, healthy joints. Of course, differences of the geometry 'in detail' due to surface irregularities of the bone of the femoral head or the acetabulum of the type described by Rushfeldt (1978), can neither be confirmed nor excluded by this study, since such irregularities cannot be detected in anterior/posterior radiograms of the pelvis.

Table 1. Age and body weight and calculated results of relative stress B_{rel} and stress B for the group of patients with idiopathic coxarthrosis and the healthy control group. The table shows the mean values (m) and the standard deviations (s) of the distributions.

	hip joints of healthy adults						patients with idiopathic coxarthrosis					
	all		males		females		all		males		females	
	m	s	ms	s	m	s	m	s	m	s	m	s
Age (years)	47.7	16.0	48.4	16.2	47.0	16.2	57.9	11.2	55.7	10.0	60.0	11.9
Body mass (kg)	68.4	11.9	74.5	12.1	62.2	7.98	74.4	13.9	80.1	11.7	68.7	11.5
Relative stress B_{rel} Gait phase 1 (1/cm²)	0.22	0.05	0.19	0.03	0.26	0.05	0.22	0.06	0.19	0.04	0.26	0.06
Relative stress B_{rel} Gait phase 2 (1/cm²)	0.45	0.08	0.41	0.06	0.49	0.07	0.44	0.09	0.39	0.07	0.49	0.09
Relative stress B_{rel} Gait phase 3 (1/cm²)	0.57	0.14	0.50	0.09	0.64	0.14	0.58	0.17	0.52	0.14	0.64	0.17
Stress B Gait phase 1 (MPa)	1.45	0.29	1.37	0.27	1.53	0.28	1.57	0.47	1.45	0.34	1.70	0.56
Stress B Gait phase 2 (MPa)	2.92	0.49	2.93	0.54	2.91	0.43	3.14	0.80	3.02	0.72	3.27	0.84
Stress B Gait phase 3 (MPa)	3.72	0.84	3.64	0.84	3.80	0.84	4.19	1.40	4.02	1.26	4.40	1.54

The mean value of the stress B was slightly higher for joints with idiopathic coxarthrosis as compared to healthy joints. This was a consequence of the finding that the body weight of the persons with idiopathic coxarthrosis was on average higher than the body weight of the healthy control group. This difference was highly significant, $P < 0.01$.

12

Within the healthy, as well as within the coxarthrosis group, the mean value of the stress B_{rel} and B was higher for joints of females than males. This is because the mean radius of the femoral head of females was smaller than that of males. However, the resulting difference in stress was less pronounced in stress B than in stress B_{rel} because the lower mean body weight of females tends to compensate partially the difference in B between the two sexes. Furthermore it was noted that, for example in the stance phase in slow gait, the stress B for males in the coxarthrosis group was lower than the corresponding value of B for females in the healthy control group.

There is no evidence of a higher incidence of idiopathic coxarthrosis in females as compared to males (Danielsson, 1964) and the difference in the mean value of B between arthrotic and healthy joints was small compared to the standard deviation of the distributions. It was therefore concluded that mechanical factors, ie compressive stress of a magnitude significantly above that level found in normal, healthy persons, is probably not of primary importance in the etiology of idiopathic coxarthrosis. The greater body weight of the coxarthrosis patients, as compared to the healthy control group, was interpreted as an effect rather than as a cause of the arthrosis (Saville & Dickson, 1968).

Surface irregularities of the bone or the cartilage of the hip joint, or local differences in the mechanical properties of the cartilage, could not be considered in the model calculation employed. Such local deviations from a spherical concentric joint with a homogeneous intermediate cartilaginous layer would result in local stress concentrations on the articular surface superimposed on the assumed cosine-shaped stress distribution. However, if such stress concentrations were primarily responsible for the development of the arthrosis one should still expect a higher incidence of arthrosis in those joints for which the calculated stress B is above the mean value of normal, healthy joints.

A high value of B may be due to a large body weight, a small radius of the femoral head, a small acetabular area, a position of the load vector close to the acetabular rim, or a combination of these factors. Comparison shows that arthrotic joints are not subject to a higher relative stress B_{rel} or a higher stress B than normal healthy joints. It is therefore inferred that our conclusion is not invalidated by the possible existence of local stress concentrations on the articular surface.

References

Brinckmann, P., Frobin, W. & Hierholzer, E. (1980a): Belastete Gelenkfläche und Beanspruchung des Hüftgelenks. Z. Orthop. 118, 107.

Brinckmann, P., Frobin, W. & Hierholzer, E. (1980b): Stress on the articular surface of the hip joint in healthy adults and persons with idiopathic osteoarthrosis of the hip joint. J. Biomech. (in press).

Danielsson, L.G. (1964): Incidence and prognosis of coxarthrosis. Acta Orthop. Scand., Suppl. 66.

Greenwald, A.S. & O'Connor, J.J. (1971): The transmission of load through the human hip joint. J. Biomech. 4, 507.

Rushfeldt, P.D. (1978): Human hip joint geometry and the resulting
  pressure distribution.   D.Sc. thesis, Massachusetts Institute of
  Technology, Dept. of Mech. Eng.
Saville, P.D. & Dickson, J. (1968): Age and weight in osteoarthrosis of
  the hip.   Arthritis. Rheum. 11, 635.

3

Forces and couples in the lumbar vertebral column during level walking at different speeds

AURELIO CAPPOZZO

INTRODUCTION

A great deal of research is still needed to elucidate the structural and functional properties of the vertebral column both in the normal and pathological state. The function of the vertebral column in the human body adds importance to knowledge concerning the mechanical loads normally acting on it. This is also a necessary starting point for the understanding of the mechanical etiology of spinal disorders and their effects.

Walking is a typical motor function of man and since the vertebral column is a very crucial part of the locomotor system it ought to be adapted functionally to the dynamics of locomotion. From this point of view, locomotion studies lend themselves to supplying information about the structural properties of the body and about the limits of exposure of the latter to mechanical stimulus.

This paper is concerned with the external forces and couples acting on the vertebral column at level L4 during level walking in the range of possible speeds of progression. These forces and couples are regarded here as the basic data for estimation of the load acting on the fourth lumbar vertebra. An elementary model of the relevant musculo-skeletal system was devised and an estimation of this load was obtained. At present, the only other information available about this load relates to the maximal value of the intradiscal pressure at level L3. It was measured in vivo during walking at a slow cadence (Nachemson & Elfström, 1970). It is unfortunate that these authors did not report the time functions of the measured pressure, therefore inhibiting consideration of the dynamic aspects of the relevant load. The forces and couples, due to the gravitational and inertial forces, were calculated using measurements of the movement of the torso, of the head and of the upper limbs. These data were obtained by means of a stereophotogrammetric technique. With this experimental method, the low frequency component of the external load could be determined. In order to have some information about its transient component, due to contacts with the ground at heel-strike, the vertical acceleration of the head was measured by means of an accelerometer mounted on a bite-bar. Similar measurements have been made by Light, McLellan & Klenerman (1979) during walking at the 'natural' cadence. Some of the measurements were

15

analysed with harmonic analysis. This analysis allowed a better insight into the characteristics of the load in relation to the biodynamic properties of the tissues on which it acts.

MATERIALS AND METHODS

The movement in space of the torso, head and upper limbs was measured photographically. Four cameras (Nikon F2) were placed in stereoscopic pairs with convergent optical axes. The test subjects carried light-emitting diodes (LEDs) firmly attached to the following anatomical landmarks, on both right and left sides: zygomatic process, acromial process, apex of the iliac crest, anterior-superior iliac spine, and external epicondyle of the humerus. These LEDs were driven by telecontrolled impulses. The duration of these was three milliseconds, at a frequency of 30 to 60 impulses per second according to stride duration (Cappozzo, Leo & Pedotti, 1975). Subjects walked along a 15 metre pathway, placed between the two stereopairs and parallel to the base-lines of the latter. During the experiments, the LEDs were made to flash and photographs were taken with the four open-shutter cameras. They were enlarged to about one-tenth of life size and printed on polyester plates. The coordinates of the images of the LEDs were measured on the photographs by means of a digitizer with a resolution of 0.1 mm. These image coordinates allowed the calculation of the true spatial coordinates of the landmarks by means of commonly used parallax equations. A foot switch was used that allowed the precise measurement of the temporal factors of the walking cycle. Body-segments movement data and stride phases were synchronised.

In order to proceed to the calculation of the external forces and couples, the mechanical model shown in Fig. 1 was devised. The portion of the torso above level L4 was represented by a rigid heavy segment joining the centroids of the bodies of L4 and C1 (hereafter these points will be referred to as L4 and C1). The former point coordinates were determined from the coordinates of the landmarks on the pelvis. This was done using geometrical information obtained from X-rays of the torso of one subject and applying scaling factors for the other subjects. The position of C1 with respect to the shoulder landmarks was obtained by means of a similar procedure. The head was represented by a rigid heavy segment passing through point C1 and the mid-point between the landmarks of the zygomatic processes. This segment was assumed to be linked to the torso segment with a spherical hinge. The shoulder girdle was represented by a weightless segment joining the centres of rotation of the shoulders and articulated with respect to the torso segment with a spherical hinge. The positions of the centres of rotation of the shoulders (SR and SL) were determined by projecting the acromial process landmarks onto a line through the approximate geometric centres of the shoulder joints. The upper limb was one rigid heavy segment as shown in Fig. 1. This was justified by the observation that the angle between arm and forearm was approximately constant during walking and needed, therefore, to be measured only once. Mass, mass moments of inertia, and position of the centre of gravity of the segments of the mechanical model were obtained from Chandler et al. (1975). It should be emphasised that the positions of the centres of gravity, particularly those of the

16

torso segment, were critical for accurate calculation of the external couples. Unfortunately, the data available in the literature are difficult to assign to a given subject. This was liable to be a major cause of error in the end results.

The stereophotogrammetric data provided regular samples of the displacement functions for the mechanical model. Relevant accelerations were calculated by means of a method based on a harmonic regression described in Cappozzo et al. (1975). This analytical procedure also provided smoothing of the experimental data.

The resultant of the inertial and gravitational forces acting on the model, its moment with respect to point L4, and the resultant of the inertia couples, were then calculated by means of equations of dynamics.

The vertical acceleration of the head was measured by means of an uni-axial accelerometer mounted on a bite-bar tailored on the subject's teeth with an acrylic resin. The measuring system had a frequency of resonance at about 130 Hz. The accelerometer used was of the Deltashear type (sensitivity = 47.1 pC/g; bandwidth = 0.2 - 9000 Hz; weight = 30 g). During the measurements, the active axis of the accelerometer would shift at varying angles from the vertical, thereby creating an error in the readings due to the superimposition of a component of the gravitational acceleration on the target acceleration. However, since the angles were small and subject to relatively slow variations, the error was small and its effect on the transient component of the acceleration considered negligible. Acceleration measurements were made while subjects walked barefoot on a hard surface.

Experiments were carried out on three young male subjects with a normal locomotor system. A total of 28 walking cycles, at speeds ranging from 0.99 to 2.35 m/s, were analysed.

RESULTS AND DISCUSSION

Figure 1 shows the three components of the resultant of the external forces and of the couples acting on the portion of the body above level L4 and resolved with respect to point L4. These results were obtained in four trial walks at different speeds of progression by a 22-year-old subject (body mass = 70 kg, mass of the portion of the body above L4 = 38 kg, height = 1.74 m). Forces and couples are to be read according to the sign convention indicated in Fig. 1.

From the patterns in Fig. 1 it can be seen that all forces and couples increase in peak-to-peak amplitude with speed. The vertical component of the force had a peak-to-peak amplitude ranging from 0.5 to 1.5 times the weight of the portion of the body above level L4. This partial weight will be referred to hereafter as W.U.B. The component of the force acting along the antero-posterior axis had a peak-to-peak amplitude ranging from 0.3 to 0.6 times W.U.B. The component acting along the latero-lateral axis had a peak-to-peak amplitude ranging from 0.2 to 0.4 times W.U.B.

The component of the external couples acting in the transverse plane (ie, about the Z axis) had a relatively small amplitude. This couple was due mainly to the upper limbs' action. The mechanical model that was used did not include the dynamic effects of the opposite torsion movements of the upper and lower trunk. Some approximate calculations

17

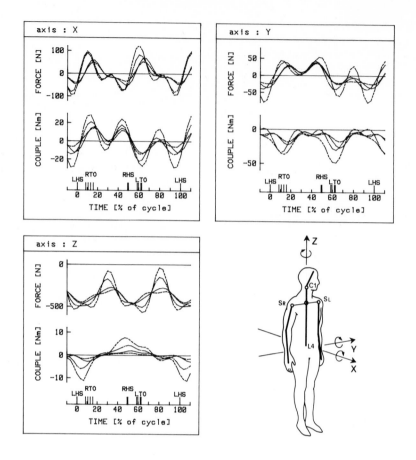

Fig. 1. External forces and couples acting on the portion of the body above level L4 and resolved with respect to the centroid of the body of L4, during walking at 1.05 (----), 1.27 (——), 1.72 (—·—), 2.24 m/s (—--—). Mechanical model of the upper portion of the body.

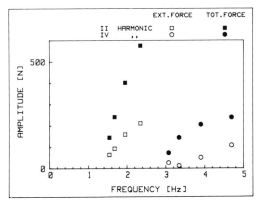

Fig. 2. Harmonic analysis of the vertical external and of the vertical total force acting on the vertebra L4 during walking at the four speeds referred to in Fig. 1

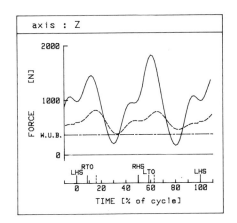

Fig. 3. Total force acting on the vertebra L4 during walking at 1.07 m/s (broken line) and at 2.24 m/s (solid line). W.U.B. is the weight of the portion of the body above the level of L4

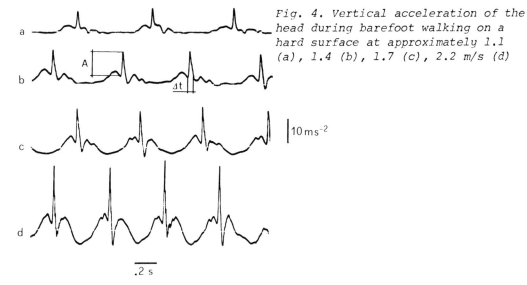

Fig. 4. Vertical acceleration of the head during barefoot walking on a hard surface at approximately 1.1 (a), 1.4 (b), 1.7 (c), 2.2 m/s (d)

19

of the inertia couples associated with these movements were made. Their maximal values were several times lower than those of the resultant couple due to the upper limbs' movement. Thus, they were deemed negligible. The component of the external couple acting in the sagittal plane (ie, about the Y axis) had, almost exclusively, a flexing action on the trunk. In one subject out of three this couple had positive peaks, ie, an extending action on the trunk as well. These peaks occurred at approximately 40 and 90 percent of the walking cycle and at the highest speeds of progression only. The component of the external couple acting in the frontal plane (ie, about the X axis) performed a lateral flexing action on the ipsilateral side of the trunk with respect to the foot in support phase.

Figure 2 depicts the amplitude spectra of the vertical component of the external force for the four trial walks referred to in Fig. 1. The amplitude of second and fourth harmonics - defined with respect to the stride period - was considerably larger than that of the other harmonics. For this reason these latter harmonics are not reported in Fig. 2. The amplitudes of both the second and fourth harmonics increased with speed. Thus, the vertical component of the external force underwent oscillations about a mean value equal to W.U.B., and its frequency content became closer to 5 Hz as walking speed increased.

In the forthcoming discussion, attention will be focused on the characteristics of the total force transmitted through the vertebra L4 and acting along the vertical axis. This force (F_{tz}) is the resultant of the relevant component of the external force (F_{ez}), referred to previously, and of the vertical component of the forces exerted by those trunk muscles whose fibres are crossed by a transverse plane at level L4. Hereafter, the forces are considered to be positive when they act so as to compress the vertebra L4.

In order to assess the type of contribution given by the muscular forces to the vertical total force build-up, a very simplified model of the spinal musculo-skeletal structure was devised. Only the erectores spinae muscles were taken into consideration as extensors and lateral flexors of the trunk relative to the pelvis. The forces exerted by these muscles were given constant moment arms (a_x, a_y) about the antero-posterior axis and the latero-lateral axis that intersect in point L4 ($a_x = 0.04$ m and $a_y = 0.05$ m). The dynamic equilibrium of the part of the body above L4 implies that the moments of the muscular forces are equal in magnitude and opposite in sign to the correspondent external couples (C_x, C_y) given in Fig. 1. This is true if ligament forces are ignored. As estimation of the total vertical force acting through the vertebra L4 was obtained using the following equation:

$$F_{tz} = \max\left[\frac{|C_y|}{a_y}, \frac{|C_x|}{a_x}\right] + F_{ez}$$

This force is given in Fig. 3 for the slowest and fastest walking trials referred to in the previous figures. For walking speeds from 1.05 to 2.24 m/s, maxima of the total vertical force ranged from two to five times W.U.B. The maximal value of the total load acting on L3 during 'slow walking', as obtained in vivo by Nachemson & Elfström (1970), ranged from 2 to 3.3 times W.U.B. The results in Fig. 3 are consistent with these in vivo measurements. It is well to emphasise here that the results of the present study cannot take into account any preload acting on the vertebra. This preload was assessed by Nachemson & Elfström (1970) in subjects in supine position.

Figure 2 shows results of the harmonic analysis of the total vertical force. The amplitude of second and fourth harmonic are both greater than those of the external vertical force.

In Fig. 4, examples of the vertical acceleration of the head against time are reported. The acceleration transient immediately following each heel strike is characterised by two peaks. The first is positive (directed upwards) and the second is negative. In the three subjects tested, the amplitude (A) of the peak of acceleration immediately following the heel strikes was in the range of 7 - 23 m/s² for all walking speeds tested. The duration (Δt) was in the range of 46 - 29 milliseconds. Amplitude increased and duration decreased as walking speed was increased. The findings of Light et al. (1979) appear to be in disagreement with these figures. For barefoot, normal walking on a hard surface, these authors reported a peak amplitude and duration of approximately 5 m/s² and 20 milliseconds, respectively. This discrepancy might be either due to different experimental conditions - a more or less resilient floor, for example - or to different transducer-teeth couplings. Differences between individuals may also be responsible.

The impulsive acceleration transmitted to the cranium through the vertebral column is, therefore, associated with an impulsive force. The amplitude of this force impulse acting on L4 can be roughly estimated by multiplying the acceleration impulse by the mass of the portion of the body above L4. Values ranging from 260 to 870 N were found. This is likely to be an underestimation of the amplitude. The energy-absorbing effects of the entire vertebral column and of the flexion-extension movements of the head with respect to the trunk have been neglected. The amplitude of the force impulse is greatly reduced when either the heel of the shoe or the floor have shock-absorbing properties (Light et al., 1979).

This discussion has not taken into consideration possible actions of the short deep muscles of the back. A synergic action of these muscles might significantly change the type of loading on the vertebral column, without having an appreciable dynamic effect. Due to the marked non-linearity of the biodynamic properties of the vertebral column, the relevant response of this structure could also be altered. These are conjectures that can only be validated by means of intramuscular electromyography.

It must be acknowledged that the model of the musculo-skeletal structure used for the estimation of the total vertical load acting on L4, fostered simplifications that are, undoubtedly, open to criticisms. Nevertheless, it is felt that the results obtained with this model, though to be considered with caution, do supply useful and reliable information concerning the most relevant aspects of the resultant load. A further model is being devised that will supply information on the components of the total force that have been ignored here. This is being done while still maintaining a degree of mistrust of over-sophisticated models.

CONCLUSIONS

The main characteristics of the total vertical force acting on the vertebral column at level L4 were assessed during level walking in the range of possible speeds of progression. It was found that the value of this force undergoes wide oscillations. The relevant component due to the muscular contraction augments the vertical external force. The frequency content of the total vertical force is characterised by a second and fourth harmonic - defined with respect to the stride period - lying in the range of 1.2 - 4.9 Hz. Following each heel strike an impulsive force superimposes upon the force due to gravity, inertia and muscular contraction as referred to above. This impulsive force is caused by the contacts between foot and floor. It is of a relatively large amplitude and occurs within a short lapse of time.

At the highest speeds of progression the frequency content of the oscillating component of the load (Fig. 2) gets closer to the 4 - 5 Hz range, where resonance phenomena have been found to occur within the vertebral column in subjects who were sitting on vibrating tables (Coermann, 1962; Dupuis, 1977). It can be tentatively inferred that the load of the vertebral column during walking can be one of the factors imposing a limit to the speed of walking. This is likely to be true not in terms of the magnitude of the load, but the decisive factor could be its frequency content.

Acknowledgements - Part of the data reduction and computing used in this study was carried out at the Bioengineering Unit, University of Strathclyde, Glasgow. The co-operation of Professor J.P. Paul is gratefully acknowledged.

References

Cappozzo, A., Leo, T. & Pedotti, A. (1975): A general computing method for the analysis of human locomotion. J. Biomech. 8, 307.

Chandler, R.F., Clanser, C.E., McConville, J.T., Reynolds, H.M. & Young, J.W. (1975): Investigation of inertial properties of the human body. Aerospace Medical Research Laboratory, Aerospace Medical Division, Air Force Systems Command, Wright-Patterson Air Force Base, Ohio, Report N.AMRL-TR-74-137.

Coermann, R.R. (1962): The mechanical impedence of the human body in sitting and standing position at low frequencies. Hum. Factors 4, 227.

Dupuis, H. (1977): Human response to vibration under different conditions. In 'Proceedings of the European symposium on life sciences research in space', ESA sP-130, pp. 327-333. Cologne Porz, Germany.

Light, L.H., McLellan, G. & Klenerman, L. (1979): Skeletal heel strike transient in normal walking in different footwear - measurements and implications. In 'Proceedings of XII international conference on medical and biological engineering'- V International Conference on Medical Physics, paper 40.2. Jerusalem, Israel.

Nachemson, A. & Elfström, G. (1970): Intravital dynamic pressure measurements in lumbar discs. Scand. J. Rehab. Med. Suppl. 1.

4

Is there compressive loading on the apophyseal joints of the lumbar spine in erect posture?

M.A. ADAMS AND W.C. HUTTON

INTRODUCTION

It has been shown that, in erect sitting, increasing the lumbar lordosis reduces pressure on the intervertebral disc (Andersson et al., 1975). However, other research has sought to demonstrate a link between low back pain and lordotic posture (Fahrni, 1975). This apparent paradox may be explained by assuming some other structure resists intervertebral compressive force in lordotic posture - the obvious candidate being the apophyseal joints.

Figure 1 shows a cross-section through one of these joints in the sagittal plane. They seem designed to resist intervertebral shear forces which act in the horizontal direction. Any resistance to the intervertebral compressive force would produce nipping of soft tissue which includes the innervated joint capsule, or high 'wedge' forces on the articular cartilage, or both. Thus, compressive load-bearing by the apophyseal joints could possibly lead to back ache, or osteoarthritic changes in the facets.

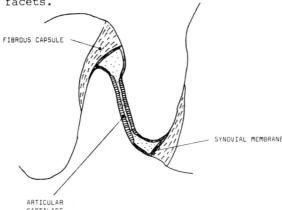

Fig. 1. A lumbar apophyseal joint cut through in the sagittal plane

The purpose of the work presented here was to determine what proportion, if any, of the intervertebral compressive force is resisted by the lumbar apophyseal joints, and to see if this is influenced by slight changes in posture. The full details of the experiment, with the complete results for 40 specimens tested, are presented elsewhere (Adams & Hutton, 1980).

METHOD

Cadaveric lumbar spines were dissected into intervertebral joints consisting of two vertebrae and the intervening soft tissue. Each joint was set in dental plaster and loaded in compression while orientated in 2° of flexion and 2° of extension. Force deformation curves were obtained. When taken over the whole lumbar spine, these small angles add up to simulate the erect sitting and erect standing postures respectively. The apophyseal joints were sawn through in the plane of the disc and the test repeated. From the differences in the curves, the role of the neural arch in resisting compressive forces was obtained. Twenty-seven of the 40 joints (Group 2) were first subjected to three hours of compressive loading to reduce the disc height by about ten percent. This loss occurs in life each day, when body weight expresses excess fluid absorbed by the discs during the night.

RESULTS

The results showed that the Group 2 joints in 2° of extension resisted 16 percent on average of the intervertebral compressive force. In all other cases, the resistance was negligible. Some joints with extreme disc narrowing or scoliosis had as much as 70 percent of the resistance to compression from the facets: these abnormal joints are not included in the average. All of these abnormal joints showed advanced degenerative changes in the apophyseal joints.
   Apophyseal joint load bearing was significantly higher at the three lower lumbar levels, but there was no significant variation with sex, age or degree of disc degeneration.

CONCLUSION

The apophyseal joints of the lumbar spine resist a substantial proportion of the intervertebral compressive force whenever the normal (for an excised spine) lordosis is increased, as occurs in erect standing. This may have implications in low back pain and spinal osteoarthritis.

References

Adams, M.A. & Hutton, W.C. (1980): The effect of posture on the role of the apophyseal joints in resisting intervertebral compressive force. J. Bone Jt. Surg., 62B, 358.
Andersson, B.J.G., Ortengren, R., Nachemson, A.L., Elfstrom, G. & Broman, H. (1975): The sitting posture: an electromyographic and discometric study. Orthop. Clins N. Am. 6, 105.
Fahrni, W.H. (1975): Conservative treatment of lumbar disc degeneration: our primary responsibility. Orthop. Clins N. Am. 6, 93.

5

Movements of painful intervertebral joints

I.A.F. STOKES AND P.A. MEDLICOTT

INTRODUCTION

Assessment of patients with painful condition of the spine relies heavily on observations of their voluntary movements of the back and of the posture that the patient adopts. In this way the diagnosis of painful conditions of the spine is similar to that of other joints of the body. However, the inaccessibility of the intervertebral joints make such examination difficult, to the extent that many painful conditions of the spine are never diagnosed or localised to an individual intervertebral joint. Previous attempts to measure intervertebral joint movements from X-ray films have been handicapped by the two-dimensional nature of the plane X-ray film. The spine has a complex three-dimensional shape and secondary or coupled movements often accompany the primary or intentional movement, such as flexion and extension or lateral bending. In addition, measurement of movement from such plane X-ray films is complicated by the magnification and distortion inherent in these.

In this study, biplanar radiography with computer analysis of measurements has been used to measure intervertebral joint motion during the voluntary movements of patients with low back pain. The intervertebral joint movement has been expressed in terms of three angles, namely those of flexion and extension, lateral bending, and axial rotation, and in terms of two linear translation movements, namely the forwards backwards (that is, shear) movement in the intervertebral disc, and the vertical component of the movement in the facet joints on either side of each intervertebral joint.

PATIENTS STUDIED

Results of measurements of 18 patients with suspected herniated nucleus pulposus in the lumbar spine are presented here. These patients were studied prospectively after they had been admitted to hospital for consideration for surgery. They were assessed by clinical examinations, myelography and plane radiography. In 11 patients who went on to surgery results of biplanar radiographic studies were also compared with the surgical findings. A more detailed description of this group of patients has been given elsewhere (Stokes et al., 1980a). It was hypothesised that a painful disc herniation would result in a limitation of those movements which tend to increase pressure on an involved nerve root. The movement of facet joints was used as a measure of this potentially painful movement since it corresponds to a closing or opening of the intervertebral foramen (Fig. 1).

METHOD

Patients were radiographed in three postures, firstly in their neutral standing position, then in maximal lateral bending to left and to the right. These movements were usually painful so the range of movement was probably limited by pain. Two radiographic exposures were made for each position of the patient to allow the biplanar technique to be used to measure the position and the orientation of each vertebra, and hence the intervertebral movements. The antero-posterior and lateral projections were normally used, although for bending to the left a lateral and postero-anterior pair of exposures was used since this gave more freedom of movement to the patient and produced a better pair or radiographic images for analysis. Films were analysed first by marking nine anatomic landmarks on each vertebra in each film. The position of these marks on each film was measured by means of a digitiser connected on-line to a PDP-11 computer. Previously the X-ray set-up had been calibrated for the position of the X-ray tubes relative to the X-ray films, so that the biplanar radiographic technique (Frymoyer et al., 1979; Brown et al., 1976; Rab & Chao, 1977) could be used to calculate three-dimensional cartesian coordinates of each of the nine landmarks on each vertebra in each of the three radiographic positions. In this study, statistical techniques were used to make use of the redundant information resulting from the use of nine anatomical landmarks. A minimum of three landmarks is necessary to define the orientation of a rigid body. It was assumed that the patient's vertebrae did not deform during these movements so that corrections could be made to the measured landmark positions, such that all nine landmarks on each vertebra maintained a constant geometrical relationship to each other.
  Details of these statistical techniques, and of the methods of measuring intervertebral movements in terms of three angles and the relative displacements in facet joints and across the intervertebral disc, have been described by Stokes et al. (1980b)

RESULTS

Each intervertebral joint was classified as being either symmetrical or asymmetrical. This classification was based on four measurements of the movements of facet joints. The movement of each of the two facet joints was measured in a left and in a right lateral bend. Intervertebral joints without disc herniation generally moved in such a way that the facet joint on the side of the bend 'closed' (reducing the size of the intervertebral foramen) and that on the opposite side 'opened' by a roughly equal amount (Fig. 2). Any intervertebral joint which did not have this pattern of 'opening' and 'closing' was classified as 'asymmetrical'.
  All joints with confirmed herniated nucleus pulposus were found to be asymmetrical (Table 1). Some patients achieved asymmetry of movement by

26

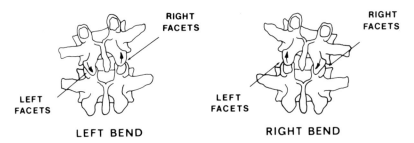

Fig. 1. *The vertical component movement of movement in facet joints was used to describe the movement of intervertebral joints from the standing position to left and right lateral bending positions*

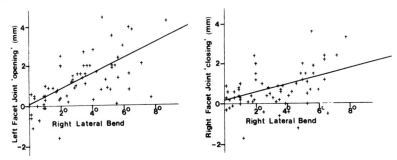

Fig. 2. *The facet joint movement which accompanied lateral bending in 70 intervertebral joints without disc herniation. In general some flexion accompanied lateral bending, so that the 'opening' of the joint opposite to the side of the bend was a little more than the 'closing' of the joint on the side of the bend. The cephalo-caudal component of the movement is shown*

Table 1. *The numbers of lumbar intervertebral joints in the 18 patients which were found to be symmetrical and asymmetrical in lateral bending. All joints with disc herniation were asymmetrical*

		asymmetry		
		yes	no	
herniated nucleus pulposus	yes	12	0	P<1% in Fischer exact test
	no	17	14	

Table 2. *The mean values of asymmetry (mm) in three groups of asymmetrical intervertebral joints. The asymmetrical joints were divided into three groups, according to pathological state*

unaffected joints in spines with disc herniation at another level (17 asymmetrical joints)	0.55	significant difference (P<1%)
intervertebral joints with disc herniation (12 asymmetrical joints)	1.98	significant difference (P<2.5%)
intervertebral joints in patients found to have no disc herniation (16 asymmetrical joints)	1.04	

avoiding lateral bend to one side in a particular joint. Other patients used flexion at that joint simultaneously with lateral bending to maintain the size of the intervertebral foramen. However, some other unaffected joints were also found to be asymmetrical based on the simple criterion. Any facet joint movement which was not in the expected direction was expressed in millimetres, and these 'magnitudes of asymmetry' were compared in three groups of intervertebral joints (Table 2). Asymmetries in 'affected' joints were significantly greater than those in 'unaffected' joints.

CONCLUSIONS

Patients with herniated nucleus pulposus in the lumbar spine were found to move asymmetrically at the affected joint in lateral bending. This asymmetry was interpreted as a way of maintaining the size of the intervertebral foramen, and avoiding pressure on a painful nerve root. This suggests that these patients achieve a fine control of movement at individual intervertebral joints. This finding has potential for improved diagnosis of the presence and anatomical level of a herniated nucleus pulposus.

Acknowledgements - Patients were studied with the permission of Professor R.B. Duthie, who advised and encouraged us in this work. Funding was provided by the Department of Health and Social Security. X-ray equipment was provided by GEC Medical Equipment Limited.

References

Brown, R.H., Burstein, A.H., Nash, C.L. & Schock, C.C. (1976): Spinal analysis using three-dimensional radiographic technique. J. Biomech. 9, 344.

Frymoyer, J.W., Frymoyer, W.W., Wilder, D.G. & Pope, M.H. (1979): The mechanical and kinematic analysis of the lumbar spine in normal living subjects in vivo. J. Biomech. 12, 165.

Rab, G.T. & Chao, E.Y.S. (1977): Verification of roentgenographic landmarks in the lumbar spine. Spine 2, 287.

Stokes, I.A.F., Wilder, D.G., Frymoyer, J.W. & Pope, M.H. (1980a): Assessment of patients with low back pain by biplanar radiographic measurement of intervertebral motion. Spine (at press).

Stokes, I.A.F., Medlicott, P.A. & Wilder, D.G. (1980b): Measurement of movement in painful intervertebral joints. Med. Biol. Eng. and Comp. 18, 694.

6

Axial forces in the forearm: their relationship to excision of the head of radius

ANDREW A. AMIS, J.H. MILLER, D. DOWSON AND V. WRIGHT

INTRODUCTION

This work was designed to examine the mode of action of the structure of the forearm in response to axial forces. A matter of particular concern was the role of the head of radius. Examination of the literature shows that excision of the head of radius is commonly accepted as part of the surgical treatment of rheumatoid arthritis (eg Laine & Vainio, 1969; Taylor, Mukerjea & Rana, 1976). The procedure provides pain relief following inflammatory joint disease, but is also used when the head of radius has been fractured. Literature relating to these post-trauma cases suggests that 50 percent may have disabling wrist symptoms (Lewis & Thibodeau, 1937; McDougall & White, 1957; Taylor & O'Connor, 1964). The appearance of wrist symptoms has been linked to the severity of use of the limbs, and it has been suggested that disruption of the distal radio-ulnar joint follows stretching of the interosseous membrane. The fibres of the membrane are arranged so that a force acting to push the radius proximally can be resisted by their tension acting in a distal direction, towards their insertions on the ulna.

There are two main sources of axial force within the forearm: external forces, acting on the hand, and internal muscle forces. The latter are predominant during voluntary actions, leading to large forces on both humero-ulnar and humero-radial articulations (Amis et al., 1979; Amis, Dowson & Wright, 1980). A maximal isometric flexion effort may cause a force of 2.5 kN on each of the elbow articulations. These forces are normally balanced so that the forearm remains in equilibrium on the humerus without ligamentous stabilising actions. It was suggested by Amis et al. (1979) that excision of the head of radius would cause the humero-radial force to be transferred to the coronoid process, and that a medial collateral ligament tension would be needed to prevent a valgus angulation. Taylor & O'Connor (1964) noted that an increase in the carrying angle occurs after this procedure.

The transmission of external forces, from the hand to the elbow, has been studied by Halls & Travill (1964) and Walker (1977), with conflicting results. Halls & Travill suggested that the radius transmitted most of the force directly from the hand to the humerus (50 to 70 percent). Furthermore, they found that cutting the interosseous membrane had very little effect on this. Conversely, Walker suggested that the radius did not transmit load directly below 100 N, when it came into contact with the capitulum, beyond which it transmitted 63 percent of any excess force. Thus they ascribed a major role to the interosseous membrane, which would mean that the humero-ulnar joint would take the major part of the force below 485 N.

A drawback of the published investigations is that a fixed load axis was used throughout each experiment, leading to each author describing a certain structural response. This situation does not normally apply – external forces may have any orientation at the hand. It should be expected that movements of the load vector would alter the distribution of forces between radius and ulna, also that collateral ligament actions would be necessary if a valgus or varus load component caused the vector to pass outside the articulation.

Experiments were undertaken to examine the structural function of the forearm, particularly the load-sharing between radius and ulna, the role of the interosseous membrane, and the effect of excision of the head of radius.

EXPERIMENTAL METHODS

1. Joint Movements

The response of the cadaveric forearm to axial forces was examined by two methods. The first of these monitored displacements of the forearm bones relative to the humerus. The second measured the forces transmitted to the humerus via each of the articulations.

Limbs were instrumented in the manner shown in Fig. 1, so that intra-articular displacements could be monitored under load. Later, measurement of the load/deflection characteristics of the excised humero-radial and humero-ulnar joints enabled the forces carried by the individual articulations in the intact limb to be found. The transducers were mounted by means of guide tubes cemented into the posterior aspect of the humerus. The holes for the guide tubes continued across the joint space, so that the displacement transducer probes could rest against the subchondral bone of the head of radius or coronoid process. The probe holes were drilled when the limb was frozen, so that cartilage fragments could not enter the joint space. The limbs were mounted by potting the humeral shaft in a socket which was clamped to the bed of a high-speed servo-hydraulic test machine. The pronated forearm was vertical and the elbow flexed 40 degrees. The posture was therefore similar to that recorded by Carlsöö & Johansson (1962) for falls forward on to the outstretched hand. It was found that the transducer outputs were very sensitive to movements of the hand. To help immobilise the distal end of the specimen, the proximal phalanges were potted into a box which was mounted on the crosshead of the test machine. Crosshead movements could be accommodated by inter-carpal joint movements. Loads of 500 N were applied to the thenar and hypothenar areas of the carpus of the dorsiflexed hand. The transducer outputs were fed to an ultra-violet galvanometric recorder, which allowed transient impact load effects to be monitored. The effect of varying the direction of the line of action of the force was studied by applying small loads by hand, so that the action of the collateral ligaments could be examined. The two limbs tested in the above manner were dissected, and 8 cm lengths of the bone shafts set into metal holders. After mounting in a compression testing machine, the joints were compressed at a rate of 9 mm/minute to produce force/displacement curves.

2. Direct Force Measurement

Despite efforts to stabilise the hand, the validity of the displacement readings was doubtful. A second experiment in which the humero-radial and humero-ulnar forces could be measured directly was designed. Furthermore, the force would be applied directly to the distal radius, so that radio-carpal movements could be eliminated. It was assumed that most of the force applied to the hand would be transmitted via the radio-carpal joint, rather than to the ulna via the triangular fibrocartilage. Although it was not known at first whether this assumption was correct, the experiment still allowed force to transfer from the radius to the ulna (via the interosseous membrane) in a normal manner. This effect has an important bearing on radial head excision.

The distal end of the specimen was prepared by cutting the soft tissues 5 mm distal to the radio-carpal joint line and then releasing the carpus from the capsule and ligaments. This ensured that the distal radio-ulnar joint was not affected. An intra-medullary rod was cemented into the distal radius, supporting a steel sphere at the centre of the wrist cross-section, 20 mm distal to the radius.

To measure the forces transmitted via the axial elbow articulations, the humeral condyles were sawn apart and mounted on force plates. The two triangular force plates were mounted 2 mm apart on strain-gauged columns. This apparatus allowed the magnitude and position of two vertical forces to be found simultaneously (see Fig. 2). The humerus was then transected 50 mm proximal to the elbow-joint line. The saw cut was inclined such that, with the forearm vertical and the elbow flexed 45°, the cut surface would rest horizontally on the force plates. A saw cut was then begun from the posterior aspect of the humerus, in a sagittal plane estimated to coincide with the superior radio-ulnar joint. The direction of the cut was checked by an anterior-posterior (A-P) radiograph. The humeral condyles were fixed by transverse pins, which prevented relative movement when the saw cut was completed. The transected surface of the humerus was excavated to provide recesses for the acrylic bone cement which was used to mount the humeral condyles on the force plates. A piece of greased card was used to keep the condyles and force plates from being linked by the cement. After setting, the card and transverse pins were removed. The apparatus and specimen assembly was then mounted in a testing machine, with the distal sphere located in a fixed socket on the load axis of the machine and the baseplate resting on a compression load cell mounted on the crosshead (Fig. 2).

For the first test, the inter-condylar cut (coinciding with the superior radio-ulnar joint) was positioned on the axis of the machine, with the vertical forearm in a neutral position of rotation. Forces up to 1.2 kN were applied, with the force plate outputs noted, so that the response to various axial forces could be examined. After this the baseplate was moved laterally and medially and a force applied at each position. With the baseplate remaining flat, the lateral movements caused the forearm bones to tilt relative to the humerus. Being bound both to each other and to the humerus by muscles and ligaments, the tilting caused some combination of relative axial movement and gaping of one articulation, therefore causing a redistribution of force on the humeral condyles under load.

In the above experiment, the line of action of the applied force was unknown. This was because the tilt of the forearm caused an unknown sideways reaction between the distal sphere and socket. To overcome this, so that the effect of varying the line of action could be studied, the baseplate was mounted on steel rollers which allowed sideways movement. The baseplate was tilted by placing packing pieces under one side. It was then moved sideways so that the forearm bones remained perpendicular to the baseplate. Thus the fixed line of action of the testing machine could be arranged to pass through the distal sphere and along the forearm at a range of angles to its axis, then, via one or other of the humeral condyles, to the baseplate (Fig. 2). A load of 600 N was applied at each position, and the resulting force noted for each condyle. At a certain inclination the forearm became unstable under a vertical load, and tilted further. This was allowed by movement of the baseplate. The consequent redistribution of force between the condyles either restored equilibrium or else one force plate was lifted from the base, indicating that a collateral ligament tension was necessary for equilibrium. The movements of the baseplate were also recorded.

The interosseous membrane was kept taut during all the experiments, so that it could exhibit a maximal effect on the load-sharing mechanism, by maintaining the forearm in a neutral position of rotation. Pronation or supination allow the membrane to slacken, as reported by Patrick (1946) and Walker (1977). The membrane must act to transfer axial force from the radius to the ulna following excision of the head of radius, but this mechanism must be accompanied by an elastic deformation of the membrane and hence a proximal movement of the radius. It is this proximal movement which may cause disruption of the distal radio-ulnar joint in vivo.

To examine the action of the forearm after radial head excision, the specimen was set vertically in the test machine after excision of the head, with the baseplate free to move sideways, and an axial load applied. The axial stiffness of the interosseous membrane was examined later, after transection of the triangular fibrocartilage of the distal radio-ulnar joint. Axial movement of the radius, caused by a cyclic load up to 600 N, was measured by a dial gauge which indicated movements of the neck of radius relative to the baseplate. The baseplate was fixed during this part of the experiment so that the measured deflections would not be affected by tilting of the forearm.

RESULTS AND DISCUSSION

It was expected that altering the position and direction of the applied load would cause the response of the forearm structure to change. The first experiment, in which displacement transducers crossed the joint

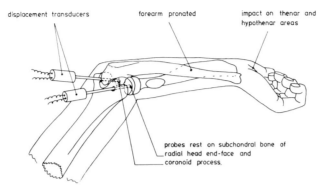

displacement transducers   forearm pronated   impact on thenar and hypothenar areas

probes rest on subchondral bone of radial head end-face and coronoid process.

Fig. 1. Experiment to examine axial forces in radius and ulna by monitoring compression of the elbow articulations

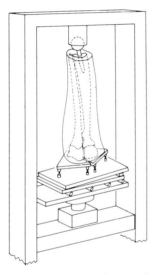

Fig. 2. Experimental set-up to measure axial forearm forces by mounting humeral condyles on force plates

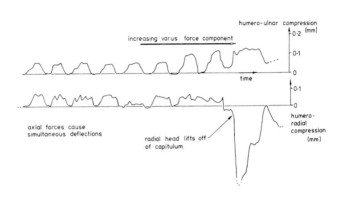

humero-ulnar compression (mm)

increasing varus force component

time

axial forces cause simultaneous deflections

radial head lifts off of capitulum.

humero-radial compression (mm)

Fig. 3. Deflections at elbow articulations caused by axial compressive forces applied to the hand

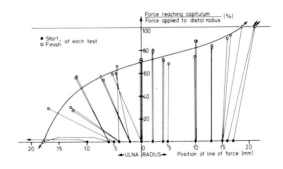

Force reaching capitulum / Force applied to distal radius (%)

• Start,
○ Finish of each test.

←ULNA | RADIUS→   Position of line of force (mm)

Fig. 4. Load-sharing characteristics, between radius and ulna, in response to compressive forces acting at various angles to the forearm axis

33

line, was therefore expected to yield results showing a trend of radial head force diminishing, while the ulnar force increased, as the position of the loading vector moved across the wrist from the thenar to the hypothenar eminence. However, this trend was not observed. The force appeared to be taken almost entirely by the axial elbow articulation which was closest to the load axis, with a quite sudden transition from one to the other during a traverse of the supinated or pronated wrist. It was not possible to prevent small movements of the radius and ulna on the surface of the humerus. These movements were sufficient to invalidate the readings of the displacement transducers, so the actual forces were not calculated from the load/deflection curves found later. Trends in the results were still apparent, however, as can be seen in Fig. 3. The humero-ulnar and humero-radial joint deflections are seen to have followed opposite trends when an increasing varus component was added to the cyclic axial force. At the limit, all the force passed to the humero-ulnar joint as the head of radius lifted off of the capitulum thus tensing the lateral collateral ligament. Similar behaviour was noted under valgus forces, but medial gaping did not occur.

Deformations of the collateral ligaments give the forearm a range of movement of approximately ten degrees on the humerus (Amis et al., 1977). The sudden transition of load carriage from one bone to the other suggested that the forearm was rotating about a pivot point situated at the elbow. To find this pivot point, double-exposed photographs were taken of the limb with the load in different directions. Grids of parallel lines attached to the forearm produced interference fringes in the double-exposure, due to slight valgus-varus rotation of the forearm. The method of Shoup & Steffen (1974) was then used to locate the centre of rotation, which was found to be in the capitulo-trochlear groove of the humerus. The sudden transition was indicative of freedom of relative movement of the forearm bones, suggesting that they were not tightly bound to each other by the interosseous membrane when the forearm was pronated or supinated. Dissections showed that this was the case, with the interosseous membrane tightening towards neutral rotation, thus confirming the results of Patrick (1946) and Walker (1977).

For the second set of experiments, in which the separated humeral condyles were mounted on to force plates, the forearm was kept in a neutral rotation posture to allow the tight interosseous membrane to give maximal transferrence of force from radius to ulna. When the forearm was loaded axially, it was found that the radius transmitted 73 percent of the applied force directly to the capitulum at all forces up to 1.2 kN.

If the radius is considered to act as a strut, pivoting at its base on the capitulum and tilted so that its distal end is on the centreline of the forearm (considering the A-P view in neutral rotation), it is apparent that it must lean on the ulna. The force transmitted to the medial lip of the trochlea will depend on the ratio of the distances of the capitular and trochlear pivot points from the line of action of the applied force. With the specimen in the posture described, this reasoning leads to 32 percent of the force being predicted to act on the trochlea. The experiment yielded 27 percent.

Tilting the baseplate allowed the load axis to pass through different parts of the elbow. When it moved laterally, the proportion of the total force (600 N) transmitted to the capitulum was increased, as seen in Fig. 4. The forearm also remained stable. This is indicated in Fig. 4 by the vertical lines between the start and finish of each test, which indicate that the baseplate did not move sideways to find an equilibrium position with a different tilt of the forearm on the humerus. When the load was applied 15 mm or more lateral to the radio-ulnar joint, it also passed laterally to the centre of the capitulum. The radius thus tilted into valgus (indicated by the horizontal shift between start and finish of each test), and transmitted the entire applied load when its axis had shifted beyond 17 mm. In this case the load platform attached to the ulna was lifted off of the baseplate, indicating that a medial collateral ligament action would restore equilibrium in an intact limb.

When the specimen was tilted so that the load axis passed through the trochlea, the specimen tended to move into varus. This behaviour may reflect the properties of the collateral ligaments of the elbow. The anterior band of the medial collateral ligament, originating from the distal face of the medial epicondyle and inserting into the medial lip of the coronoid process, tightens as the elbow extends. This structure is therefore well suited to prevent valgus angulation of the extended forearm. In contrast, the lateral collateral ligament, which dissipates into the annular ligament and deep fascia of the supinator muscle origin, does not have a direct bone-to-bone restraint on the head of radius. This will facilitate forearm movements into varus, because the head of radius is not tightly restrained from lifting off of the capitulum, as demonstrated in Fig. 3.

The forearm was more stable when an axial force caused a shift into valgus rather than varus. The opposite tendency would be expected from study of the elbow joint, since the trochlear surfaces alone can be stable. However, examination of the function of the forearm shows that axial forces in vivo tend to be transmitted in such a way that the humero-radial joint, rather than the medial side of the elbow, is compressed. Carlsöö & Johansson (1962) for example, showed that, in a fall forwards on to the outstretched hand, the humerus is rotated inwards and the forearm semi-pronated. This posture causes the palm to face downwards and the elbow joint, with the lateral side uppermost, is loaded in the manner just described. Similarly, a backward fall is accompanied by external humeral rotation and forearm supination to place the palm downwards, a posture which again compresses the head of radius and tenses the medial ligament. This mechanism may also explain a function of carrying angle, which leaves the pronated forearm with a slight valgus angulation and hence produces a tendency for axial forces to load the elbow in the desired manner.

The final stage of the experiment was to examine the function of the forearm after excision of the head of radius. Application of an axial force to the specimen caused it to compress in a stable manner, in a vertical posture, until a force of 100 N was reached. The forearm then moved into valgus, so that the load axis shifted 1 cm radially. This position was presumably held by medial collateral ligament tension up to a force of 150 N, when the specimen suddenly collapsed into valgus, tearing the medial condyle from its force plate. This behaviour is the same as that suggested by Amis et al. (1979) for an excised joint loaded by internal muscle actions. It appears that all axial compression force is concentrated on to the lateral edge of the coronoid process, and that this force is augmented by the tensile force in the medial collateral ligament. Thus the integrity of the forearm structure depends on this ligament after excision of the head of radius.

Tests of the axial stiffness of the interosseous membrane gave an average value of 275 N/mm at 500 N. This value is the average of three load cycles up to 600 N, following three which exhibited a diminishing permanent axial deformation. This specimen had been embalmed, a process which tends to stiffen collagenous structures by increasing inter-molecular cross-linking, so a fresh specimen would probably have a lower stiffness: Walker (1977) estimated 200 N/mm. Both of these values are considerably less than those for the radial and ulnar articulations which have stiffnesses of approximately 1.4 and 1.8 kN/mm respectively at 500 N. The interosseous membrane, being much more compliant, will therefore have little chance to transmit much force from the radius to the ulna. It is therefore suggested that the fibres of the membrane act primarily to transmit the tensions of the deep flexor muscles of the forearm back to the radius so that the radio-carpal joint is compressed by their actions, and not the head of ulna and triangular fibrocartilage. The membrane compliance is such that external forces will move the radius only one or two mm proximally after excision of its head. However, the considerably greater muscle forces which act on the radius of an active person, giving humero-radial forces up to 2.5 kN, will be sufficient to disrupt the distal radio-ulnar joint.

CONCLUSION

The experimental results reported here confirm a major role for the humero-radial joint in the function of the forearm and elbow, and demonstrate some consequences of excision of the head of radius on the stability of the elbow and disruption of the distal radio-ulnar joint. The results of a muscle force analysis (Amis et al., 1979) were also confirmed. It is suggested that radial head excision should not be undertaken lightly, and that prosthetic replacement should be considered for active patients.

Acknowledgements - A.A. Amis was in receipt of funds from: the Science Research Council, the Arthritis and Rheumatism Council, and the Leeds and Harrogate Area Health Authorities during part of this work.

Thanks for technical assistance are due to Miss McPherson, Charing Cross Hospital; Mr. Johnson, University College and Mr. Chaperlin, Imperial College.

References

Amis, A.A., Dowson, D., Wright, V., Miller, J.H. & Unsworth, A. (1977): An examination of the elbow articulation with particular reference to the variation of the carrying angle. Eng. Med. 6, 76.

Amis, A.A., Dowson, D., Wright, V. & Miller, J.H. (1979): The derivation of elbow joint forces and their relation to prosthesis design. J. Med. Eng. Technol. 3, 229.

Amis, A.A., Dowson, D. & Wright, V. (1980): Elbow joint force predictions for some strenuous isometric actions. J. Biomech. 13, 765.

Carlsöö, S. & Johansson, O. (1962): Stabilisation of, and load on, the elbow joint in some protective movements. Acta Anat. 48, 224.

Halls, A.A. & Travill, A. (1964): Transmission of pressures across the elbow joint. Anat. Rec. 150, 243.

Laine, V. & Vainio, K. (1969): Synovectomy of the elbow. In: 'Early synovectomy in RA', ed W. Hÿmans, W.D. Paul & H. Herschel, pp. 117-118. Amsterdam: Excerpta Medica Foundation.

Lewis, R.W. & Thibodeau, A.A. (1937): Deformity of the wrist following resection of the radial head. Surg. Gyn. Obstet. 64, 1079.

McDougall, A. & White, J. (1957): Subluxation of inferior radio-ulnar joint complicating fracture of radial head. J. Bone Jt. Surg. 39B, 278.

Patrick, J. (1946): A study of supination and pronation with especial reference to the treatment of forearm fractures. J. Bone Jt. Surg. 28B, 737.

Shoup, T.E. & Steffen, J.R. (1974): On the use of moire fringe patterns for the experimental kinematic analysis of plane motion. Mechanism and Machine Theory 9, 131.

Taylor, A.R., Mukerjea, S.K. & Rana, N.A. (1976): Excision of the head of radius in rheumatoid arthritis. J. Bone Jt. Surg. 58B, 485.

Taylor, T.K.F. & O'Connor, B.T. (1964): The effect on inferior radio-ulnar joint of excision of head of radius in adults. J. Bone Jt. Surg. 46B, 83.

Walker, P.S. (1977): Human joints and their artificial replacements. Springfield: C.C. Thomas.

7

Do minimum principles apply to joint loadings?

J.C. BARBENEL

INTRODUCTION

During function there are forces present at the skeletal joints. The forces have components due to externally applied loads, to the weight of the limbs and the accelerations produced during movement. In addition there are forces generated by muscles functionally associated with the joints. The magnitude of the externally applied forces may be measured directly and those due to the weight and the motion of the limb segments may be estimated from kinematic data and some suitable quantitative model.

The forces in the muscles, and therefore the joint forces, cannot be obtained from such measurements. They may, in theory, be calculated from the equations of equilibrium for a suitable skeletal segment. Unfortunately most joints have several muscles associated with them and this produces more variables than there are equilibrium equations, which precludes a unique solution. The simplest way of overcoming this problem is to group the muscles on a functional basis, until the number of unknown variables is equal to the number of available equations. This technique has been used to assess the forces acting in the hip (Paul, 1965; 1967), the knee (Morrison, 1968), elbow (Nicol et al., 1977) and metacarpophalangeal joints (Berme et al., 1977).

An alternative method is to select from all the possible solutions one that satisfies some additional condition. The additional condition is usually an optimality constraint requiring that the solution satisfy some minimum principle. Such minimum principles have extensive applications in the physical sciences, but the basis for their use in biological systems is unsubstantiated.

The present paper reports an investigation of the applicability of two minimisation constraints to a simple joint-muscle system - the temporomandibular joint and the jaw muscles.

The mandible was assumed to be stationary, and in the rest position, but applying an occlusal force. The conditions are equivalent to those occurring during biting with the posterior teeth.

MATERIAL AND METHODS

Anatomy

The mandible consists of a horizontal, curved bar of bone - the body - from the posterior ends of which two rami project upwards. The rami are oblong, nearly flattened plates surmounted by two processes separated by the mandibular notch. The anterior process is the coronoid; the posterior is the condylar process, the apex of which is the condylar head which articulates with the articular fossa of the temporal bone.

The temporomandibular joint connects the mandible with the rest of the skull via the articulating surfaces formed by the temporal bone and the condylar head. The joint is completely divided into two by a fibrous plate, the articular disc, the circumference of which is attached to the capsule which encloses the joint. The joint is strengthened by the sphenomandibular and the stylomandibular ligaments and by local thickenings of the capsule.

The following elevator muscles of the mandible were considered:
The temporal muscle which arises from the temporal fossa and the lateral wall of the skull. The fibres converge to form a tendon which is inserted into the coronoid process of the mandible.
The masseter muscle arises from the lower border and the deep surface of the zygomatic arch and is inserted over most of the outer surface of the ramus.
The median or internal pterygoid muscle arises from an area above and behind the tooth-bearing part of the maxilla. The fibres run backwards and downwards to be inserted on to the deep surface of the ramus. The area of insertion of the muscle on the deep surface of the ramus closely resembles the masseter insertion on the outer surface of the ramus.

The depressor muscle retained in the analysis was:
The lateral or external pterygoid muscle arises from two heads, one above the other, in the region of the origin of the median pterygoid muscle. The fibres converge postero-laterally towards the condylar head and fuse close to the point of intersection. The muscle is inserted into the neck of the condyle and into the capsule of the temporomandibular joint.

Lines of action of the muscles

Attempts to assess the lines of action of the elevator muscles have been made by Carlsöö (1952), who used a questionable technique, and by Mainland & Hiltz (1934), who assessed the lines of action from the direction of the superficial fibres of the muscle.

In order to include the influence of deep fibres of the muscle in the analysis, a dissection was undertaken to determine the position of centroids of area of origin and insertion of the masseter, temporal and internal and external pterygoid muscles. The assumption was made that the line joining these points was the line of action of the relevant muscle. This is a reasonable assumption only for those actions in which the whole of the muscle is active.

The results obtained from the dissection were referred to three orthogonal axes; the x axis was directed along the intercondylar axis, the y axis parallel to the Frankfort plane, and the z axis directed at right angles to the other two (Fig. 1).

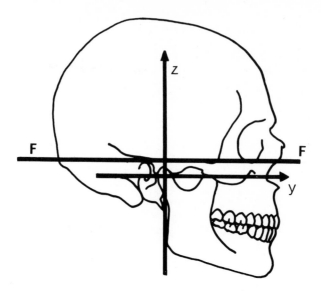

Fig. 1. Coordinate axes. The x axis is directed inwards along the intercondylar axis. The y axis is parallel to the Frankfort plane (FF)

The results obtained for the alignment of the elevator muscles were compared with those of Mainland and Hiltz. They were in good agreement and all results were pooled to produce mean values (Table 1).

Analysis

The forces acting on the mandible at the stage of biting when the jaw is stationary are:
1. Occlusal load. The load was assumed to act equally on each side of the mandible and to have a total magnitude of L. It was directed at an angle θ to the z axis.   The occlusal load had a moment about the x (intercondylar) axis of

   $$L.(Y \cos \theta + Z \sin \theta)$$

   where Y and Z were the coordinates of the point where the line of action of the occlusal load L intersected the occlusal plane.
2. Muscle forces. The mandible was assumed to be in the rest position with the muscles on each side acting equally. The muscle forces considered were the masseter (F_M), temporal (F_T), and the internal and external pterygoid muscles (F_I) and (F_E).   The force in each muscle was assumed to be equal on each side.
3. The temporomandibular joint force. The force acting on each condyle was assumed to have a magnitude R, and to act at an angle Φ to the z axis.

   When the mandible is at rest under the action of these forces there are three equations of equilibrium, which involve the experimentally determined direction cosines of the muscle force components. They are:

1. the sum of all the vertical (z) force components is equal to zero, or

$$0.84F_M + 0.84F_T + 0.78F_I - 0.17F_E - R\cos\Phi - L\cos\theta = 0 \qquad \ldots (1)$$

2. the sum of the horizontal (y) force components is equal to zero

$$0.55F_M - 0.46F_T + 0.50F_I + 0.91F_E - R\sin\Phi - L\sin\theta = 0 \qquad \ldots (2)$$

3. the sum of the moments of the forces is equal to zero.

Taking the moments about the intercondylar axis yields

$$2.7F_M + 2.6F_T + 2.3F_I - L(Y\cos\theta + Z\sin\theta) = 0 = 0 \qquad \ldots (3)$$

Table 1. *Values of mean and standard error in the mean of muscle force parameters*

muscles	direction cosines			moment arm about inter-condylar axis (cm)	no. of specimens
	x	y	z		
masseter	-0.12±0.02	0.55±0.04	0.84±0.02	2.7±0.2	4
temporalis	-0.18±0.03	-0.46±0.03	0.84±0.01	2.6±0.17	4
internal pterygoid	0.38±0.03	0.50±0.05	0.78±0.04	2.3±0.17	4
external pterygoid	0.39	0.91	-0.17	0.0	1

The three equations contain the four variables associated with the occlusal loading, which may be taken as the independent variables. The dependent variables are the muscle forces and the magnitude and direction of the joint force - a total of six unknown quantities. The difference between the number of unknown quantities and the number of equations, which is typical of the problem found in attempting to formulate and solve equilibrium equations for body segments, means that the values of the unknowns cannot be obtained by direct solution of the equations.

There are additional limitations on the muscle forces which cannot be negative. This requirement and the equations of equilibrium are equivalent to the 'zero sum two person game', which can be converted into a simple linear programming problem (Gass, 1975). This allows the introduction of additional constraints which requires the solution of the equation to minimise (or maximise) some additional function called the objective function, which is a linear combination of the non-zero variables.

RESULTS

Solutions were obtained for two objective functions, one of which minimised the sum of the forces in the jaw muscles, the other the magnitude of the resultant force at the temporomandibular joint.

Minimum Muscle Force

The objective function to be minimised was the unweighted sum of the muscle forces:

$$F_M + F_T + F_I + F_E \quad \text{and}$$

$$F_M \geqslant 0; \quad F_T \geqslant 0; \quad F_I \geqslant 0 \text{ and } F_E \geqslant 0$$

The equations of equilibrium (equations 1, 2 and 3) were additional linear constraints on the solution.

The solutions of these equations were obtained by systematically varying $\cos\Phi$, $\cos\theta$ and Y and the minimum value of the objective function located.

The solutions were obtained as a function of Y and θ, the two independent variables which described the location and direction of the occlusal load. All the solutions predicted that for the sum of the muscle forces to be a minimum, the masseter would be the only active muscle.

Minimum Joint Force

Unlike the muscle force the joint force may be negative, representing a tensile force supported by the joint capsule and the associated ligaments. It could not, therefore, appear in the objective function explicitly. In order to overcome this difficulty the joint force, and the objective function, was obtained from the first of the equilibrium equations. The function to be minimised was therefore:

$$\frac{1}{\cos\Phi} (0.84F_M + 0.84F_T + 0.78F_I - 0.17F_E - L\cos\theta) = R$$

This value of R was used to eliminate the joint force from the second equilibrium equation, and the resulting equation and the moment equilibrium equation were additional constraints on the solution. Solutions were once again obtained by varying $\cos\Phi$, $\cos\theta$ and Y.

The solutions obtained predicted that only the temporal and masseter muscles would be active if the joint force was a minimum.

DISCUSSION AND CONCLUSION

A necessary condition for either of the two minimum solutions to be true is that the predicted muscle activity should agree with that occurring during normal biting. The qualitative results of the analysis predicting which muscles should be active, allows a particularly simple comparison. It is possible to show by palpation, or electromyography, that during symmetrical biting the masseter, temporal and internal pterygoid muscles are certainly active. Electromyographic evidence suggests that the external pterygoid may also be active. Both the minimum muscle and minimum joint force solutions predict that the internal pterygoid muscles would be inactive, and that it is clear, therefore, that neither of these minimum principles applies during normal function.

The number of muscles predicted as being active cannot be greater than the number of equilibrium equations, and this suggests that a suitable choice of objective functions could lead to the prediction that the masseter, temporal and internal pterygoid muscles could be active.

A critical examination of the equations shows, however, that the minimum muscle force solution is determined by the moment equation (3) only. The muscle with the largest moment arm was the masseter, and this satisfied the moment equation while exerting the minimum force. The two force equilibrium equations (1 and 2) were satisfied by the force in the masseter muscle, and by $R\cos\Phi$ and $R\sin\Phi$, neither of which variables modified the magnitude of the objective function. The use of weighted muscle forces in the objective function (Penrod, Day & Singh, 1974; Chao & An, 1977; Pedotti, Khrishnan & Stark, 1978) may alter the particular single muscle which satisfies the moment equation, but will not introduce activity in additional muscles.

The joint force could be negative, and could not, therefore, appear in the objective function. The need to eliminate this variable reduced the number of independent equations to two, which becomes the maximum number of active muscles. As with the minimum muscle force constraint, the minimum joint solution cannot be modified so that it predicts three muscles are active.

The overall conclusion must be that there is no evidence from this study that either of the minimum principles employed is applicable to normal function.

References

Berme, N., Paul, J.P. & Purves, W.K. (1977): A biomechanical analysis of the metacarpo-phalangeal joint. J. Biomech. 10, 409-412.

Carlsöö, S. (1952): Nervous co-ordination and muscular function of the mandibular elevators. Acta Odont. 10, Suppl. 11.

Chao, E.Y. & An, K.N. (1977): Graphical interpretation of the solution to the redundant problem in biomechanics. ASME Paper, 77-Bio-1.

Gass, S.I. (1975): Linear programming. McGraw-Hill, New York.

Mainland, D. & Hiltz, J.E. (1934): Forces exerted in the human mandible by the muscles of mastication. J. Dent. Res. 14, 107-114.

Morrison, J.B. (1968): Bioengineering analysis of force actions transmitted by the knee joint. Biomed. Eng. 3, 164-170.

Nicol, A.C., Berme, N. & Paul, J.P. (1977): A biomechanical analysis of elbow joint function. In 'Joint replacement in the upper limb', London: I. Mech. E.

Paul, J.P. (1965): Studies of forces transmitted by joints II - engineering analysis. In 'Biomechanics and related bioengineering topics', ed R.M. Kenedi, Oxford: Pergamon Press.

Paul, J.P. (1967): Forces transmitted by joints in the human body. Proc. I. Mech. E. 181, 3J, 875.

Pedotti, A., Krishnan, V.V. & Stark, L. (1978): Optimization muscle force sequencing in human locomotion. Math. Biosci. 38, 57-76.

Penrod, J., Day, D. & Singh, F. (1974): An optimization approach to tendon force analysis. J. Biomech. 7, 123-129.

8

A loading and stress analysis of the patella

R.J. MINNS AND P.M. BRAIDEN

INTRODUCTION

Many hypotheses have been put forward to account for the appearance of lesions on the articular surface of the human patella and other joints of the body. Changes in the biochemistry of the cartilage and bone matrix have always accompanied chondromalacic lesions (Lund & Telhag, 1978). Nutritional and vascular alterations in chondromalacic patellae have also been noted (Hirsch, 1944; Bjorkstrom & Goldie, 1980). However, these changes have all been associated with unfavourable loading of the patella rather than a consequence of metabolic changes.

Three types of patellar articular cartilage lesions have been identified (Ficat & Hungerford, 1977). The first type is an open chondromalacic lesion usually confined to the medial and/or 'odd' facet (Goodfellow et al., 1976b) in which the surface appears fibrillated with tufts of collagen fibres exposed. These lesions have been seen clearly at arthroscopy (Leslie & Bentley, 1978). The second type of lesion, called 'basal degeneration' by Goodfellow et al. (1976b), is a closed chondromalacic lesion in which the surface appears normal but the deeper layers are disordered. On palpation the cartilage feels 'spongy'. This lesion usually occurs mainly in the more central zones of the patella.

The third type of lesion has a hard glistening surface appearance and is elastically very hard to the touch. This lesion has been characterised histologically by Ficat & Hungerford (1977) by the presence of extremely dense bundles of randomly organised collagen fibres which dominate the lesion. This lesion is usually confined to the lateral aspect of the patella and has been associated clinically with the 'extreme lateral pressure syndrome'.

These three types of lesion can be identified radiologically by position and appearance. Could these lesions be related to different types of loading and stresses within the patella? This was the question tackled in this study. The stresses within the patella arise from contact loads applied to the articular surface, muscular and tendon forces along the superior and inferior edges, and medial and lateral ligament and retinucular loads. The muscle loads can be applied obliquely by the 'Q' angle effect (that is the line of pull of the quadriceps muscle and the patellar ligament (Insall, Falvo & Wise, 1976)) which produces bending on the patella. Patella shape varies tremendously and we identified six axial-view shapes using the classification of Wiberg (1941). We included the effect of shape in our studies since this may alter significantly the magnitude and position of the stresses within the patella.

Our stress analysis model used measurements of the loading, shape, movement and material properties. Results were obtained for the magnitude and position of the stresses under different physiological conditions, and were related to the positions and type of lesion observed clinically.

MATERIALS AND METHODS

Figure 1 shows the sequence of events leading to the stress analysis of the patella.

Fifteen subjects of an average age of 31 years were tested using equipment to measure movement and load on upstairs, downstairs, and level walking, and when performing a 'knee bend'.

Patella Movement

In order to measure the angular position of the patella, a goniometer was built which allowed sagittal plane movement during knee flexion to be measured. This measurement relied on the assumption that the patellar tendon increased very little in length. A thermosetting plastic sheath which was securely fastened to the subject's calf, and an adjustable portion on its proximal end, allowed the experimenter to position a small hinged runner centrally on the patella. This followed the sagittal movement during knee flexion. Mounted on this runner was a transducer that was used in the angle measuring system. The angle measuring system used a polarised light goniometer to measure three angles: those of the thigh, calf, and patella in the sagittal plane. The variation of the angles during the four tested activities was recorded by an ultra-violet light recorder. The accuracy of this patella movement recording was checked on two subjects by lateral X-rays at three angles of knee flexion.

Ground to Foot Reaction Force

The force between the ground and the foot was measured by four miniature compression load cells positioned under the heel, first, third to fifth metatarsal heads, and the big toe of sandals worn by the subjects. The position of each load cell relative to the ankle axis was checked by lateral X-rays and the horizontal position by vertical X-rays. The output of each load cell was amplified, and the individual and total loads were recorded on the same ultra-violet strip chart recorder as the angular movements. A time marker on the recorder allowed cadence and step time to be calculated.

Other measurements of each subject were the tibia length, patellar tendon lever arm, hamstring/gastrocnemius lever arm and patellar tendon/tibia angle. These data were used in calculations of the loads passing through the patellar tendon, the quadriceps mechanism, the patello-femoral joint force and the tibio-femoral joint reaction. These forces were calculated by considering the static equilibrium of the patella,

45

the shank and foot. Assumptions were made about the loads passing through the hamstrings and gastrocnemius muscles and their effect on the patellar loads. For the stress analysis it was assumed that equilibrium was provided by the quadriceps muscle group, and although the weight of the calf and foot were taken into account (6 per cent of body weight), inertial forces were not.

Material Properties

The mechanical properties required for the stress analysis were Young's modulus (E) and Poisson's ratio (ν). The stress analysis reported here assumes isotropy, so only a single value of E and ν for each material was used. This simplification is currently being investigated by mechanical testing of specimens to relate the mechanical properties to anatomical site and degree of degeneration. The values of Young's modulus and Poisson's ratio for subchondral bone and articular cartilage in unconfined compression were obtained from our own recordings (Minns, Higginson & Atkinson, submitted for publication) and those for cancellous and cortical bone from Reilly & Burnstein (1974).

Contact Loading Areas

After obtaining the values and direction of the patello-femoral joint force it is necessary to know where this force acts on the patella section. It is generally agreed that for the lower values of knee flexion the contact areas occur centrally nearer the inferior pole and progress proximally with increased knee flexion (Goodfellow et al., 1976a; Townsend et al., 1977; Matthews, Sonstegard & Henke, 1977). In the model we used, the positions of load on the patella articulating surface nodes at four separate horizontal levels were deduced from published data.

Distribution of Patella Material

The stress analysis required data on the distribution of the four materials considered in the model. These were obtained by cutting postmortem patellae at four horizontal sections, obtaining radiographs of the surface and estimating the proportions of the materials by thickness, distribution and length. Seven vertical sections were also taken from other postmortem patellae. The distributions found at horizontal mid-section agree closely with those in horizontal sections prepared by Abernethy et al. (1978). A mid-vertical section used in the model is shown in Fig. 4. This shows the material distributions and loadings which were calculated.

Stress Analysis

The PAFEC finite element programme was used to calculate the three principal stresses occurring within all the elements of the model, together with the maximum shear stresses and principal stress directions. Output was in both numerical and graphical form. This allowed stress values to be obtained for each element and at any node in the model field.

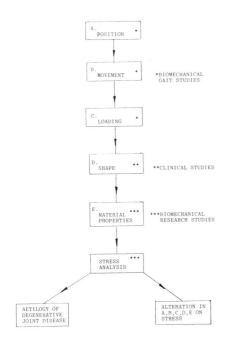

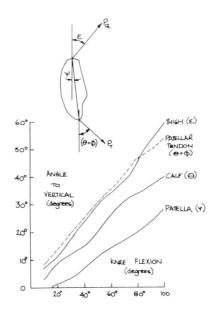

Fig. 1. Sequence of analyses used in computational analysis of stresses acting within the patella

Fig. 2. Sagittal plane movement of the patella relative to the thigh and calf during flexion whilst performing a squatting activity

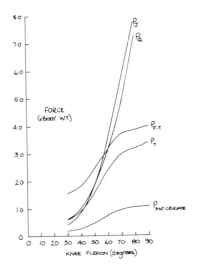

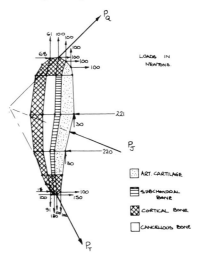

Fig. 3. Forces acting on the patella during a squat exercise. Patello-femoral joint reaction (P_J), quadriceps tension (P_Q), tibio-femoral joint force (P_{FT}), patellar tendon tension (P_T). It was assumed there were antagonistic muscle actions

Fig. 4. Vertical mid-section of the patella used by the computer model. The three loads acting on the patella are resolved into nodal loads. The distribution of the four materials used in the model is shown

47

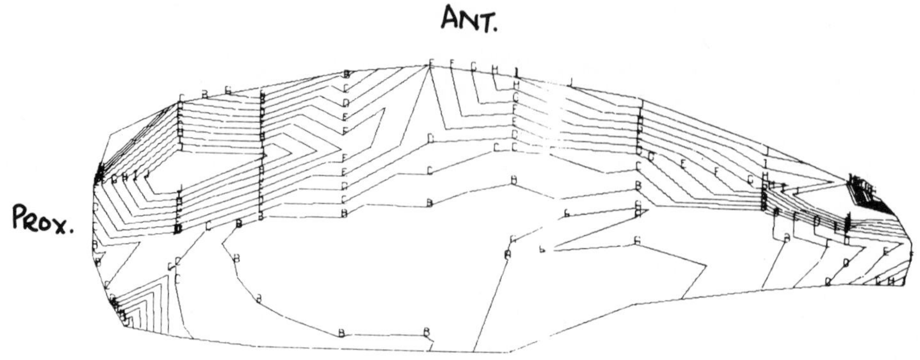

Fig. 5. Computer plot of stresses within the patella. Maximum principal (most positive) stress ($\times 10^6$): A-A-A 1.69E+00, B-B-B 7.46E+00, C-C-C 1.32E+01, D-D-D 1.90E+01, E-E-E 2.47E+01, F-F-F 3.05E+01, G-G-G 3.63E+01, H-H-H 4.20E+01, I-I-I 4.78E+01, J-J-J 5.35E+01 (scale 4.5510E+00:1)

ACTIVITY	FOOT REACTION FORCE	MAXIMUM VALUES (x BODY WEIGHT)										MAXIMUM* ARTICULAR CARTILAGE STRESSES MPa.	
		NO ANTAGONISTS		$P_{HAM} = P_T$		$P_{GAS} = P_T$		$P_{HAM} = 1.BW$		$P_{GAS} = 1.BW$			
		P_{FT}	P_J	P_{FT}	P_J	P_{FT}	P_J	P_{FT}	P_J	P_{FT}	P_J	Shear	Tensile
Level Walking	1.27	2.94	1.56	6.9	1.98	9.50	2.7	3.85	2.0	3.90	2.07	4.53	8.0
Upstairs	1.20	3.51	3.18	5.65	6.0	10.37	12.2	3.85	3.8	4.15	4.11	7.92	15.0
Downstairs	1.95	5.87	5.75	10.39	11.4	18.65	22.1	6.36	6.4	6.66	6.7	18.5	32.5

Table 1. Maximum values of patello-femoral joint reaction (P_J), and tibio-femoral joint force (P_{FT}) during level walking, walking upstairs and walking downstairs. Antagonistic muscle actions were calculated by assuming a variation of muscle tension with patellar tendon tension, and at a constant value of body weight, and their effects on P_J and P_{FT} are shown. The last two columns show the maximum shear and tensile stresses acting on the articular cartilage. *Tensile stress on surface, shear stress at subchondral bone/cartilage interface

RESULTS AND DISCUSSION

Forces on the knee and patella which were calculated for this study are summarised in Figs. 3 and 4. Typical stresses within the patella calculated from our model are shown in Fig. 5, and some forces and resultant stresses are summarised in Table 1. Only rigorous X-ray photogrammetry has been undertaken to describe patella movement (Veress et al., 1979). This is costly, damaging to the patient and involves static measurements. Using the goniometer described, we were able to track the sagittal rotation of the patella dynamically by non-invasive means. Measurements of patellar movement are shown in Fig. 2.

If the patella followed a course midway between the femur and tibia during squatting, the patella would remain nearly vertical. However, because of the articulation of the patella in the femoral groove and condylar shape, the patella follows a movement closer to the tibia. If the angle of the patellar tendon is added to the tibia it closely follows a rotation similar to the femur, but in the other direction. This would suggest that for a squatting activity the loading vectors are similar to those reported by Matthews et al. (1977). However we have found that this is not the case for the other activities we analysed.

The loadings we calculated were all very dependent on the lever arm of the patellar tendon, and thus a family of curves can be obtained. As the lever arm is increased there is a corresponding decrease in all the loads. If the lever arm is doubled, all the loads calculated were approximately halved. As a consequence of changes in loading with lever arm, the contact stresses will also decrease with an increase in patellar tendon elevation. This has been shown experimentally by Ferguson et al. (1979). For an average lever arm of 3.7 cm, the variation of loads associated with patella/knee loading are shown in Fig. 3 for a 'knees bend'. The patello-femoral joint force and the quadriceps mechanism tension rise sharply above 45° of knee flexion, whilst the patellar tendon tension and more interestingly the tibio-femoral force level off above 70° of knee flexion.

Contact stresses at the patello-femoral surfaces have been estimated for various activities using information on contact areas and loading (Matthews et al., 1977; Seedhom & Tsubuku, 1977). However, lesions have been seen all over the patellar surface, in particular areas which appear to have little or no contact with the femoral surface (Bentley, 1978; Goodfellow et al., 1976b). A preliminary stress analysis suggested that there exist areas of cartilage which are subjected to high tensile, compressive or shear stress under certain loading conditions (Minns, Birnie & Abernethy, 1979). These could produce lesions similar in appearance to those seen in articular cartilage (Minns, Steven & Hardinge, 1977), as well as the bony changes predominantly seen within the medial cortex of the patella (Darracott & Vernon-Roberts, 1971). The results from the stress analysis performed in this study indicate similar values of stress occurring in similar regions. An example of the distribution of the tensile and compressive stresses and their localisation is given in Fig. 5. As expected, high tensile stresses occur anteriorly and distally with compressive stresses on the articulating surface. Computer generated results detail the three principal stresses in the three planes and the maximum shear stresses and their angles to the vertical, horizontal and medio-lateral directions. The maximum shear stresses at the subchondral bone/ articular cartilage interface and maximum tensile stresses on the articular surface for three activities studied are shown in Table 1. The maximum shear stresses existed in all activities and loading conditions in the central regions of the patella, whilst the maximum tensile stresses occurred medially on the periphery and maximum compressive stresses on the central lateral region. All these values occurred at a maximum loading, greatest 'Q' angle (caused by the obliquity of the quadriceps/patellar tendon loading mechanism) and with high loads in the lateral retinaculum. These stresses may account for the localisation of the three types of lesion observed (Ficat & Hungerford, 1977) in particular they may account for the mechanism and position of the shear fatigue lesion (Minns, 1976).

Clinically, our results would suggest that compressive stresses could be reduced if the high lateral retinacular loads were reduced. This might be achieved by a surgical procedure similar to that described by Merchant & Mercer (1974). The medially-placed tensile stresses that arise could be reduced by correct alignment of the patellar tendon/ quadriceps mechanism. However, the alignment must be reduced accurately since a small lateral component of load would still produce harmfully high tensile stresses medially. We would not advocate removal of the articular cartilage as this would decrease the patellar tendon lever arm and consequently increase the patella loads, but also subject exposed subchondral bone to higher tensile and shear stresses.

References

Abernethy, P.J., Townsend, P.R., Rose, R.M. & Radin, E.L. (1978): Is chondromalacia patellae a separate clinical entity? J. Bone Jt. Surg. 60B, 205.

Bentley, G. (1978): The surgical treatment of chondromalacia patellae. J. Bone Jt. Surg. 60B, 74.

Bjorkstrom, S. & Goldie, I.F. (1980): A study of the arterial supply of the patella in the normal state, in chondromalacia patellae and in osteoarthrosis. Acta Orthop. Scand. 51, 63.

Darracott, J. & Vernon-Roberts, B. (1971): The bony changes in 'chondromalacia patellae'. Rheum. Phys. Med. 11, 175.

Ferguson, A.B., Brown, T.D., Fu, F.H. & Rutkowski, R. (1979): Relief of patellofemoral contact stress by anterior displacement of the tibial tubercle. J. Bone Jt. Surg. 61A, 159.

Goodfellow, J., Hungerford, D.S. & Zindel, M. (1976a): Patello-femoral joint mechanics and pathology. I: Functional anatomy of the patello-femoral joint. J. Bone Jt. Surg. 58B, 287.

Goodfellow, J., Hungerford, D.S. & Woods, C. (1976b): Patello-femoral joint mechanics and pathology. II: Chondromalacia patellae. J. Bone Jt. Surg. 58B, 291.

Hirsch, C. (1944): A contribution to the pathogenesis of chondromalacia of the patella. A physical, histologic and chemical study. Acta Chir. Scand. 90, Suppl. 83.

Insall, J., Falvo, K.A. & Wise, D.W. (1976): Chondromalacia patellae. A prospective study. J. Bone Jt. Surg. 58A, 1.

Leslie, I.J. & Bentley, G. (1978): Arthroscopy in the diagnosis of chondromalacia patellae. Ann. Rheum. Dis. 37, 540.

Lund, F. & Telhag, H. (1978): Content and synthesis of nucleic acids in the cartilage in chondromalacia patellae. Acta Orthop. Scand. 49, 535.

Matthews, L.S., Sonstegard, D.A. & Henke, J.A. (1977): Load bearing characteristics of the patello-femoral joint. Acta Orthop. Scand. 48, 511.

Merchant, A.C. & Mercer, R.L. (1974): Lateral release of the patella. A preliminary report. Clin. Orthop. 103, 40.

Minns, R.J. (1976): Cartilage ulceration and shear fatigue failure. Lancet 1, 907.

Minns, R.J., Steven, F.S. & Hardinge, K. (1977): Osteoarthrotic articular cartilage lesions of the femoral head observed in the scanning electron microscope. J. Path. 122, 63.

Minns, R.J., Birnie, A.J.M. & Abernethy, P.J. (1979): A stress analysis of the patella, and how it relates to patellar articular cartilage lesions. J. Biomech. 12, 699.

Reilly, D.T. & Burstein, A.H. (1974): The mechanical properties of cortical bones. J. Bone Jt. Surg. 56A, 1001.

Seedhom, B.B. & Tsubuku, M. (1977): A technique for the study of contact between visco-elastic bodies with special reference to the patello-femoral joint. J. Biomech. 10, 253.

Townsend, P.R., Rose, R.M., Radin, E.L. & Raux, P. (1977): The biomechanics of the human patella and its implications for chondromalacia. J. Biomech. 10, 403.

Veress, S.A., Lippert, F.G., Hou, M.C.Y. & Takamoto, T. (1979): Patellar tracking patterns measurement by analytical X-ray photogrammetry. J. Biomech. 12, 639.

Wiberg, G. (1941): Roentgenographic and anatomic studies on the femoropatellar joint with special reference to chondromalacia patellae. Acta Orthop. Scand. 12, 319.

9

Designing the human knee

JOHN O'CONNOR, JOHN GOODFELLOW AND EDMUND BIDEN

INTRODUCTION

The magnitudes of the forces transmitted by the various structures of a joint, tendons, ligaments and articular surfaces, depend not only on the nature of the external loads and the degree of muscle action but on the geometry of the joint structures. The geometrical information required for the calculation of such forces is usually obtained by direct anatomical measurement. Not all of these measurements are easy to make with sufficient accuracy. Some, such as the position of the line of action of the compressive force transmitted between the femur and the tibia, are hardly amenable to direct measurement.

However, the geometrical arrangements of the tendons, ligaments and articular surfaces are not independent of each other. Goodfellow & O'Connor (1978) have demonstrated that there is an intimate relationship between the geometry of the cruciate ligaments and the shapes of the articular surfaces of the tibio/femoral joint. When the dimensions of the cruciate ligaments and the distance apart of their attachment points on each bone are measured in one position of the joint, an attempt can be made to calculate the shapes of the surfaces which will articulate with each other without interpenetration or distraction while maintaining the ligaments at constant length in all positions of the joint.

The object of developing a theoretical model of the human knee is to define the minimum number of geometrical quantities which must be measured on cadaver specimens to allow subsequent calculation of the movement of the bones upon each other and the forces transmitted by the joint structures. Algebraic formulae for movements and forces are obtained in terms of geometrical quantities such as the lengths of ligaments and tendons and the location of their attachment points on the bones.

A sagittal-plane model of the knee is described in which the soft tissues are represented as straight-line tension-bearing elements of constant length and the bones and their articular surfaces are taken to be rigid. Ignoring external forces which could cause varus-valgus angulation or tibial rotation, we consider only the means by which the model knee can induce extension or resist flexion in the presence of external loads. Despite such crude approximations, the results of the analysis are found to agree quite well with the results of experiments on cadaver knees.

FORCES AT THE KNEE

Figure 1 shows two ways in which the tibia could be loaded by an external force W tending to flex the knee, Fig. 1a being a simulation of quadriceps strengthening exercises with the femur fixed and a weight hung from the tibia, Fig. 1b being a simulation of flexed knee stance. In both cases, the knee has to provide a resultant vertical force W and a couple M, Figs. $1a_2$, $1b_2$. The resultant force has a tensile component tending to distract the joint in one case and a compressive component in the other. The joint structures can provide the couple M only by some combination of compressive stress on the articular surface of the tibia and tensile stress in the soft tissues along the lines of their fibres. Figures $1a_3$ and $1b_3$ give a statically-equivalent description of the joint force and couple, consisting of the forces N and R normal and the force F tangential to the tibial plateau. The compressive force N can be provided by contact between the femur and the relatively flat tibial plateau, but the frictionless articular surfaces cannot provide the tension force R or the shearing force F. These latter must be provided by some combination of tension forces in the soft tissues.

The precise combination of soft tissue forces whose resultant is equivalent to the forces R and F cannot be determined from statics alone, because the forces must also produce compatible deformations of the soft tissues. We avoid the problem of analysing compatible deformations by making some assumptions. Near full extension, the patellar tendon in the human knee is directed slightly posterior to the tibial axis while at high angles of flexion it is directed slightly anterior. This suggests that the force in the rearward-looking patellar tendon could combine with that in forward-looking anterior cruciate near full extension, the posterior cruciate making no contribution while, at high angles of flexion, the force in the forward-looking patellar tendon could combine with that in the rearward-looking posterior cruciate, the anterior cruciate making no contribution. At some intermediate position of flexion, at which one cruciate has just shed its load and the other is about to accept its load, the patellar tendon could act alone to provide the forces R and F. These assumptions have the virtue that, in any position of the joint, only three joint forces - the compressive force between femur and tibia, the patellar tendon force and the force in one or other of the cruciates - are needed to keep the tibia in equilibrium and the values of these forces can be obtained directly from statics.

The assumptions just described are illustrated in Fig. 2 which also includes the geometrical quantities which must be known before the joint forces can be calculated. The forces R and F in Fig. 1 are statically-equivalent to the forces in the soft tissues. Their resultant must pass through either 0_1 in Fig. 2a, or 0_2 in Fig. 2b, where the lines of action of the patellar tendon force and either the anterior or the posterior cruciate force intersect.

The caption to Fig. 1 gives expressions for the forces R, F and N for both methods of loading the joint. Whereas the shear force F depends

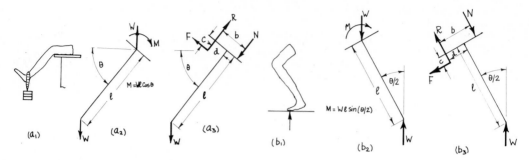

Fig. 1. (a)$_1$ *Leg lifting under external load W* (a)$_2$ *The joint has to provide a force W and a couple M* (a)$_3$ *Statically equivalent forces on the tibia.* $F/W = \cos\theta$;

$$N/W = (\frac{\ell}{b} - \frac{c}{b}) \cos\theta - \frac{d}{b} \sin\theta; \quad R/W = (\frac{\ell}{b} - \frac{c}{b}) \cos\theta + (1 - \frac{d}{b}) \sin\theta$$

(b)$_1$ *Flexed knee stance under external load* (b)$_2$ *The joint has to provide a force W and a couple M* (b)$_3$ *Statically equivalent forces on the tibia.* $F/W = \sin(\theta/2)$;

$$N/W = (\frac{\ell}{b} - \frac{c}{b}) \sin(\frac{\theta}{2}) + \frac{d}{b} \cos(\frac{\theta}{2}).$$

$$R/W = (\frac{\ell}{b} - \frac{c}{b}) \sin(\theta/2) - (1 - \frac{d}{b}) \cos(\theta/2)$$

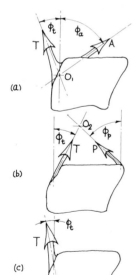

Fig. 2. *The combination of soft tissue forces to give the forces R and F of Fig. 1*

(a) *In the early stages of flexion, the force A in the anterior cruciate ligament acts with the force T in the patellar tendon.*

$A = (R \sin\Phi_t - F \cos\Phi_t)/\sin(\Phi_a + \Phi_t)$;

$T = (R \sin\Phi_a + F \cos\Phi_a)/\sin(\Phi_a + \Phi_t)$

(b) *At high angles of flexion, the force P in the posterior cruciate ligament acts with T.*

$P = (R \sin\Phi_t + F \cos\Phi_t)/\sin(\Phi_p + \Phi_t)$

$T = (R \sin\Phi_p - F \cos\Phi_p)/\sin(\Phi_p + \Phi_t)$

(c) *The intermediate position at which the patellar tendon acts alone.*

$T = F/\sin\Phi_t = R/\cos\Phi_t$

In the absence of external load and muscle action, the two cruciates can act together to balance a compressive force N between the articular surfaces, then

$T = 0; \quad A/N = \sin\Phi_p/\sin(\Phi_a + \Phi_p); \quad P/N = \sin\Phi_a/\sin(\Phi_a + \Phi_p)$

only on the values of the load W and the angle of flexion θ, the normal forces R and N in addition depend explicitly on the location of the points O_1 and O_2 and on the location of the tibio/femoral contact point as well as on the value of the external lever arm ℓ.

The caption to Fig. 2 gives expressions for the forces in the patellar tendon, and in the cruciate ligaments, in terms of the forces R and F and of the angles Φ_t, Φ_a and Φ_p which the lines of action of the tendon and ligament forces make to the tibial axis. Thus, to calculate the joint forces in any position, we need to know the angle of flexion, the length of the tibia, and six quantities characteristic of the joint, the three distances b, c and d (Fig. 1) and the three angles Φ_t, Φ_a and Φ_p (Fig. 2). In the next section, we consider the quantities which must be measured in order to obtain b, c, d, Φ_t, Φ_a and Φ_p for all positions of the joint.

GEOMETRY OF THE KNEE

Figure 3a shows a photograph of a human knee from which the lateral femoral condyle has been removed. It shows the femur connected to the tibia by the cruciate ligaments. The two ligaments and the two bones form a four-bar linkage. Kapandji (1970) and Huson (1974) demonstrated that the action of this linkage is mainly responsible for the distinctive motion of the femur on the tibia during flexion and extension - backward rolling with forward sliding during flexion, forward rolling with backward sliding during extension. Although it is well known that the fibres in the two ligaments are not uniformly tight in all positions of flexion and extension, we shall study the model of the cruciate mechanism shown in Fig. 3b in which the ligaments are represented by straight bars of constant length, connected to the tibia at A and B and to the femur at C and D.

The angle α, Fig. 3b, which the femoral attachment line CD makes to the tibial attachment line AB, is directly related to the angle of flexion. Figure 3a suggests that α is zero and CD is parallel to AB when the joint is flexed to about 50°, ie that $\alpha \simeq 50°$ when the joint is fully extended. Then the angle of flexion θ as defined in Figs. 1 and 2 is related to α by $\alpha = \alpha_o - \theta$ where α_o is the value of α at full extension. The axis of the femur then makes an angle $\pi/2 - \alpha_o$ to CD.

Inclination of the Cruciates to the Tibia

If the lengths of the cruciates a and p and the distances apart of their attachments to the femur f and to the tibia t are known (from measurement), we can calculate the inclinations Φ_a and Φ_p of the ligaments from the geometry of Fig. 3b. The appropriate formulae are given in the caption to Fig. 3. Note that the values of the angles depend on the relative rather than the absolute lengths of the bars in the mechanism of Fig. 3b.

Geometry of the Tibio/Femoral Articular Surfaces

We imagine the tibia to be rigidly fixed to the link AB of the cruciate mechanism, the femur to the link CD. The relative movement of the bones during flexion and extension is then entirely controlled by the changing geometry of the mechanism. The bones require articular surfaces which can transmit the compressive force N from one to the other. There is a wide variety of choice.

Goodfellow & O'Connor (1978) have shown that the point P in Fig. 3b, where the ligaments cross, is the Instant Centre of the joint. The two curves which are the loci of P with respect to the two bones also define the shapes of the articular surfaces, one attached to each bone, which would roll without sliding upon each other as the joint flexes and extends. For a given cruciate mechanism, the shapes of the non-sliding articular surfaces are unique. However, if the articular surfaces of the bones make contact with each other above the loci of P, the femoral surface would slide backwards as well as roll backwards on the tibia during flexion; if they make contact below the loci of P, the femur would slide forwards while rolling backwards on the tibia during flexion, as do the surfaces of the natural joint. There is therefore a wide variety of possible pairs of articular surfaces which can be compatible with a given cruciate mechanism, each pair giving a different combination of rolling and sliding. We can choose the shape and location on its bone of one of the articular surfaces and calculate the shape of the mating surface for the other bone.

In the present study, we take the tibial plateau to be flat, perpendicular to the tibial axis and lying in the plane AB of the ligament attachments. If the articular surfaces are not to interpenetrate or lose contact, the velocity of the point on the femoral surface in contact with the tibia must always be tangential to the tibial plateau. For each position of the joint, the only point which satisfies this condition is the point F in Fig. 3b which lies on a line through the instant centre P perpendicular to the tibial surface. The distance AF is then a direct measure of the position of the contact point on the tibial surface and a formula for its value is given in the caption to Fig. 3. If the articular surfaces are considered to be frictionless, PF is the line of action of the compressive force transmitted between the femur and the tibia.

The construction to find the shape of the mating femoral surface is indicated in Fig. 3c. The cruciate mechanism moves from ABCD to ABC'D' when the angle of flexion increases by a small amount. Relative to the tibia, the instant centre moves from P to P' and the contact point from F to F'. The point N at which the line PF intersects BC moves to N', the line NF on the femur moving to N'F". If the change in flexion angle between these two positions is sufficiently small, we can regard the segment of the femoral surface F"F' as a portion of a circular arc, with centre at 0' where the line F"N' intersects P'F'. Making the distance ON equal to O'N, the centre of curvature 0 of the femoral surface is found for the position ABCD and the radius of curvature is the height OF. Note that the centre of curvature of the femoral surface at the contact point can move both with respect to the tibia and the femur, and the radius of curvature at the contact point can also vary with the position of the joint. Since the distance F"F' between neighbouring contact points on the femoral surface clearly exceeds the distance FF' on the tibial surface, the femur slides forwards while rolling backwards on the tibia during flexion. This construction demonstrates quantitatively the intimate relationship between the geometry of the

a

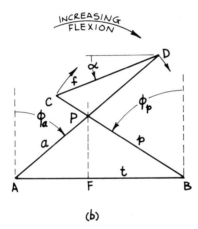

(b)

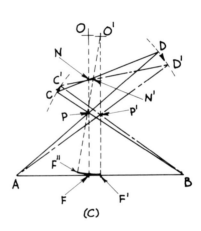

(C)

Fig. 3. (a) A human knee with the medial femoral condyle removed,
exposing the four-bar cruciate mechanism   (b) Diagram of the cruciate
mechanism. AB of length t is the tibia, CD of length f is the femur, AD
of length a is the anterior and BC of length p is the posterior cruciate
respectively. The axis of the femur makes an angle $\pi/2 - \alpha$ with CD.
The angle α and the angle of flexion θ are related by $\theta = \alpha_o - \alpha$. The
inclinations Φ_a and Φ_p of the cruciates to the tibial axis are given by

$$2aD^2 \sin \Phi_a = (D^2+a^2-p^2)(t+f \cos \alpha) - f \sin \alpha \sqrt{4a^2D^2-(D^2+a^2-p^2)^2}$$

$$2pD^2 \sin \Phi_p = (D^2+p^2-a^2)(t+f \cos \alpha) + f \sin \alpha \sqrt{4p^2D^2-(D^2+p^2-a^2)^2}$$

where $D^2 = t^2+f^2+2ft \cos \alpha$. The point of contact of the femur and the
tibia lies at F. The distance AF is given by $t \tan \Phi_a/(\tan \Phi_p+\tan \Phi_a)$
(c) The construction to find the centre of curvature of the femur at its
contact point with the tibia

57

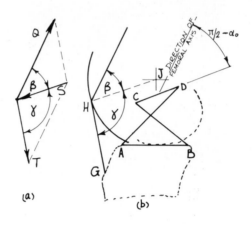

c

Fig. 4. (a) The patella as a three-force member, T the patellar tendon force, Q the quadriceps tendon force, S the patellar/femoral force. Q/T = sinγ/sinβ; S/T = (β+γ)/sin β   (b) The model of the patellar mechanism. The point H is fixed in the patella. The quadriceps tendon is parallel to the femoral axis. The patellar track on the femur is a circle, centred at J of radius JH. GH is the patellar tendon (c) X-ray of a human knee showing that the quadriceps tendon is parallel to the femur

articular surfaces at a joint and the geometry of the soft tissue array spanning the joint.

The construction leaves open the possibility that the articular surfaces can transmit compressive forces and the soft tissues tension forces even in the absence of external forces or muscle action. If they do, such a set of forces must be self-equilibrating, the resultant tension force being equal and opposite to the resultant compressive force, both on the same line of action. If the force in the patellar tendon is zero (no muscle action), the forces in the two cruciate ligaments could act together to balance the compressive force (Fig. 2). The resultant of the cruciate forces passes through P, Fig. 3. The components of the cruciate forces parallel to the tibial plateau act in opposite directions and can have equal magnitudes in all positions of the joint, their components perpendicular to the tibial plateau can add to give a resultant through P equal and opposite to the compressive force. Formulae for the ligament forces, expressed as fractions of the compressive force, are given in the caption to Fig. 2. They show that the ligament forces in the unloaded joint can vary with the position of the joint, a result which may be consistent with the observation that different fibres in the anterior cruciate of a cadaver knee are tight in different positions of flexion when the joint is passively manipulated. Note that such forces would be additional to the forces transmitted by the joint structures in the presence of external loads or muscle action.

The geometry of the cruciate mechanism and associated tibio/femoral articular surfaces has given us three of the quantities needed for the calculation of the forces needed to resist flexion, Φ_a, Φ_p and the line of action of the compressive force. To complete the calculation, we must locate the centre of the soft tissue forces, 0_1 or 0_2 in Fig. 2, and the position of the tibial axis in relation to the knee. A study of the patellar mechanism is required.

The Patellar Mechanism

In the sagittal plane, the patella sits in equilibrium mainly under the action of the tension forces Q and T in the quadriceps and patellar tendons and the compressive force S applied by contact with the femur, Fig. 4a. For equilibrium, the lines of action of these three forces must meet at a single point, H in Fig. 4b.

In our model of the patellar mechanism, the three forces intersect at the same point H in the patella for all positions of the joint. In addition, the point H also lies on a circular track on the femur, with centre at J and radius JH. The patellar tendon is attached to the tibia at G and to the patella at H and the distance GH is constant. As the femur rolls backwards on the tibia during flexion, so does its circular patellar track, carrying with it the point H. As the flexion angle changes, the angle Φ_t which the patellar tendon makes with the tibial axis varies in a manner which can be calculated when the dimensions of the cruciate and patellar mechanisms have been chosen. The point H always lies at the intersection of two circles, a circle of radius GH and centre fixed at G in the tibia and a circle of radius JH and centre J moving with the femur.

This model fixes immediately the lines of action of the forces T and S.

Figure 4c shows a radiograph of a human knee in which, fortuitously, the patellar and quadriceps tendons are clearly shown. The quadriceps tendon lies closely parallel to the axis of the femur. It was observed in Fig. 3 that the line of the femoral attachments CD makes an angle α_o to the tibial plateau AB when the joint is fully extended, that CD is parallel to AB when the joint is flexed to α_o. In any position of the joint, the axis of the femur and therefore the line of action of the quadriceps force makes an angle $\pi/2 - \alpha_o$ with CD (Fig. 4b). Figure 3a suggests that α_o is about 50°.

From this model, we can calculate the patellar tendon angle Φ_t and, with the cruciate angles Φ_a and Φ_p, establish the locations 0_1 and 0_2 of the centres of the soft tissue forces. In addition, the caption to Fig. 4 gives formulae for the quadriceps and patellar-femoral forces as ratios Q/T and S/T of the force in the patellar tendon. The force ratios depend only on the angles β and γ (Fig. 4), which separate the lines of action of the patellar-femoral force from those of the quadriceps and patellar-tendon forces respectively. Both these angles change as the joint flexes. Thus, the kinematics and statics of the patellar mechanism are intimately related to those of the tibio/femoral joint. The forces in the quadriceps and patellar tendons differ from each other if the angles β and γ differ. There is therefore a distinction between the patellar mechanism and the simple frictionless pulley with which it is often compared.

The Tibial Axis

Specification of the patellar mechanism completes all but one of the geometrical quantities required for the force formulae in Figs. 1 and 2. The values of b and c (Fig. 1), are known when the locations of 0_1 and 0_2 have been determined. There remains the quantity d, the distance of the soft tissue force-centre from the tibial axis. Where does the knee-joint lie in relation to the tibial axis?

There are various assumptions we could make but we shall fix on one. In the situation of Fig. 1a, consider the tibia hanging under its own weight W at 90° of flexion. Assume that the tibial axis passes through the centre of gravity of the limb and is vertical in this position. The joint structures have to provide an equal and opposite force W and zero couple. The simplest system of forces at the joint which could maintain the tibia in equilibrium in this position would be tension in the patellar tendon and posterior cruciate with zero compressive force between the articular surfaces (Fig. 2b). The line of action of the tibial weight force would then pass through 0_2 in this position. We therefore take the tibial axis to pass through 0_2 when the joint is flexed to 90°. This implies that the compressive force between the bones is zero at 90° flexion when the limb is loaded as in Fig. 1a.

Calculations

The development of the sagittal plane model has identified the geometrical quantities which must be known before the movement of the bones at the joint and the forces transmitted by the joint structures can be calculated. They are the lengths of the four links of the cruciate mechanism, the position within the femur of the centre of its patellar track and the radius of that track, the position on the tibia of the patellar tendon attachment and the length of the tendon, the angle of flexion α_o at which CD is parallel to AB. In principle, these are all quantities which can be measured on cadaver specimens. In practice, such measurements may not all be easy to make, although they may be easier than trying to detect the changing orientation of a ligament or tendon with position. Ligaments and tendons are not straight-line elements of constant length attached at single points to the bones but bundles of flexible fibres attached over finite areas. It is not possible to assign a single length to a ligament nor to locate its point of attachment on a bone with precision.

We shall compare the predictions from the model with independent measurements of the shape of the femoral articular surface, the movement of the tibio/femoral contact areas, the force in the anterior cruciate ligament and the ratio of the quadriceps to patellar tendon forces. Calculations of these quantities were carried out for a number of combinations of model dimensions and the combination which best fits the experimental results is shown in Fig. 5, with its dimensions given in the caption. Further calculations are still in hand. If a combination of dimensions can be found which gives satisfactory prediction of all aspects of the mechanical behaviour of cadaver knees in the sagittal plane, such dimensions may then be deemed to represent the effective lengths of ligaments and tendons, and the effective location of their attachment points in that plane.

RESULTS

Shape of the Femoral Articular Surface

Figure 5 includes the calculated shape of the femoral surface which articulates without interpenetration or distraction with a flat tibial plateau. For comparison, the outlines of sagittal sections through the lateral and medial femoral condyles of a cadaver knee are also shown. The calculated shape represents a reasonable compromise between the two anatomical sections. Figure 5 also shows the calculated track on the femur of the centre of curvature of the femoral surface of the model. This has a shape generally similar to that described by Kapandji (1970).

Movement of the Tibio/Femoral Contact Point

For the model dimensions quoted above, the contact point between the femur and the tibia and the line of action of the compressive load moves posteriorally through a distance of 22.5 mm when the joint is flexed from full extension to 90° of flexion.

Kapandji (1970, p. 99) shows diagrams of the menisci at full extension and 90° of flexion. The geometrical centres of the areas on the tibia covered by the menisci move backwards 6 mm on the medial side and 12 mm on the lateral side. These distances are rather less than our calculated movement of the contact point. However, it must be difficult to locate the centre of pressure of the forces transmitted through the menisci. Kapandji notes that, while the menisci are tightly interposed between the articular surfaces at full extension, the femur makes contact only with the posterior portions of the menisci in flexion.

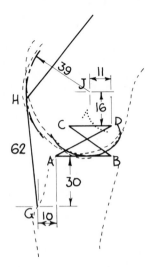

Fig. 5. Dimensions of the model. AB = 35,
AD = 4 , CD = 27, BC = 32, α_0 = 55°. All
lengths in mm. The solid line is the
calculated shape of the femoral surface which
articulates with a flat tibial plateau. The
chain-dotted line is the model patellar track.
The dashed outlines of sagittal sections through
medial and lateral condyles of a human femur are
shown for comparison. The dotted line is the
calculated path on the femur of the centre of
curvature of its contact point with the tibia

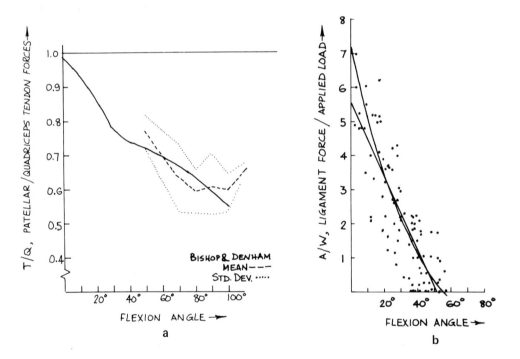

a

b

Fig. 6. (a) Left: the ratio of forces in the quadriceps and patellar
tendons as determined by Bishop & Denham (1977). The solid line is the
result of the present calculations   (b) Right: the force in the
anterior cruciate ligament as determined by Malcolm & Daniel (1980).
The straight line is the least squares fit of data from eight specimens.
The curved line is the result of the present calculations

Thus, the distances he quotes are likely to underestimate the movement of the line of action of the compressive force.

Ratio of Quadriceps and Patellar Tendon Forces

Bishop & Denham (1977) have measured the forces in the quadriceps and patellar tendons of cadaver knees and expressed their results as a ratio. Upper and lower bounds for this ratio are plotted against flexion angle in Fig. 6a. The solid line in Fig. 6a is the result of our calculations. There is reasonable agreement between their measurements and our results. This comparison is a test not only of our model of the patellar mechanism, but also of the model cruciate mechanism, since the relationship between the angles β and γ, Fig. 4, depends in part on the motion of the femur on the tibia.

Force in the Anterior Cruciate Ligament

Fortunately, during the course of this work, independent experimental evidence became available to us. Malcolm & Daniel (1980) have attempted to measure the force in the anterior cruciate ligament during a simulation of quadriceps strengthening (Fig. 1a). With the femur fixed horizontally, a weight hung from the ankle and the knee joint intact, various positions of flexion were obtained by lengthening a wire attached to the quadriceps tendon. A precise optical method was used to determine the antero-posterior location of the tibia relative to the femur in each position of flexion. The anterior cruciate was then removed and replaced by a wire threaded through a Teflon (p.t.f.e.) tube. For each of the previous positions of flexion, the force in the ligament replacement wire required to restore the antero-posterior location of the bones to its previously corresponding value was measured. The value of this force was deemed to equal the force in the anterior cruciate of the intact knee.

The results of experiments on eight human cadaver knees were kindly provided to us prior to publication and are shown in Fig. 6b. The straight line is the least squares fit for all the data. The curved line is the result of our calculation, using the dimensions of the model quoted above.

DISCUSSION

The comparison between experimental and theoretical results is generally satisfactory, although not completely so. The shape of the femoral surface, the magnitude of the force in the anterior cruciate ligament, and the ratio of quadriceps to patellar tendon forces are calculated with reasonable accuracy. However, the calculated excursion of the tibio/femoral contact point exceeds the experimental estimates. The predicted variation of the quadriceps tendon force (not reported here) also exceeds experimental measurements. We are currently attempting further refinement of the model in search of closer agreement.

The calculated movement of the tibio/femoral contact point could be reduced by assuming the tibia to have a convex articular surface. More recent sections through cadaver knees have revealed that, while the point of attachment to the tibia of the anterior cruciate ligament lies reasonably close to the tibial plateau, that of the posterior cruciate lies substantially below at the rear of the joint. Our further calculations will take account of these factors.

The present work has concentrated on the action of the knee in resisting flexion or inducing extension. We are planning a further development to account for the action of the posterior structures in extension or inducing flexion. Goodfellow & O'Connor (1978, Fig. 9) demonstrated how the anterior cruciate ligament combines with the posterior capsular ligament to provide the tensile component of the couple which prevents hyper-extension. This suggests a similar complementary role for the cruciates in resisting extension, the anterior cruciate acting with the posterior structures in the early stages of flexion and the posterior cruciate acting in the later stage of flexion.

CONCLUSIONS

(1) The theoretical analysis demonstrates quantitatively the intimate relationship between the geometry of the soft tissue array spanning the knee joint and the geometry of its articular surfaces. (2) It adds further support for the view that the cruciate ligaments mainly control the backwards movement of the femur on the tibial plateau during flexion. (3) It identifies the particular geometric quantities to be determined by experiment to allow study of the motion of the bones and the forces transmitted between them in the sagittal plane. (4) Its main novelty is a description of the complementary roles of the two cruciates in developing forces at the knee necessary to resist flexion. In the early stages of flexion, the patellar tendon acts with the anterior cruciate, at high flexion with the posterior cruciate. Only at about 50° of flexion are both cruciates unloaded.

Acknowledgement - We wish to thank the Arthritis and Rheumatism Council for their support of this work.

References

Bishop, R.E.D. & Denham, R.A. (1977): A note on the ratio between tensions in the quadriceps tendon and infra-patellar ligament. Eng. Med. 6, 53.

Goodfellow, J. & O'Connor, J. (1978): The mechanics of the knee and prosthesis design. J. Bone Jt. Surg. 60B, 358.

Huson, A. (1974): The functional anatomy of the knee joint: the closed kinematic chain as a model of the knee joint. In 'The knee joint', pp. 163-168. International Congress Series No. 324. Amsterdam: Excerpta Medica.

Kapandji, I.A. (1970): The physiology of the joints, Volume 2, Lower Limb. London and Edinburgh: Churchill Livingstone.

Malcolm, L. & Daniel, D. (1980): A mechanical substitution technique for anterior cruciate ligament force determination. Proceedings of the Orthopaedic Research Society, Atlanta.

10

Three-dimensional measurement of forces on the knee

M.W. WHITTLE

PURPOSE

The object of the study was to aid in the diagnosis and assessment of disorders of the knee joint, by calculating the forces transmitted by the ligaments, tendons and articular surfaces, in normal subjects and in a range of pathological conditions.

Amongst the most difficult orthopaedic conditions to diagnose are soft tissue injuries of the knee, particularly injuries involving the menisci and the ligaments. Accurate diagnosis, and particularly an assessment of the severity of an injury, is necessary before deciding whether conservative or operative treatment is indicated (Ginsburg & Ellsasser, 1978).

It is anticipated that the force transmitted by different joint structures during walking will prove to be a more accurate guide to the presence and degree of injury than conventional methods of clinical examination.

METHOD

In order to determine the forces transmitted by joint structures, it is necessary either to instrument the structures involved directly, which is generally impractical, or to measure the ground reaction force and the position of the limb, and to calculate the forces within the joint. This study uses the latter approach, by means of a force plate to measure the ground-reaction force vector, and two or more television cameras to determine the location of reflective markers attached to anatomical landmarks on the subject's limbs (Fig. 1).

Two Kistler force plates are used, which provide a description of the magnitude, direction and point of application of the ground-reaction force. The force plate signals are sampled by an analogue-to-digital converter on-line to a Digital PDP-11/34 computer.

The television cameras are also on-line to the computer, through an interface developed by Jarrett (1978). The anatomical markers show up as bright spots in the field of view of the cameras, and the coordinates of these spots are stored on computer disc for later analysis.

In order to provide a complete three-dimensional measurement system, the field of view of the television cameras is calibrated each time the

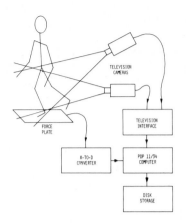

Fig. 1. Scheme of the measurement system

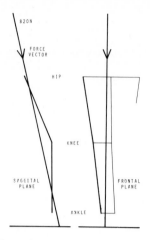

Fig. 2. Limb position and force vector at point of maximal flexor moment in a normal subject

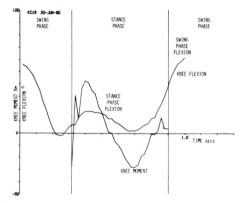

Fig. 3. Angle of knee flexion and knee moment in normal subject

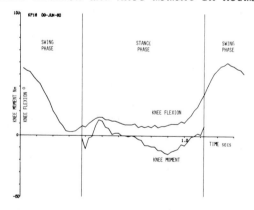

Fig. 4. Angle of knee flexion and knee moment in patient with meniscal tear

system is used, by taking in data from a frame on which reflective markers are situated at known locations. Two-dimensional least squares fitting is used to establish the best fit between the image of the calibration points on the television tube and their known position in three-dimensional space. The constants derived from this calibration are used to calculate the three-dimensional location of the markers on the subject's limbs.

RESULTS

The measurement system has just become operational, and to date only preliminary studies have been performed. Figure 2 shows at one instant of time the relative positions of the limb and the force vector in the sagittal and frontal planes in a normal subject. Figure 3 shows recordings during one stance phase of the knee angle and the moment about the knee in the sagittal plane in the left knee of the same normal subject. Figure 4 shows the same measurements in a patient with a torn lateral meniscus in the left knee. This second record demonstrates a reduced cadence, a decreased stance phase flexion, and a marked reduction in both flexor and extensor knee moments.

DISCUSSION

A great deal has been published on the measurement of knee joint forces in walking. Many of the earlier studies used only one type of data (kinetic or kinematic), or used both types of data but made only two-dimensional measurements. Those earlier workers who made three-dimensional measurements used either electrogoniometers, which tend to modify the patient's gait, or three-dimensional (biplanar) cine photography, which is an accurate but very labour intensive measurement technique.

There are two basic approaches to measuring the positions of the limb in space - to determine the coordinates of markers over anatomical landmarks, or to determine the position of the foot and the angles of the limb segments, and hence to calculate 'up the leg' from the floor. The latter approach is undoubtedly less accurate, but is currently being used successfully in clinical practice (Johnson & Waugh, 1979).

A variety of methods are available for measuring the three-dimensional location of anatomical landmarks. Cine photography is probably the most accurate method, but the time taken to analyse the data makes it unsuitable for routine measurements or for large scale studies. Methods in which electrical devices, such as light emitting diodes or photocells, are fixed over the anatomical markers are accurate, but generally limited in range, and are subject to a certain amount of interference with the patient's gait because of the need for wires to connect with the devices. The television system is very flexible, in terms of distance and viewing angle, and the subject is generally not aware of the presence of the markers. Data collection is extremely rapid, so that analysis can be completed within a few minutes. Preliminary estimates of the accuracy of the present system indicate a standard deviation of measurement of 3-4 mm in all three dimensions.

Measurement of the foot-ground reaction force and the position of the limb in space permits calculation of the knee moment, which will eventually be followed by the use of a mathematical model to derive the forces within the joint.

References

Ginsburg, J.H. & Ellsasser, J.C. (1978): Problem areas in the diagnosis and treatment of ligament injuries of the knee. Clin. Orthop. 132, 201.

Jarrett, M.O. (1976): A television/computer system for human locomotion analysis. PhD thesis, University of Strathclyde, Glasgow.

Johnson, F. & Waugh, W. (1979): Method for routine clinical assessment of knee-joint forces. Med. Biol. Eng. Computing 17, 145.

11

Force plate studies of patients undergoing hip joint replacement

S. KHODADADEH, I.A.F. STOKES AND M.W. WHITTLE

INTRODUCTION

Patients with hip diseases have been shown to walk with a reduced movement of the hip joints (Murray et al., 1972) and in such a way that the total loading on the hip joint is decreased (Paul & McGrouther, 1975). The object of the present study was to develop measurement techniques which could be used to assess the effect of osteoarthritis of the hip on simple parameters of gait and to establish to what extent replacement of the hip joint with a prosthesis affected the measured parameters.

METHOD

Patients were assessed using a walkway equipped with two 'Surrey' force plates, and two 'Kistler' force plates. The 'Surrey' plates were positioned side-by-side to record the vertical reaction force over two or more paces (Fig. 1), and the 'Kistler' plates were placed diagonally so that a six-component description of the force on each limb could be recorded separately. The results of three walks over each pair of force plates were analysed. The patients were also examined clinically and assessed for the degree of disability. The following gait parameters were measured before and after total hip replacement:

Magnitude of first peak of vertical load on each limb (kN)
Magnitude of second peak of vertical load on each limb (kN)
Time to the first peak of vertical load on each limb (msec)
Time to the second peak of vertical load on each limb (msec)
Durations of the vertical load on the limbs (stance phase) (msec)
Double support time (time for which load was imposed on both limbs) (msec)
Area under the vertical force/time recording (N-s)
Stride length (mm)
Step length (mm)
Walking base (the distance between footprints, perpendicular to the walking direction) (mm)

Methods of deriving these parameters are shown in Figs. 1 and 2.

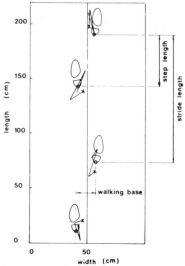

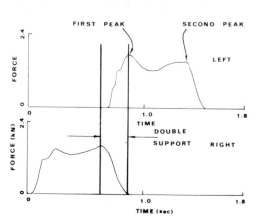

Fig. 1. Definition of gait
parameters from footprints. The
distance between footprints made by
powder on the patient's shoes was
measured and compared with indirect
measurements given by positions of
the centre of pressure on the
'Surrey' force plates. (0 = initial
measured position; X = initial
computed position)

Fig. 2. Definition of the
parameters of loading on the limbs,
and the timing of peak loads and
time of 'double support'

PATIENTS STUDIED

Forty-two patients were studied before, and about six months after,
Charnley total hip replacement. Of these, 27 were female (age range 52-
78 years), and 15 were male (age range 48-70 years). Patients were
divided into three groups according to the condition of their limbs:
Group A - unilateral involvement (23 patients), Group B - bilateral
involvement, one hip already replaced (11 patients), and Group C -
bilateral involvement, no previous hip operation (8 patients).

RESULTS

1. No significant correlation was found between the clinical assessment
of the patients and quantitative measurements of gait.
2. Pre-operative findings:
   (i) Patients with unilateral hip disease showed asymmetry in both the
timing and magnitude of limb loading. Mean time to reach the first peak
load was 407 msec (s.d. = 162.2) for the non-operated limb, and 362 msec
(s.d. = 190.5) for the operated limb. This difference is significant at
the P<2.5 per cent level. Similar observations were found for the
magnitude of the vertical peak loads. The mean first peak load on the

non-operated limb was 0.70 kN, s.d. = 0.14, on the operated limb 0.67 kN, s.d. = 0.13, P<2.5 per cent; and the mean second peak load for non-operated limbs was 0.71 kN, s.d. = 0.10, operated limbs 0.68 kN, s.d. = 0.13, P<2.5 per cent.

(ii) Patients with bilateral hip disease were much more symmetrical in their gait; no significant differences were seen in these patients between gait measurements of their two limbs.

3. Post-operative findings:

(i) After operation, patients with unilateral hip disease showed a return towards symmetrical gait. Mean time to reach the first peak load was 259.5 msec (s.d. = 122.3) for the non-operated limb, and 325 msec (s.d. = 156.7) for the operated limb. This difference is significant at the P<0.1 per cent level.

(ii) Patients with bilateral hip disease retained their pre-operative gait symmetry after surgery.

4. The major differences in gait pattern following operation were a decrease in the stance phase duration (pre-operative mean, 1073 msec, s.d. = 283, and post-operative mean, 951 msec, s.d. = 214, P<0.1 per cent), and an increase in stride length (pre-operative mean, 928 mm, s.d. = 15, post-operative mean, 1065 mm, s.d. = 14.7, P<0.1 per cent).

CONCLUSIONS

By investigating the symmetry of walking before and after hip replacement surgery, some parameters of gait associated with a painful hip have been identified. The most significant differences between asymptomatic and treated hips were the duration of loading and stride length, with some differences in the measurements of the magnitude of limb loading.

References

Paul, J.P. & McGrouther, D.A. (1975): Forces transmitted at the hip and knee joint of normal and disabled persons during a range of activities. Acta Orthop. Belg. 41, 78.

Murray, M.P., Brewer, B.J. & Zuege, R.C. (1972): Kinesiologic measurements of functional performance before and after McKee-Farrar total hip replacement. J. Bone Jt. Surg. 54A, 237.

12

Adaptive mechanics - the skeleton's response to mechanical stress

L.E. LANYON

INTRODUCTION

During the last century the assumption that the primary role of bone was a structural one would never have been questioned. The weight of the literature, such as it was, reflected this opinion. Ward was performing simple loading experiments on cubes of cancellous bone as early as 1838 and the ideas of Meyer and Wolff that bone tissue was optimally arranged to withstand stresses, the distribution of which could be mathematically predicted, was supported by Kock's detailed analysis of the proximal femur in 1917. From that time until the present day the rise of the biochemically based disciplines has shifted the standpoint from which most people approach bone physiology.

The principal methods now used to study the mechanical properties and behaviour of isolated pieces of bone are essentially the same as those which were available at the start of the century. These traditionally rely either on loading whole bones, bone fragments or bone-shaped models with apparently suitable loads, or mathematical modelling of bone-like shapes subjected to such loads. Despite the sophistication made possible by techniques such as finite element analysis, the fundamental assumptions on the manner of loading and the limitations on the method of loading outside the body are the same as those experienced a hundred years ago. Research on the mechanical properties of bone tissue has led from the use of simple criteria of the strength of materials into the uncertainties of anisotropic analysis of heterogeneous partially visco-elastic material. Such considerations when applied to problems of clinical significance, such as finite element models of total hip replacement, produce programmes of increasing complexity (ie Svensson, Valliappan & Wood, 1977; Tarr et al., 1979). While each additional complication may edge such models closer towards reality the improvements which result from altering the minutiae of the geometry and physical properties of the material are small compared with the large imponderable assumptions on the manner and distribution of loading which are inevitable in the analytical approach.

REMODELLING OF BONE AND SOFT TISSUE

Skeletal biomechanics is not, and should not be, confined to considering in isolation the properties of the materials and the loading situation of the structures concerned. The most exciting and clinically relevant challenge lies in determining the living relationships of these tissues, and the organs of which they are part, with the mechanical tasks which they perform. The cellular populations of bone and soft tissue make little structural contribution to the immediate physical properties of the material which they have produced. By virtue of their remodelling capability however these cells can swiftly transform the tissue's characteristics. There are many factors which influence connective tissue cells to form, control the mineralisation of, and subsequently maintain or remodel their matrix. The most fascinating of these, and that most relevant to a consideration of their structural role, is the mechanism whereby the tissue's mechanical circumstances influence cellular activity to adapt the character, mass, and orientation of the matrix in a structurally appropriate manner. It is the structural appropriateness of this response which suggests that it is adaptive in nature. In the bony skeleton it is this adaptive response which is responsible throughout growth and after maturity for maintaining a match between the shape of the whole bone, the orientation of its internal architecture, and the mass of its tissue. In soft tissues functional adaptation occurs; but, since these structures transmit tension, they are self-aligning and their gross shape is neither constant nor critical nor needs to be adapted.

Most studies on the structure to function relationship in bone and soft tissues have inevitably been qualitative. Usually the mechanical input to the system has been changed and the tissue's response observed. Those experiments involving regimes of increased activity have shown that animals which have been exercised develop larger muscles, larger tendons and larger bones than those which have not. The most striking example of functional adaptation caused by exercise is the observation quoted by Jones et al. (1977) that professional tennis players have 35 per cent more bone in the humerus on their playing, rather than their non-playing, sides. In bones the response to high levels of activity is that the structure's mass increases but its material properties stay constant (Tschantz & Rutishauser, 1967; Chamay & Tschantz, 1972; Woo et al., 1979). In tendons, intermittent strain produces a rapidly recoverable change in properties (Weisman, Pope & Johnson, 1979) but increased exercise alters not only the long term properties of the tissue but also increases the mass of the structure (Woo et al., 1979). Thus increase in activity from a pre-existing level causes a positive adaptive response in these tissues, whereas decrease causes a reduction in the ultimate strength of tendons and ligaments and a loss of bone tissue (Marotti & Marotti, 1965; Burkhart & Jowsey, 1967; Player et al., 1979; Donaldson et al., 1970).

The inference is clear, therefore; in both soft and hard tissues the 'normal' amount of tissue present represents an equilibrium position in which the tissue's mechanical environment determines an appropriate tissue mass and orientation, and in soft tissue appropriate material properties. The origin of the regulatory stimulus is still obscure. Bone and collagenous tissue are the recipients of mechanical activity, not its instigators. The immediate effect of functional activity in these tissues is unaffected by the metabolism of their cellular

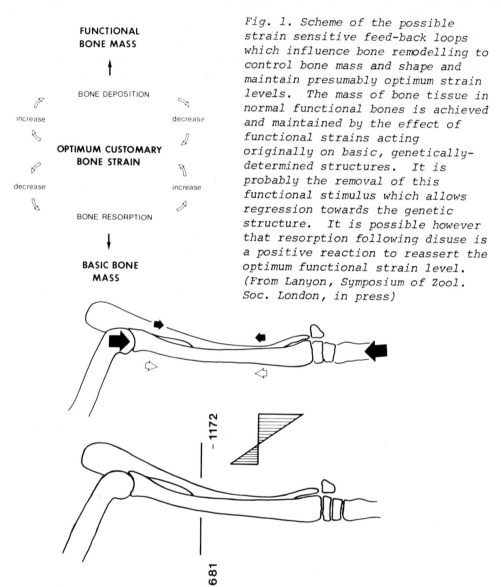

FUNCTIONAL
BONE MASS

↑

BONE DEPOSITION

increase

decrease

OPTIMUM CUSTOMARY
BONE STRAIN

decrease

increase

BONE RESORPTION

↓

BASIC BONE
MASS

Fig. 1. Scheme of the possible strain sensitive feed-back loops which influence bone remodelling to control bone mass and shape and maintain presumably optimum strain levels. The mass of bone tissue in normal functional bones is achieved and maintained by the effect of functional strains acting originally on basic, genetically-determined structures. It is probably the removal of this functional stimulus which allows regression towards the genetic structure. It is possible however that resorption following disuse is a positive reaction to reassert the optimum functional strain level. (From Lanyon, Symposium of Zool. Soc. London, in press)

-1172

681

Fig. 2. (a) Principal origins of load in sheep radius. Loading through its joint surfaces (large black arrows) will cause bending with the cranial (convex) surface in longitudinal tension and the caudal (concave) surface in longitudinal compression. Tension in the flexor muscles on the concave surface (small black arrows) supports the animal during its stance phase and contributes to this bending. Only tension in the extensor musculature on the convex surface (open arrows) or relocation of the bone's cortices towards the compressive surface could neutralise this bending. (b) The strain situation on the sheep radius at peak strain during walking. The cranial (convex) surface of the radius is under longitudinal tension strain (681 x 10^{-6}) the caudal (concave) surface is under longitudinal compression (-1172 x 10^{-6}). The bone's natural curvature accentuates the bending within the bone which arises due to compression through the joint surfaces and tension in the flexor musculature. (From Lanyon, Symposium of Zool. Soc. London, in press)

population. In bone it has been supposed that the stimulus which influences mass arises from the strain pattern which is induced by functional activity within the tissue. It has become a generally accepted idea that the mass of tissue present is adjusted until a, presumably optimum, functional strain level is achieved (Fig. 1). This optimum strain, which is likely to be a property of the tissue, will be at a compromise level ensuring tissue economy on the one hand and an adequate fatigue life with respect to the strains produced by coordinated activity on the other. The disadvantage of high functional strains is clearly the level of tissue damage that they would induce. The disadvantage of low strains could simply be that transportation of superfluous tissue is wasteful of energy to the whole organism. Since the only purpose of high bone mass is a structural one, there is likely to be an inbuilt tendency to reduce bone mass to a minimum compatible with structural competence. However, repetitive intermittent strain may not simply provide bone tissue with an indication of its mechanical circumstances but may actually aid the physiology of the osteocyte population, possibly by facilitating movement of fluid or providing a beneficial electrical environment. If this were the case regulation of tissue mass could be maintained by an active feedback in both positive and negative directions. The remodelling goal of the whole bone would therefore presumably be directed to establishing this optimum level of functional tissue strain uniformly throughout the skeleton.

EXPERIMENTAL STUDIES

The distribution of stress throughout bone tissue may be controlled by not only adjusting the mass of the tissue but also the shape of the structure. The axial mode of bone loading is the one which presents the highest safety factor to failure with greatest tissue economy. Bone is strongest in compression and the least strain is engendered for the highest load if it is applied axially. In cancellous bone the precise and apparently advantageous orientation of trabeculae in the direction of the principal tensile and compressive strains (Koch, 1917; Lanyon, 1974) has been regarded as an adaptation to achieve for these bone elements the advantages of axial loading, and to avoid the high strains associated with bending. The position and manner of loading of whole bones makes it inevitable that they are subjected to bending moments. It was Frost's idea (1973) that these moments could be partially or completely neutralized by moments in the opposite direction generated by the curvature of the bone (Fig. 2a). These curvatures, which are characteristic of many long bones, develop as a result of functional activity (Lanyon, 1980), and so Frost's idea that their development has a positive functional advantage would be a logical one. Unfortunately for the general applicability of this concept, although overall compression is the normal loading mode for some bones, in others the curvatures which they develop seems to increase rather than neutralize the bending caused by their manner of loading (Fig. 2b).

One consequence of loading a bone simultaneously in compression and bending is that a uniform load distribution is impossible. Since strain gauge studies have also shown that cortical thickness is not proportional to load it follows that a uniform strain distribution is

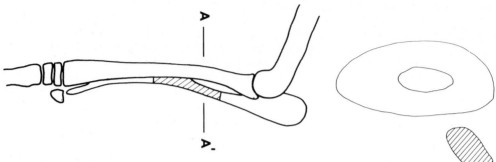

Fig. 3. (a) Left: a lateral outline traced from a radiograph of a sheep radius and ulna illustrating the cranially convex curvature of the radius and the area (shaded) of the ulna removed in the overload experiment described in the text. (b) Right: transverse outlines traced from sections taken at the level A-A on Fig. 2a. The upper section shows the normal radius with the much smaller ulna adjacent to the lateral edge of its caudal surface. The new bone formation which resulted over a one year period following removal of the ulna is shaded on the lower section. Although the cranial (upper) surface experienced the greater 20% functional overstrain the new bone formation was predominantly deposited on the caudal surface which had only a 10% overstrain but a higher absolute normal strain (see Fig. 2b). (From Lanyon et al. Trans. Orthop. Res. Soc. 1980)

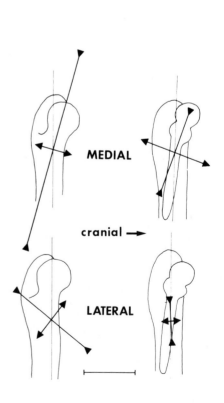

Fig. 4. Outlines taken from lateral radiographs of the femora of sheep with and without a femoral component of a total hip prosthesis. An indication of the pure principal strains during walking on the medial and lateral side of the bone is illustrated. The direction of each line indicates that of the principal strain, the length is proportional to the size of the strain the label represents 200×10^{-6}.

(From Lanyon et al. Trans. Orthop. Res. Soc. 1979)

not possible either (Lanyon & Baggott, 1976; Lanyon, Magee & Baggott, 1979). Thus, although the bone tissue may have similar properties in different regions, the strain distribution throughout the structure is not uniform and some areas must normally be strained more than others. The sheep radius illustrates this situation: there is a disparity in normal functional strain levels between cranial and caudal cortices of 1.8:1 (Fig. 2b). Despite this, when peak walking strain levels are increased by only 10-20 per cent (by removing the ulna) this results in adaptive new bone formation. The new bone is deposited, not in the region of greatest overstrain, but in the region of greatest absolute strain (Lanyon et al., 1980). Its effect is not simply to restore the normal walking strain level, since after adaptation these strains were actually less than normal (Fig. 3).

This result is remarkable in a number of ways. Although the functional strain levels were elevated by the ulnar osteotomy these levels could easily have been achieved by the animal walking slightly faster. Thus adaptive remodelling was induced not only by levels of strain which were physiological for bone tissue but by levels which could easily have been encountered in that particular location. This fact, coupled with the overcompensation in local strain levels which was the result of remodelling, suggests that it is not these levels alone, but possibly also the pattern of strain distribution throughout the structure, which influences bone remodelling. The small re-organisation of strain pattern which produced an adaptive change in this experiment should be compared with the more radical re-organisation normally associated with internal fixation and prosthetic joint replacement.

PROSTHETIC JOINTS

The most successful joint replacement is that of the hip. Nevertheless, despite the success of this procedure, loosening of the prosthesis, endosteal resorption of the femur, and calcar resorption are all too common complications. Although there is no agreement on the origin of the loosening process the traditional, mechanically-based explanation for the resorption, and in many cases total obliteration of the calcar, which is commonly associated with loosening, is that this region of bone is protected from functional stress by the presence of the prosthesis. Considerable effort has been devoted to designing prostheses with collars which rest upon the calcar. The intention of this procedure being that the collar will transmit longitudinal compressive loads to the bone in this region so re-establishing the stimulus to maintain its normal architecture (Oh & Harris, 1979). Although there is no bone strain data from the situation in humans in vivo, animal studies have shown that the presence of the femoral component does reduce peak longitudinal compressive locomotor strains on the surface of the calcar by some 60 per cent while at the same time increasing tensile hoop strains by 31 per cent (Lanyon et al., 1979) - Fig. 4. This indicates a substantial re-organisation of surface strain compared to that just referred to in the radius overload experiment. However, the manner of bone-loading produced through a prosthetic femoral component is so different from that through a normal proximal femur that the strain distribution within the bone cortex may differ even more substantially than the surface strain measurements suggest. When it is considered that changes in customary surface strain in the sheep radius as small as 10 per cent have been shown to induce adaptive remodelling it is perhaps not surprising that this should also occur following even more substantial changes to the loading situation of the femur after total hip replacement. It is unfortunate, however, that in this case the remodelling should be deleterious to the fixation. Stabilisation of fractures with stainless steel fracture plates similarly affects the strain regime of the bone fragments reducing functional strains immediately beneath the plate by 80 per cent (Lanyon et al., 1979). This strain reduction, like that associated with the total hip prostheses, results in nett resorptive remodelling (Akeson et al., 1976) which in this case, because it occurs within the cortex, is not deleterious to the fixation but reduces the strength of the whole bone, so predisposing it to refracture. Designs of prostheses and fracture fixation devices which reduce functional strains in the bone tend to produce bone resorption, but it is not necessarily inevitable that this should be so. It is, however, a substantial challenge to design implants so that they are capable of fulfilling their own mechanical function, by withstanding the loads to which they must be subjected, and yet so distribute load to their host bone that they do not induce remodelling deleterious to the fixation.

FIXATION OF FRACTURES

In fracture fixation devices, the use of materials other than metals with properties closer to those of bone is proving to be one means of reducing stress protection and the resulting resorptive remodelling which leads to a decrease in bone strength (Moyen et al., 1978; Bradley et al., 1979). Since it is self-evident that the pre-operative situation is compatible with normal bone remodelling it is an empirically sound objective to attempt to restore this situation after both internal fixation and prosthetic replacement. In our present state of ignorance this also seems a safe course to take, particularly since we neither understand what constitutes a satisfactory strain environment nor how or why this varies from place to place. At present the mechanical analysis on which the design of any new implant is based can only be relevant to the construction of the implant itself. Except in the most general way, it cannot be influenced by any knowledge of how the host structures will react after it has been implanted, because this knowledge is only available by inference from trial-and-error comparisons.

Our lack of knowledge of the interaction between bones and their mechanical environment is highlighted in relation to implant surgery. Such surgery is usually made necessary as a result of mechanical failure in the skeleton. No biological system could be expected to withstand more than a certain proportion of motor cycle or car accidents so skeletal inadequacy cannot be claimed in these situations. Fractures of overwhelming traumatic origin are, however, less common than those resulting from nearer normal functional loads in patients with reduced and inadequate bone mass.

OSTEOPOROSIS AND AGING

Bone loss occurs in both sexes after the age of 50 (Dequeker, 1975). This loss places a sizeable proportion of the female population at risk from fracture under the loads involved in everyday activities (Riggs, 1979). During the first 50 years of a normal person's life-span the amount of bone in the skeleton is maintained appropriate to the mechanical demands made upon it. This match can potentially be a close one, because the same loading situation which provides the stimulus for adaptive remodelling is also that which causes the damage to the bone's structure. In addition to mechanical events there are of course many hormonal, biochemical and dietary factors which affect the balance of bone remodelling. The predominance of females in the population which sustains fractures, the steeper decline in bone mass after the menopause, and the post-menopausal state of elderly women, has concentrated practically all efforts towards finding a biochemical lesion responsible for the aetiology of this condition and an appropriate biochemical treatment for it. Despite these efforts there still appears to be no satisfactory hormonal or biochemical treatment which can, over the long term, shift the balance of bone remodelling away from resorption and towards apposition. Indeed in Riggs' recent review (1979) he concluded that after 40 years clinical investigation at the Mayo Clinic they had found that only combined therapy with fluoride (which has unpleasant side effects) could cause an increase in bone-forming surfaces. He proposes that 'because fluorohydroxyapatite crystals are larger than those of hydroxyapatite it is possible that the flow of piezo-electric current in bone is increased and that this stimulates osteoblasts'. It is perhaps significant that almost inadvertently Riggs has suggested a biochemical treatment that would depend for its success on bone's mechanical strain regime, since the electric potentials which develop in bone and are responsible for flow of charge are generated by intermittent strain within the bone tissue. Indeed, although it would be foolish to ignore the significance of hormonal changes and biochemically based influences in the aetiology of osteoporosis, a definition of the condition is that there is a reduction of bone mass to the extent of mechanical incompetence. In other words the largely unstudied mechanism which is acknowledged to be responsible during the first three quarters of our life for maintaining a normal, mechanically competent structure, fails to do so in old age - particulary when the hormonal balance following the menopause favours bone resorption. The mechanically sensitive remodelling response of the skeleton is still present (Dickson, 1977); it is just no longer effective in preventing a steady decline in bone mass, despite the fact that customary intermittent bone strains should be increasing as the bone available to take functional loads decreases. This deficiency may reflect a failure of the bone cells to respond appropriately to a continuing or, perhaps, increasing stimulus. Alternatively the mechanical 'input' to the skeleton in elderly people may no longer provide the cellular population of bones with a suitable stimulus. It has for instance been suggested (Lanyon & Hartman, 1977) that if functional strains were to influence bone cells through strain-related potentials then only strains imposed above certain strain rates would provide a remodelling stimulus whereas strains at any rate will cause damage. Thus the increasing strains which accompany decreasing bone mass are inappropriate as a stimulus, unless applied at sufficiently high (youthful) strain rates. Whatever the reason for the failure of the mechanically-sensitive response effectively to maintain appropriate bone mass, the balance of skeletal remodelling in the elderly is still influenced by the bone's mechanical circumstances. Immobilisation, inactivity and bed rest still lead to negatively-balanced remodelling and calcium loss, whereas restored function leads to increased bone mass (Dickson, 1977). In dogs Uhthoff, Jaworski & Liskova-Kiar (1979) have demonstrated not only the reversibility of immobilisation osteoporosis but also that, in dogs of different ages, different bone surfaces are involved. Although it would be foolish to ignore the substantial hormonal contribution to the aetiology of age-related osteoporosis, the influence of mechanical factors in this condition, although sometimes alluded to, has never been systematically investigated.

TISSUE REMODELLING AND DEGENERATIVE DISEASE OF JOINTS

The relationship of functional bone-loading to osteoarthrosis has received more attention and there are reports that in rabbit knee joints at least intermittent loading can cause stiffening of the subchondral bone masses and that this may be associated with cartilage overload and joint degeneration (Simon et al., 1972; Radin et al., 1973). Patients who have low bone mass tend to be protected from osteoarthrosis while those with high mass are most at risk (Foss & Byers, 1972).

If the relationship between bone-remodelling and mechanical stress underpins the aetiology of osteoporosis and osteoarthrosis, as well as being fundamental to the use of the implants which are increasingly used to treat these conditions, then it appears to be one of the most significant and most-neglected relationships in orthopaedic science today. Our ignorance of the nature of this relationship in calcified tissues is only surpassed by that in relation to cartilage and soft tissue.

References

Akeson, W.H., Woo, S.L-Y., Rutherford, L., Coutts, R.D., Gonsalves, M. & Amiel, D. (1976): The effects of rigidity of internal fixation plates on long bone remodelling. Acta Orthop. Scand. 47, 271.

Bradley, G.W., McKenna, G.B., Dunn, H.K., Daniels, A.V. & Statton, W.O. (1979): Effects of flexural rigidity of plates on bone healing. J. Bone Jt. Surg. 61A, 866.

Burkhart, J.M. & Jowsey, J. (1967): Parathyroid and thyroid hormones in the development of immobilisation osteoporosis. Endocrinology 81, 1053.

Chamay, A. & Tschantz, P. (1972): Mechanical influences in bone remodelling. Experimental research on Wolff's Law. J. Biomech. 5, 173.

Dequeker, J. (1975): Bone and ageing. Ann. Rheum. Dis. 34, 100.

Dickson, R.A. (1977): The effect of synovectomy on function and bone density in the rheumatoid hand. Proc. Br. Orthop. Res. Soc.

Foss, M.V.L. & Byers, P.D. (1972): Bone density, osteoarthrosis of the hip and fracture of the upper end of the femur. Ann. Rheum. Dis. 31, 259.

Frost, H.M. (1973): 'Bone modelling and skeletal modelling errors.' Springfield, Ill.: Charles C. Thomas.

Koch, J.C. (1917): The laws of bone architecture. Am. J. Anat. 21, 177.

Jones, H.H., Priest, J.D., Hayes, W.C., Tichenov, C.C. & Nagel, D.A. (1977): Humeral hypertrophy in response to exercise. J. Bone Jt. Surg. 59A, 204.

Lanyon, L.E. & Baggott, D.G. (1976): Mechanical function as an influence on the structure and form of bone. J. Bone Jt. Surg. 58B, 436.

Lanyon, L.E. & Hartman, W. (1977): Strain-related electrical potentials recorded from bone in vitro and in vivo. Calc. Tiss. Res. 22, 315.

Lanyon, L.E., Paul, I.L., Thrasher, E.L., Rubin, C.T., Liebmann, V.L., Simon, S.R., Rose, R.M. & Radin, E.L. (1979): In vivo strain measurements of bone and prosthesis following total hip replacement. Trans. Orthop. Res. Soc., 37.

Lanyon, L.E., Baggott, D.G. & Goodship, A.E. (1979): Strain protection and bone remodelling induced by dynamic compression plates - an experimental study in vivo. Trans. Orthop. Res. Soc., 167.

Lanyon, L.E., Magee, P.T. & Baggott, D.G. (1979): The relationship of functional stress and strain to the processes of bone remodelling. An experimental study on the sheep radius. J. Biomech. 12, 593.

Lanyon, L.E., Goodship, A.E., O'Connor, J.A. & Pye, C.J. (1980): A quantitative study on the functional adaptation of bone. Trans. Orthop. Res. Soc., 296.

Lanyon, L.E. (1980): The influence of function on the development of bone curvature. An experimental study on the rat tibia. J. Zool. (in press).

Marotti, G. & Marotti, F. (1965): Topographic-quantitative study of bone tissue formation and reconstruction in inert bones. In 'Calcified tissues'. Proc. Third Europ. Symp. on Calcified Tissues, ed H. Fleisch, H.J.J. Blackwood & M. Owen. Berlin: Springer Verlag.

Moyen, B.J-C., Lahey, P.J.Jr., Weinberg, E.H. & Harris, W.H. (1978): Effects on intact femora of dogs of the application and removal of metal plates. J. Bone Jt. Surg. 60A, 940.

Oh, I. & Harris, W.H. (1978): Proximal strain distribution in the loaded femur. An in vitro comparison of the distributions in the intact femur and after insertion of different hip replacement femoral compounds. J. Bone Jt. Surg. 60A, 75.

Player, J.S., Klein, L., Heiple, K.G., & Goldberg, V.M. (1979): Biomechanical strength and collagen turnover in disuse models of the ligament-bone complex. Trans. Orthop. Res. Soc., 292.

Radin, E.L., Parker, H.G., Pugh, J.W., Steinberg, R.S., Paul, I.L. & Rose, R.M. (1973): Response of joints to implant loading. III. J. Biomech. 6, 51.

Riggs, B.L. (1979): Post menopausal and senile osteoporosis: Current concepts of aetiology and treatment. Endocrinol. Japan S.R. No. 1, 31.

Simon, S.R., Radin, E.L., Paul, I.L. & Rose, R.M. (1972): The response of joints to impact loading - II. In vivo behaviour of subchondral bone. J. Biomech. 5, 267.

Svensson, N.L., Valliappan, S. & Wood, R.D. (1977): Stress analysis of human femur with implanted Charnley prosthesis. J. Biomech. 10, 581.

Tarr, R.R., Lewis, J.L., Jayson, D., Sarmienter, A., Schmidt, J. & Latta, L.L. (1979): The effect of materials, stem geometry and collar-calcar contact on stress distribution in the proximal femur with total hip. Trans. Orthop. Res. Soc., 34.

Tschantz, P. & Rutishauser, E. (1967): La surcharge mecanique de l'os vivant. Les deformations plastiques initiales et l'hypertrophie d'adaptation. Ann. Anat. Path. 12, 233.

Uhthoff, H.K., Jaworski, Z.F. & Liskova-Kiar, M. (1979): Age specific activity of bone envelopes in experimental disuse osteoporosis and its reversal. Trans. Orthop. Res. Soc., 125.

Ward, F.O. (1838): 'Outlines of human osteology'. London.

Weisman, G., Pope, M.H. & Johnson, R.J. (1979): The effect of cyclic loading on knee ligaments. Trans. Orthop. Res. Soc., 24.

Woo, S.L-Y., Ritter, M.A., Sanders, T.M., Gomez, M.A., Garpin, S.R. & Akeson, W.H. (1979): Long term exercise effects on the biomechanical and structure properties of swine tendons. Trans. Orthop. Res. Soc., 23.

13

The effect of externally applied loads on bone remodelling in the radius of the sheep

J.A. O'CONNOR, A.E. GOODSHIP, C.T. RUBIN AND L.E. LANYON

INTRODUCTION

The concept that the shape and structure of bones are directly influenced by their mechanical circumstances was proposed in the late 19th century (Wolff, 1892). Recent observations have supported this view. Increased physical activity as in professional athletes results in an increase in bone mass (Jones et al., 1977) whereas bed rest or immobilisation result in a decrease (Donaldson et al., 1970; Uhthoff & Jaworski, 1979). This mechanically-based influence on bone-remodelling is commonly supposed to be dependent on the strain produced within the bone tissue as a result of functional loading (Bassett, 1968).

Hert & his co-workers (1971 and 1972) investigated bone's mechanically-related adaptive response, assessing the new bone formation which resulted from artificial loading of the tibiae of rabbits. However, the loads they applied to the bone were chosen arbitrarily to be within the physiological strain range, and neither the normal functional strains in that region nor those artificially induced were measured directly. Although the stimulus for adaptive remodelling is almost certainly related to strains which occur within bone tissue there is considerable circumstantial evidence that the bone's cellular population may be influenced by strain-generated electrical potentials rather than strain itself. The size of these potentials generated within wet bone tissue is dependent upon both the magnitude of the strain and the rate at which it is applied (Black & Korostoff, 1974; Lanyon & Hartman, 1977). In the experiments reported here the intention was to determine the effect of strain and strain rate on adaptive bone remodelling in the sheep's radius. Both the normal (in locomotion) and artificially-imposed mechanical strain regimes were assessed using rosette strain gauges bonded to the bone surfaces in vivo.

METHOD

1. Locomotor Studies

Rosette strain gauges were bonded to both the cranial and caudal mid-shaft surfaces of the radius of sheep using the technique previously described (Lanyon, 1976). The animals were exercised on a treadmill at varying speeds and the resulting strain patterns were recorded. The changing size and direction of the principal strains were calculated throughout a number of strides at each speed.

2. *Loading of the Sheep Radius in vivo*

Using the technique previously described (Goodship et al., 1980), metal prostheses were inserted and bending loads were applied, in vivo, to the radii of sheep in the cranio-caudal plane. Both the strain level and strain rate were varied, but all regimes were applied at 0.5 Hz for one hour per day for a period of six weeks. The changes in bone mass which occurred during this experimental period were followed by direct photon absorptiometry. Fluorescent bone labels were given in single intravenous doses at weekly intervals so that sequential new bone formation could be studied at post-mortem in hard tissue sections.

The sheep were divided into four different treatment groups:

a. Loaded to produce strain levels below those induced during walking, at normal walking strain rates.

b. Loaded to produce strain levels higher than those induced during walking, at normal walking strain rates.

c. Loaded to produce strain levels higher than those induced during walking, at higher than walking strain rates.

d. Loaded to produce strain levels higher than those induced during walking, at lower than walking strain rates.

The normal reference walking speed for sheep was taken as being one metre per second. The strain level was taken to be the peak principal strain value throughout the stride and the figure for strain rate was found by estimating the maximum strain change occurring during both the loading and unloading phases of the stride, over an interval of 0.025 s.

RESULTS

1. *Locomotor Studies*

The magnitude of the peak principal strains on the radius during locomotion increased with speed, but in a non-linear manner, since they were also dependent on the animal's gait. Peak strain magnitude increased steadily through the walk and trot, but decreased at the trot to gallop transition. The manner of loading assessed by the principal strain direction on each cortex, and the relative strain values on opposing cortices, remained almost constant with increased speed. Both the on (loading) and the off (unloading) principal compressive strain rates were linearly related to the speed of the sheep despite changes in gait. Figure 1 shows the relationship between locomotor speed and these parameters for the caudal surface of the sheep radius.

The mean principal longitudinal strains recorded from the radii of eight sheep walking at one metre per second were +937 (s.e. = 5) microstrain and -1294 (s.e. = 9) microstrain. The mean strain rates (in microstrain per second) at which these were imposed were 8000 (s.e. = 500) and 15 000 (s.e. = 1100) and the strain rates at which these were released were 14 000 (s.e. = 900) and 26 000 (s.e. = 2500). The values given are those for the cranial and caudal surfaces respectively.

The artificial pattern of loading produced a strain change pattern

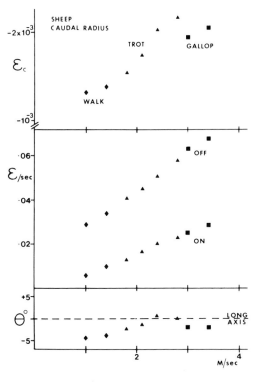

Fig. 1. The peak principal compressive strain, its rate of imposition and release, and its angle to the bone's long axis, as a function of locomotor speed

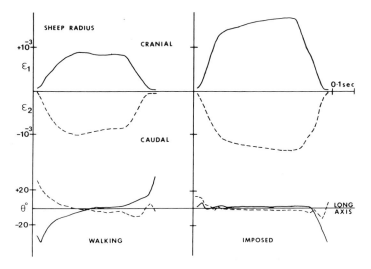

Fig. 2. The principal strains together with their angle to the bone's long axis occurring on the sheep's radius during one locomotor cycle and one typical imposed cycle

similar to that occurring during walking, in which the principal
variables were peak strain and strain rates. The similarity between
the walking pattern and a typical artificial loading pattern can be seen
in Fig. 2.

2. In-Vivo Bone Loading

a. Photon absorptiometry

Bone mineral content (BMC) of the radius and ulna of the sheep was
measured in the mid-shaft region using 241 Americium as the source. The
results obtained over the six-week experimental period, from six sheep
in the four different treatment groups used, are presented in Fig. 3.

In Gp A, loaded at lower peak strain levels than normally occur during
walking (550-660 compared to 900-1300 microstrain) but at strain rates
in the range encountered during walking at one metre per second (6-18 x
10^{+3} compared to 8-26 x 10^{+3} microstrain per second), there was a 3 per
cent decrease in BMC about mid-way through the experimental period,
which returned to within 1 s.d. of the mean BMC at termination.

In Gp B, loaded at higher peak strain levels (1000-1700 microstrain)
than normally occur during walking and at strain rates (12-31 x 10^{+3}
microstrain per second) in the range encountered during walking at one
metre per second, a small increase in BMC was maintained over the six-
week period.

In Gp C, loaded at higher peak strain levels (1100-1900 microstrain)
than normally occur during walking but at faster strain rates (15-66 x
10^{+3} microstrain per second), there was a substantial increase in BMC
over the whole of the experimental period, resulting in a 20 per cent
increase in BMC by termination. One sheep was terminated at $3\frac{1}{2}$ weeks
due to prosthetic loosening, and at this point an estimate of the BMC of
its radius and ulna was similar to the estimate of BMC of the other
sheep shown in this group.

In Gp D, loaded at higher peak strain levels (1000-1500 microstrain)
than normally occur during walking but at very slow strain rates (2-6 x
10^{+3} microstrain per second), resorption occurred. This is seen to be
greatest at three weeks, being some 7 per cent less than the original
BMC, and at termination 5 per cent less than at the start.

b. Hard tissue histology

The results obtained using direct photon absorptiometry were confirmed
upon histological evaluation of bone changes, defined by fluorescent
bone labels, viewed under ultra violet light. Figure 4 summarises these
results, in terms of bone newly deposited and resorbed from cranial and
caudal surfaces of the sheep's radius. Deposition was assessed in terms
of the maximum width of newly deposited fluorescent-labelled bone and
resorption was assessed by comparison in width with the cortices of the
control leg.

In Gp A, loaded at peak strains lower than walking at walking strain
rates, no new bone was deposited. In all the other groups peak strains
were higher than those occurring during walking. In the normal strain
rate group (B), there was a small amount of new bone deposited both
cranially and caudally. In the fast strain rate group (C) there was a

86

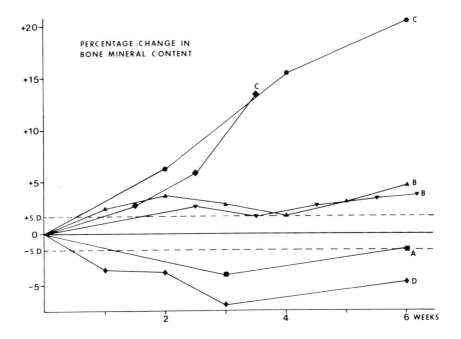

Fig. 3. The results from photon absorptiometry of the loaded radius in six sheep from the four groups, A, B, C and D

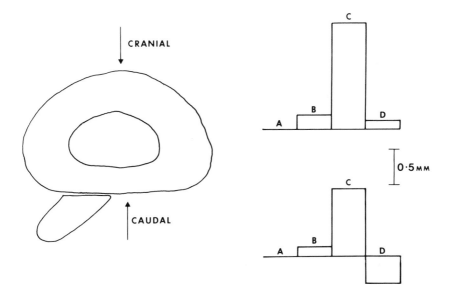

Fig. 4. Thickness of new bone deposited or resorbed from the cranial and caudal surfaces of the loaded sheep's radii

much larger amount of new bone deposited. In the slow strain rate group (D) net resorption occurred, new bone being deposited on the cranial periosteal surface, but resorption occurring on the caudal periosteal surface. In all groups, very little change was seen endosteally.

Internal intracortical remodelling also varied both in amount and in type between the four different treatment groups. In Gp A, where no appositional changes were seen, there was a small amount (65 osteons) of secondary osteonal remodelling in the ulna. In Gps B and C in which new bone deposition was seen, it was accompanied by a large amount of secondary osteonal remodelling in both the radius and ulna. This was marginally higher in Gp C (1020, s.e. = 20) compared to Gp B (820, s.e. = 50), again paralleling the appositional changes. In Gp D, however, in which net resorption occurred, no secondary osteonal remodelling was seen, but rather cancellisation and partial infilling of the inner half of the whole circumference of the radius occurred.

DISCUSSION

The predominant physical activity which affects the limb bones in quadrupeds is locomotion. Rosette strain gauges bonded to the surface of these bones allow functional strain to be recorded during the deformation cycle occurring at each stride. The information which can be obtained from these gauges is the changing size and direction of the principal strains and the rate at which strain is imposed and released. Our results from the sheep radius show that as the speed of locomotion increased the principal strain angle changed very little on each surface. The ratio of peak strains on opposite cortices also remained constant, indicating that despite changing gaits the manner of load application to the radius of the sheep remained essentially the same. However, both the peak strain and strain rate increased with speed of locomotion, the latter linearly and the former non-linearly, since there was a fall-off in the peak strain value at the trot to gallop transition. These results are consistent with previous work both in other species and other limb bones (Lanyon & Rubin, 1980).

Both peak principal strain and strain rate are mechanical parameters varying with the level of physical activity. In these artificial loading experiments on the radius of the sheep we investigated the effect of changes in these parameters on the adaptive remodelling response of bone. The radii were loaded in cranio-caudal bending which was similar to that occurring during locomotion. Peak strain and strain rate were the major variables since cycle length and number of cycles were kept constant. Whenever peak strain levels above those occurring during walking were imposed, new bone was produced. The type of response obtained was related to the strain rate used. The over-strain between these groups did not differ markedly, the major variable being strain rate. However, not only did the peak strain differ between the two groups which were loaded using a strain rate in the normal walking range, but the strain rate also differed between these groups. In Gp A no remodelling response was obtained and the strain rate was at the lower end of the range. In Gp B, a small amount of new bone deposition was stimulated and the strain rate was towards the higher end of the range. This difference in strain rate, the difference in peak strain, or a combination of the two, could account for the different responses between these groups.

The net resorption obtained in Gp D suggests that deformation at physiological levels but at low strain rates may actually be a stimulus for resorption. However, a small amount of new bone deposition occurred on the cranial surface of the radius, along with this resorption from the caudal surface. This bone drift in a caudo-cranial direction would, if continued, result in a change of bone shape by increasing the bone curvature. This increase in curvature, coupled with the decrease in bone mass, could be a remodelling response which increases both peak strain and strain rate on the surface of the bone and re-establishes normal values of these.

The internal intracortical remodelling response is also differed between the various groups. There was little or no response at normal walking peak strain and strain rate but as peak strain rate increased so did the amount of intracortical remodelling. However, though peak strain was higher than that occurring during normal walking in the low strain group (D) a large amount of intracortical resorption occurred. This parallels the adaptive response in terms of deposition and resorption and may suggest that both responses were interlinked, and were related to the same stimuli.

The responses resulting from the differing loading regimes suggest that there may be an adaptive or remodelling 'goal' which optimises either peak strain, strain rate, or both. Since strain-generated potentials do exist in bone in vivo and their size is related to both peak strain and strain rate (Black & Korostoff, 1974; Lanyon & Hartman, 1977) it may be these potentials which are providing the link between mechanical circumstances and the bone cell population.

When a bone is deformed at a physiological rate, polarisation occurs between the two opposite surfaces but the potential difference decays quite rapidly, because of movement of charge or charge equilisation. When that deformation is released and the bone is allowed to return to its original state an opposite polarisation occurs, which again decays rapidly. Below a strain rate of $4 \times 10^{+3}$ microstrain per second negligible potentials are recorded because charge movement can cancel the potential formed by charge separation as fast as it occurs. At strain levels above this the size of the potential is related to both strain magnitude and strain rate. If peak strain is constant the peak potential increases (non-linearly) with strain rate. If strain rate is constant above a certain minimum the potential increases linearly with peak strain (Lanyon & Hartman, 1977).

In the group of animals loaded at low strain rates it is doubtful whether any potentials occurred, although as a consequence there would be considerable movement of charge. In the other groups whose bones were loaded to produce the same peak strains, the strain rates were sufficient to produce potentials. The higher the strain rate the higher was the potential and the less was the movement of charge.

Our results support the hypothesis that the occurrence of piezoelectric potentials, greater in size than occur during normal activity, stimulate both the amount and rate of bone deposition. Movement of electric charge greater than that which normally occurs in vivo results from loading at a slow strain rate, and this may also stimulate bone-remodelling, but not in the same manner. This is consistent with the idea that adaptive bone-remodelling which results in bone's optimum mechanical performance is controlled not by mechanical events directly, but by the electrical environment they produce. Movement of charge and size of potentials developed may have different effects. Thus while vigorous physical activity leads to an increase in bone mass (Jones et al., 1977), slower, less vigorous activities may actively lead to resorption. This could explain the failure of exercise regimes adequately to prevent the progress of osteoporosis.

References

Bassett, C.A.L. (1968): Biologic significance of piezoelectricity. Calc. Tiss. Res. 1, 252.

Black, J. & Korostoff, E. (1974): Strain-related potentials in living bone. Ann. N. Y. Acad. Sci. 238, 95.

Donaldson, C.C., Hulley, S.B., Vogel, J.M., Hattner, R.S., Bayers, J.H. & McMillan, D.E. (1970): Effect of prolonged bed rest on bone mineral. Metabolism 19, 1071.

Goodship, A.E., Lanyon, L.E., Nicopoulos, A. & O'Connor, J.A. (1978): A technique for investigating the response of bone to changes in its mechanical environment. J. Physiol. 277, 39P.

Hert, J., Liskova, M. & Landa, J. (1971): Reaction of bone to mechanical stimuli. Part I. Continuous and intermittent loading of tibia in rabbit. Folia Morph. 19, 290.

Hert, J., Pribylova, E. & Liskova, M. (1972): Reaction of bone to mechanical stimuli. Part 3. Microstructure of compact bone of rabbit tibia after intermittent loading. Acta Anat. 82, 218. .

Jones, H.H., Priest, J.D., Hayes, W.C., Tichenor, C.C. & Nagel, D.A. (1977): Humeral hypertrophy in response to exercise. J. Bone Jt. Surg. 59A, 204.

Lanyon, L.E. (1976): The measurement of bone strain in vivo. Acta Orthop. Belg. 42, suppl. 1, 98.

Lanyon, L.E. & Hartman, W. (1977): Strain related electrical potentials recorded in vitro and in vivo. Calc. Tiss. Res. 22, 315.

Lanyon, L.E. & Rubin, C.T. (1980): Loading of mammalian long bones during locomotion. J. Physiol. (in press).

Uhthoff, H.K. & Jaworski, Z.F.G. (1978): Bone loss in response to long-term immobilisation. J. Bone Jt. Surg. 60B, 420.

Wolff, J. (1892): 'Das Gesetz der Transformation der Knochen'. Berlin: A. Hirschwald.

14

Strength of the distal radius

J.D. CURREY AND A. HORSMAN

INTRODUCTION

A bone will break in a fall if it has to absorb too much energy. In
general the soft tissues absorb much more energy than bones. Soft
tissues are by definition more compliant than bones, yet they are not
notably weaker, and so they will be much more efficient at this task.
Nevertheless the bones must often be strongly loaded and their ability
to absorb energy without fracture will become important.

In this paper we report initial results on a study on the human radius
which, among other things, shows how the ability of the radius of women
to absorb energy decreases with age.

MATERIALS AND METHODS

Twenty-eight radii, taken post-mortem from 14 women, were tested. In no
case had the subject suffered from a disease that particularly affects
bone. The bones were roughly cleaned and, prior to mechanical testing,
the bone mineral content of each specimen was determined by photon
absorptiometry. The absorptiometric system, which has been described
elsewhere (Horsman et al., 1977), uses a gadolinium-153 source, which
emits 42 keV X-rays, and a multiwire proportional counter (MWPC) as the
detector. The system produces a two-dimensional transmission image of
the object under investigation from which the object thickness (g/cm^2)
can be derived at any selected point. (The image is displayed on a
colour television monitor by the controlling computer.) In practice
each specimen was immersed in a water bath between the source and MWPC
detector and carefully positioned so that the resulting image was a
postero-anterior projection. The exposure time was 250 sec and the
total count both in the baseline and object exposures was approximately
10^7. Using the most distal point of the radius as a reference, 1 cm-
wide zones traversing the full width of the bone were defined by means
of cursors superimposed on the image. The centre line of each zone was
orthogonal to the long axis of the bone, and for the most distal zone
(site 1) was 1 cm from the tip. Six adjacent zones were evaluated, the
computer producing an 'area total' (AT 1-6) by integration of the object
thickness at all points within each zone. For purposes of this paper,
only the zones at the level of the strain gauges (see below) are
reported. The area total for any zone is proportional to the total bone

mineral content within the zone boundaries. With the exposure factors used here the precision of the area totals was approximately 2 per cent.

The bones were then more thoroughly cleaned of periosteum and associated soft tissue and the articular surface potted in resin. During all these and subsequent operations, including the mechanical testing, the bone was kept moist and frozen at -15°C betweenwhiles. Four 'TML' triple-element foil strain gauges (Type FRA-2), length 2 mm, were attached to the bone. The method of Lanyon (1976) was used, with minor modifications. Two gauges were fixed on opposite sides of the bone about 25 mm above the tip of the styloid process, and two about 70 mm above the tip. At the lower level there is a very thin sheath of cortical compact bone surrounding the cancellous bone of the interior. At the high level there is virtually no cancellous bone inside the quite thick shell of compact bone. These two zones are called 'low level' and 'high level' in this paper from now on.

Each specimen was then loaded in an 'Instron' table model compression machine. To ensure uniform loading of the flat end at the top, half a glass marble was placed on top of the bone beneath the platen (Fig. 1). The bone was then loaded rather slowly, at a rate of 5 mm per min, to a load of 600 N. This was well below the strength of each specimen. The output from the strain gauges was displayed on a 'Bryans 45000 UV' oscillograph. The information from triple-element strain gauges allows the principal strains to be calculated. The principal strains lie at right angles to each other, and are the greatest and least strains occurring at that point on the surface. In most cases the direction of the principal compressive strain was very nearly along the long axis of the bone. At each level the mean value of the two principal compressive strains, one from each side of the bone, was used in further analysis. These values did not differ from each other in any consistent way according to which side of the bone they were on. Using the mean value eliminates any effects introduced by the bone bending slightly. The specimens were then sawed through transversely about 45 mm from the styloid tip. In one specimen from each pair, chosen randomly, as much as possible of the cancellous bone was removed by scraping with a reamer. However, great care was taken not to damage the cortical shell. The specimens were then loaded to failure in a 'Howden' compressive tester at a rate of 50 mm per min, the test taking a few seconds. The greatest load borne before failure was measured. This always occurred just before the sudden drop in load that indicated that the cortex had split. Strain gauges were not used in this part of the experiment. Instead the stiffness of the whole specimen was measured. The load-deformation curve was quite linear till very close to failure. The stiffness of the specimen was considered to be inversely proportional to the deflection at 5 kN divided by the original length of the specimen. The original lengths of the specimens were all virtually the same, about 45 mm. The deformation at the fracture load was also recorded.

In four pairs of bones the strain at the upper level was not measured, because the specimen was too short. In one pair of bones the mineral content was not measured. In two bones the deformations at failure were not measured (by mistake).

RESULTS

Bone Mineral Content

This was about the same at the low and the high levels. The paired comparison t-test gave $t_{24} = 1.28$; not significant. It decreased markedly with age (Fig. 2a). The radius at the lower level loses about 0.44 per cent mineral per year between ages 40 and 90 years. At the upper level it loses about 0.36 per cent per year.

Strain

Not surprisingly, there was an inverse relationship between strain at 600 N and the mineral content (Fig. 2b). The relationship between strain and mineral content is different at the two levels in the bone. The strain is always greater at the lower level for a given amount of mineral. The lower level has more cancellous bone than the higher level. Since the total amount of bone is the same at the two levels, this implies that the cancellous bone is more compliant, per unit mass, than compact bone. This agrees with the findings of Carter & Hayes (1977). The difference is marked, the lower level of the bone being, on average over all ages, about 1.7 times more compliant than the upper level. There is an indication that the strain increased with age more in the lower level than in the upper level. The ratio of lower strain to upper strain is described by:

Ratio = 0.96 + 0.011 (age in years), $t_8 = 1.84$ $P \simeq 0.1$.

The ratio of lower level strain to upper level strain increased from about 1.3 to 1.9 over the age range examined.

Stiffness

The deflection of the intact bones, as measured at 5 kN, was inversely related to the amount of mineral:

Deflection = .022 - .0057 (mineral content), $t_{10} = 3.3$ $P < 0.001$.

The compliance of the bone without trabeculae was slightly increased.

Load at Failure

The greatest load borne by bones with their trabeculae intact decreased with age by about half, from 5.6 kN at 40 years to 2.6 kN at 90. However this relationship does depend, at the moment, rather heavily on one result from a single 39-year-old (Fig. 2c). The specimens that had had the trabeculae removed were weaker than their intact pairs by about 25 per cent. The strength is almost a linear function of bone mineral (Fig. 2d) as we have reported previously (Horsman & Currey, 1976).

Deflection at Failure

An important finding was that the deflection at failure was unaffected by age or by the amount of mineral present in the bone (Fig. 3). Nor did the presence or absence of trabeculae have any effect on the deformation at failure. It seems as if the bone fails when the

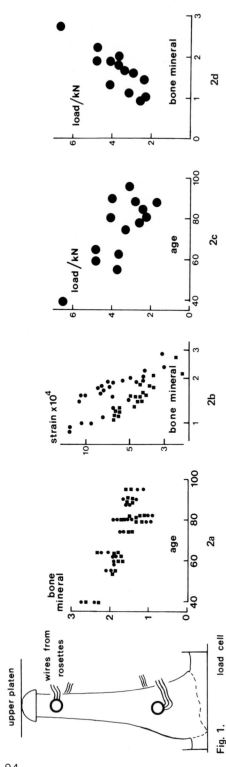

Fig. 1. The test set-up. Thick circles represent
the rosette strain gauges. At each level there are
two rosettes, on opposite sides of the bone

Fig. 2. (a) Mineral content in arbitrary units
versus age. Circles: lower level on bone; squares:
upper level. The linear equations describing the
distributions are: Lower level; mineral = 3.23 −
.022 (age in years) t_{24} = 5.7 P<<0.001. Upper
level; mineral = 2.94 − .018 (age in years)
t_{24} = 6.1 P<<0.001. (b) Mineral content versus
strain at 600N. Circles: lower level; squares:
upper level. Note how the lower level bone has a
greater strain at any given mineral content. The
distributions have been linearised by taking
logarithms. Lower level; log microstrain = 2.05 −
1.05 (log mineral) t_{22} = 5.9 P<<0.001. Upper level;
log microstrain = 1.83 − .99 (log mineral)
t_{16} = 7.6 P<<0.001. (c) Strength versus age. The

equation describing the distribution is: load at
failure = 7.91 − 0.059 (age in years)
t_{12} = 3.9 P<0.005. (d) Strength versus mineral
content. The equation is: load at failure = 0.36 +
2.08 (mineral content) t_{11} = 3.9 P<0.005.

deformation in the cortical shell exceeds some value.

DISCUSSION

Imagine a radius, inside an arm, that has to absorb a certain amount of energy in a fall. What is the best disposition of the bone material so that it nowhere reaches a strain at which it will break? We can consider the bone as consisting of a number of segments of length L. If a segment has a cross-sectional area of bone material (excluding marrow) A, if it behaves linearly and is loaded elastically to a load P, then the energy stored is P/2 x ΔL where ΔL is the change in length.

= P/2. ϵ.L. where ϵ is the strain
= (P/2) P/AE. L where E is the modulus of elasticity
= $P^2 L/2AE$

For equilibrium, the force all along the bone must be the same. (We are not considering stress waves here.) There will be some value of strain, P/AE, which will be greater than the material can bear. Since P and E are the same at all levels, so too should A be, because then the strain will be the same everywhere, and the whole bone will, in the best situation, be loaded to just under the failure strain. The maximum force in the bone will be determined by the greatest value of P/A. If one part of the bone has twice the cross-sectional area of another, the strain and therefore the total energy stored will be half that stored in the more slender part. However, things are more complicated if the modulus of elasticity varies as well as the area. If the value of failure strain is fixed, but the value of E in the fatter segment is half that in the slender segment, then the energy stored in each segment will be the same.

The experimental results given above show that the radius is more compliant near its end than higher up. The reason for this may be related to the need to prevent the very weak synovial cartilage from being very highly stressed between high spots on the two stiff ends of bones. The compliance of the bone will allow more evenly distributed loading of the cartilage. However the amount of bone mineral per unit length is about the same. As mentioned before, the end of the radius consists of a thin shell of compact bone surrounding a core of cancellous bone. The compact bone, being very thin, will not contribute greatly to the stiffness, which will be determined by the stiffness of the cancellous bone. Carter & Hayes (1977) have shown that in bone

strength $\propto \rho^2$, $E \propto \rho^3$, where ρ is the bulk of density and E is the modulus of elasticity

As a result, the stiffness of bone declines more rapidly than its strength as it becomes more cancellous. At the end of the radius the compact sheath and the cancellous core are acting almost in parallel; that is, the strains in each will be the same. Now, stress = strain x modulus of elasticity. As the modulus of elasticity of the cancellous core is less than that of the sheath the core will be at a lower stress than the sheath. However, it will not break first, because, compared with compact bone, its strength is relatively greater than its modulus of elasticity. In effect, the compact sheath has to bear a

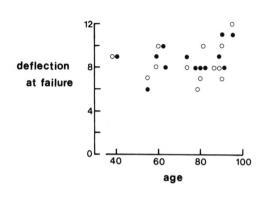

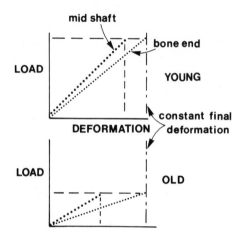

Fig. 3. Deflection at failure
(change in length/original length)
$x10^3$ versus age

Fig. 4. Diagram of energy
absorption in the radius. The
bones of both ages break at the
same deformation. The energy
absorbed per unit length in
different parts depends on the load
and the stiffness and is shown by
the areas under the dotted curves.
In young bones the mid shaft is not
much stiffer than the end, so when
the end breaks the energy in the
mid shaft is quite high. In the
old bone the disparity in the
energy absorbed in the two regions
is much greater. Because there is
much more volume in the shaft than
at the end, this results in a
considerable loss in energy-
absorbing ability of the bone as a
whole

disproportionate amount of the load. The compact sheath is breaking at a load which is determined largely by its own meagre cross-sectional area, which results in a breaking strain being reached at a relatively low load. It is a matter of common observation that the radius when loaded longitudinally tends to break at the end.

The results reported here show that the static strength of the end of the radius declines with age, concomitantly with a reduction in the amount of mineral. However, the situation may be worse than this (Fig. 4). The results of the strain gauge experiments probably show that the lower level's stiffness declines more rapidly than that of the upper level. Because the deformation at failure is effectively constant, and because the bone fails when any part of it is loaded to a strain greater than it can bear, the disparity in the amount of energy absorbed by the end and by the shaft of the bone increases with age.

Acknowledgements - JDC was supported by the Arthritis and Rheumatism Council.

References

Carter, D.R. & Hayes, W.C. (1977): Compressive behavior of bone as a 2-phase porous structure. J. Bone Jt. Surg. 59A, 954.

Horsman, A. & Currey, J.D. (1974): Densitometric and mechanical properties of the distal radius. Proc. Symp. on bone mineral determination. Stockholm. Document AE-489, Volume 1.

Horsman, A., Reading, D.H., Connolly, J., Bateman, E., Glasgow, W. & McLachlan, M.S.F. (1977): Bone mass measurement using a xenon-filled multiwire proportional counter as detector. Phys. Med. Biol. 22, 1059.

Lanyon, L.E. (1976): The measurement of bone strain in vivo. Acta Orth. Belg. 42, Suppl. 1, 98.

15

Evaluation of bone strength and integrity by vibration methods: identification of in-vivo excitated modes

J. VANDECASTEELE, G. VAN DER PERRE, R. VAN AUDEKERCKE AND M. MARTENS

INTRODUCTION

Results of in vivo vibration response analyses in one point of the ulna have been published previously, eg resonant frequency measurements (Jurist, 1970) and mechanical impedance measurements (Thompson, 1973). In both types of measurements, mathematical models were fitted to the experimental data by these authors.

Jurist correlated his results with the state of osteoporosis in a number of patients. However, it was pointed out by Doherty et al. (1974) that results of one-point vibration response measurements can only be interpreted in terms of bone mechanical properties (EI) when the excitated vibration modes are correctly identified. Our aim is to identify these vibration modes and to correlate these with the mechanical properties of human long bones by a technique called 'modal analysis'.

METHODS

Modal analysis is the analysis of the vibration modes of a mechanical structure. The structure (in our case a long human bone) is excited in a given point by a time-varying force (from a hammer impact or by an electromagnetic vibrator). The resulting acceleration is measured in a representative set of measuring points (Fig. 1). The input signal (force, as a function of time) as well as the output signal (acceleration as a function of time) are represented as a summation of a number of N harmonic signals each having its own amplitude and phase by Fourier transformation:

$$F(f) = F_n(nf_o) \text{ and } A(f) = A_n(nf_o), \ (n = 1,N)$$

$f_o = 1/T$, is the basic frequency, where T is the measurement time length. N is determined by conditions of digital signal processing. The function $A(f)/F(f)$ plotted versus frequency is called the transfer function. The latter is determined in each measurement point (Fig. 1).

Peaks are observed in these transfer functions at distinct frequency values corresponding to the natural frequencies of the structure. The associated mode shapes can be calculated from the transfer functions in the set of measurement points.

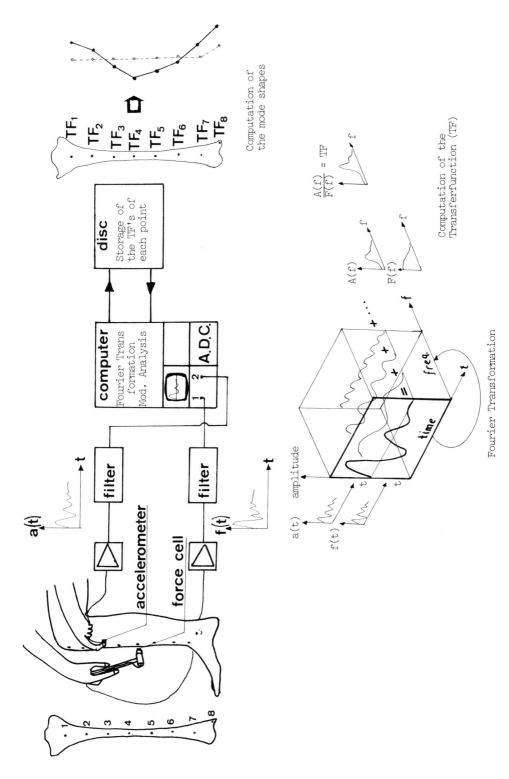

Fig. 1. Method of modal analysis

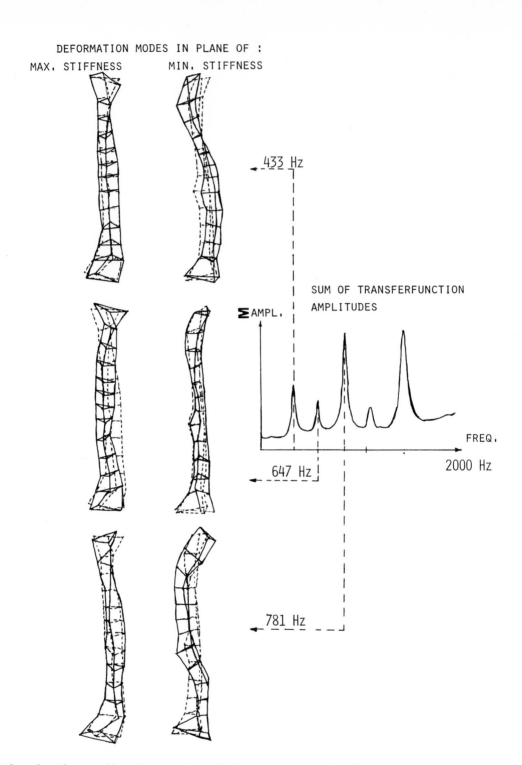

DEFORMATION MODES IN PLANE OF :

MAX, STIFFNESS   MIN, STIFFNESS

433 Hz

SUM OF TRANSFERFUNCTION
AMPLITUDES

Σ AMPL.

FREQ,

2000 Hz

647 Hz

781 Hz

Fig. 2. Three vibration modes of the dry excised tibia

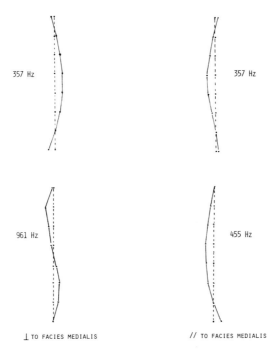

357 Hz

357 Hz

961 Hz

455 Hz

⊥ TO FACIES MEDIALIS   // TO FACIES MEDIALIS

Fig. 3. Vibration modes of dry tibia filled with fat to simulate bone marrow

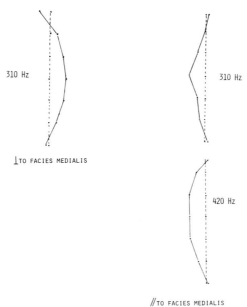

310 Hz

310 Hz

⊥ TO FACIES MEDIALIS

420 Hz

// TO FACIES MEDIALIS

Fig. 4. Vibration modes of a fresh tibia

101

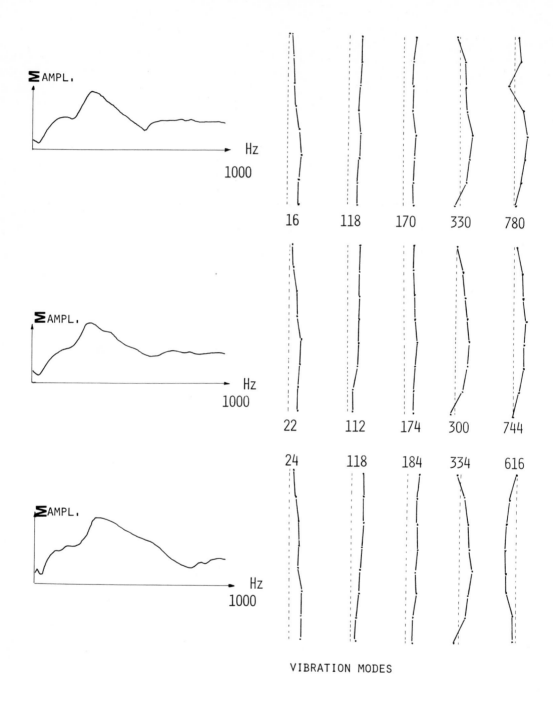

VIBRATION MODES

Fig. 5. In vivo measurements of three tibiae. In each case the
frequency/peak amplitude plot is shown, alongside the mode shape of the
bone at five significant frequencies

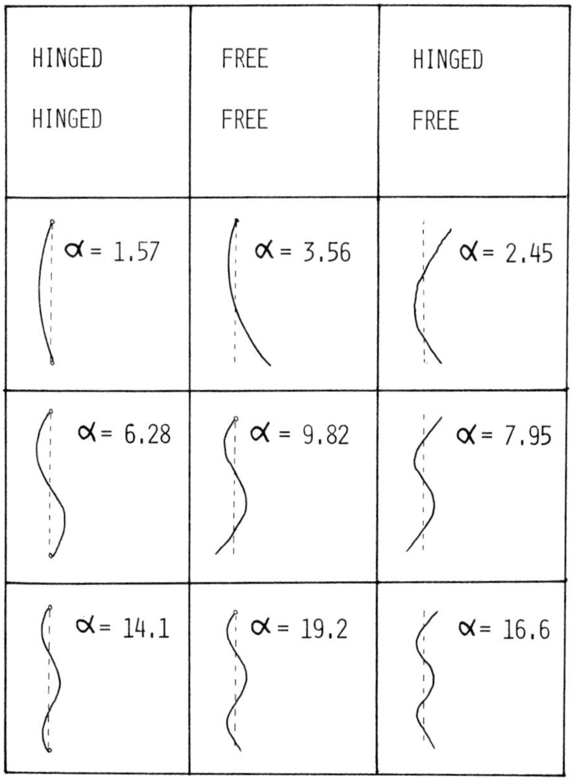

HINGED HINGED	FREE FREE	HINGED FREE
$\alpha = 1.57$	$\alpha = 3.56$	$\alpha = 2.45$
$\alpha = 6.28$	$\alpha = 9.82$	$\alpha = 7.95$
$\alpha = 14.1$	$\alpha = 19.2$	$\alpha = 16.6$

$$F_o = \sqrt{\frac{E I}{u\ I^4}} \cdot \alpha$$

Fig. 6. Bending modes of uniform beams, showing dependence on the degree of constraint and rigidity at the end couplings

In the simplest case, ie purely elastic structures (with no damping) with uncoupled modes, this technique reduces to the measurement of the transfer function amplitude at a given resonant frequency in all points (Fig. 1).

We are developing modal analysis applications in the following two problem areas of orthopaedic biomechanics:

1. The analysis of the effect of orthopaedic implants (fixation devices and joint replacements) on the dynamic behaviour of long bones (Van Audekercke et al., 1980).

2. The development of a reliable vibration technique for the assessment of bone strength and integrity in vivo and the monitoring of fracture healing.

In the latter study, our first aim is to identify the mode shapes of the tibia in vivo. To become familiar with the structure to be studied we first simulated the in vivo condition of the tibia approximately with a dry excised tibia, before using fresh excised bones, and finally bones in vivo.

RESULTS AND DISCUSSION

Resonant frequencies were determined and vibration modes were identified for two dry excised human tibiae (Fig. 2). Two distinct modes were clearly identified. These corresponded to bending along the two principal axes of inertia of the bones. The first mode, situated in the plane normal to the medial face (minimum flexural rigidity) had an eigenfrequency between 430 and 700 Hz, while the second mode, in the plane parallel to the medial face (maximum flexural rigidity), had an eigenfrequency at 640-930 Hz. A third mode was identified at ±780 Hz. This was a double bending mode in the plane of minimum stiffness (Fig. 2).

One tibia was loaded with an organic substance, simulating bone marrow. In this case, the first mode was identified at 357 Hz principally in the plane normal to the medial face. A very small component of this mode was observed in the plane parallel to the medial face, but because of poor signal to noise ratio, this mode was not clearly identified. The second mode in the plane perpendicular to the medial face occurred at 455 Hz, while the double-bending mode in the plane parallel to the medial face had an eigenfrequency at 961 Hz (Fig. 3).

Two fresh human tibiae were analysed. The first two modes were again easily identified. Again, the first mode had a very small component in the plane parallel to the medial face (Fig. 4).

Finally, modal analysis, involving acceleration measurements in a network of points, was made in vivo on tibiae of 20 men of age 23 ± 2 years (Fig. 1). The peaks in the transfer functions from in vivo measurements were very diffuse in comparison with those obtained from intact dry tibiae. This is a result of pronounced damping of the soft tissues (Fig. 5). This caused some problem in the exact identification of resonant frequencies and mode shapes.

In this mode-identification work, we now interpret the resonances lower than 300 Hz as rigid body modes and the ±300 Hz vibration mode as a single-bending mode. This hypothesis however is still to be confirmed by further experimental and model analyses.

THEORETICAL ANALYSIS AND IMPLICATIONS

Figure 6 shows the relation between resonant frequencies and the mechanical properties of uniform beams for different modes and boundary conditions:

$$f_o = \frac{EI}{u\ell^4} . \alpha$$

with EI: flexural rigidity - E = Young's modulus,
$\qquad$ I = second moment of area
$\quad$ u : mass per unit length
$\quad$ ℓ : length of the beam
$\quad$ α : factor which takes account of the influence of the boundary conditions

The boundary conditions, ie the type of fixation of the beam in its ends, have a large influence on the resonant frequency of the beam (α ranging from 1.57 to 3.56 for the first bending mode).

As soon as the in vivo excited vibration modes of the tibia are correctly determined, an analogous expression can be set up for a human tibia (or ulna). In this way the mechanical properties of a human long bone can be determined from its resonant frequencies and the type and quality of its connections in the joints. We hope to assess the state of healing of a fracture from a comparison of the transfer functions, mode shapes and damping parameters of the fractured tibia with those of the contralateral intact bone.

References

Doherty, W.P., Bovill, E.G. & Wilson, E.L. (1974): Evaluation of the use of resonant frequencies to characterise physical properties of human long bones. J. Biomech. 7, 559.

Jurist, J.M. (1970): In vivo determination of the elastic response of bone I. Method of ulnar resonant frequency determination. Phys. Med. Biol. 15, 417.

Thompson, G.T. (1973): In vivo determination of bone properties from mechanical impedance measurements. Aerospace Med. Assoc. Annual Science Meeting Abstracts, 7-10 May, Las Vegas, Nevada, USA.

Van Audekercke, R., Van der Perre, G. & Martens, M. (1980): Analysis of the dynamic behaviour of long bones and orthopaedic implants. First World Biomaterials Congress, Vienna, April 8-12, 1980.

16

Safe stress levels at the screw interface of an external fixator for long bone fractures

J.D. HARRIS, M. EVANS AND J. KENWRIGHT

INTRODUCTION

The treatment of difficult long bone fractures by external fixation is attracting wide surgical interest at present in view of the advantages this technique offers. For fractures with major soft tissue damage, and ununited fractures, external fixation gives the surgical team control over the degree of rigidity or flexibility required, over the alignment and compression of the fracture, and unimpeded access to the soft tissue at the site of the fracture.

Whilst opinions vary as to the degree of rigidity in a fracture required for optimum bone healing, two factors have emerged: first, that excessive movement, particularly in shear, will delay or prevent bone healing, and second that a high degree of rigidity is needed for shattered and unsupporting fractures which may incorporate bone grafts. With external fixation a highly rigid system can be modified to provide increased flexibility, even during rehabilitation, but the reverse is not true. An essentially flexible system will not be able to provide the stability which is required for the management of some types of fracture.

An analysis of bone stresses involved when a fractured limb is loaded axially is presented here. This is based on predictions of deflection of a rigid single frame system, the Oxford External Fixator, which represents the minimum equipment needed to orientate and hold two parts of a fractured bone. This system is as rigid as current single and double frame fixators which have been tested (Kempson, 1980).

FIXATOR GEOMETRY

The basic Oxford External Fixator comprises two bone screws in each part of the fractured bone, a frame member to provide a rigid exoskeleton, and clamping devices to hold the bone screws firmly to this external frame. Figure 1 shows this minimum system. A longitudinal force on the limb, as in partial weight-bearing, applies stress to all the active components of the system. In the example chosen no support is provided by contact between the bone ends.

The system deflects as a result of the load applied and stresses are also produced in the bone itself as a reaction to the forces transmitted by the bone screws.

Three types of deflection result from the application of longitudinal loading to the bone:

1. Axial deflection, which is movement tending to close the fracture. This is principally produced by the bending of the bone screws and the deformation of the bone due to the induced compressive forces at the screw/bone interface. Both of these are caused by the bending moment 'M' produced in the clamp and in the bone (Fig. 1). Bending of the mainframe member in a typical application is sufficiently small to be ignored.

2. Angulation, which is defined as the bending of the system in the plane of the bone and support column. Significant deflection in this plane will occur because of relative movement between the screw and the bone, and the screw and the clamp. These movements are caused by tensile and compressive forces in the screw. Again, deflection of the main column can be ignored.

3. Rotation. This is deflection of the system on an axis parallel to the axis of the bone screws. It results from axial loading with the bone screws inserted out of line. A drilling jig can be used to minimise such misalignment. Although perfect alignment is not practical, every effort to minimise this should be made as its effect will be to provide additional bone stresses which, as will be shown later, can be dangerously high.

The effects of applying partial body weight to a limb supported by a strong external fixator system will be within the safe limit of the mechanical components. However, these forces react on the bone at its interfaces with the screws. Under certain conditions these forces can be critically high, leading to loosening of the screws, and bone necrosis. This is particularly the case when the fixator components deflect, as in Fig. 2. Of equal importance is the diameter of the bone screws.

STRUCTURAL ANALYSIS

The forces transmitted through the components of the fixator were calculated by considering equilibrium of the structure. This analysis has been reported for a number of configurations of the fixator by Evans, Kenwright & Tanner (1979). This gave the forces transmitted between the bone and bone pins, from which estimates of the direct and shear stresses in the bone could be calculated (Figs. 2 and 3). Safe levels for these forces and stresses were deduced from experimental results.

Hughes & Jordan (1972) established pull-out forces for different sizes of screws in cortical bone, under single application of load. Klip & Bosma (1978) showed the creep limit for pins of different diameter subject to sustained bending loads. Denne et al. (1978) determined the safe stress levels for screw fixation into cortical bone when repeated cyclic loading was applied to the screw (see Figs. 4 and 5). This last work was specifically designed to establish safe levels of stress for this study.

FORCES

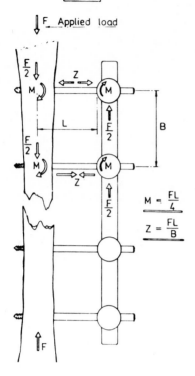

$$M = \frac{FL}{4}$$

$$Z = \frac{FL}{B}$$

Fig. 1. The Oxford External Fixator, showing the directions of forces when the bone is axially compressed

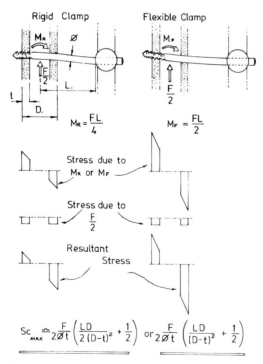

$$Sc_{MAX} \stackrel{\sim}{=} \frac{F}{2\emptyset t}\left(\frac{LD}{2(D-t)^2} + \frac{1}{2}\right) \quad \text{or} \quad \frac{F}{2\emptyset t}\left(\frac{LD}{(D-t)^2} + \frac{1}{2}\right)$$

Fig. 2. Rigidity in fixator stiffness markedly affects bone stress. A comparison between freely rotating and fixed screw clamps, using simplified analysis of stress levels

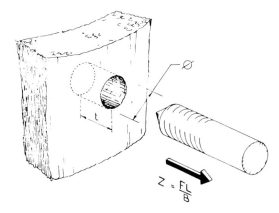

$$Z = \frac{FL}{B}$$

Shear Stress = $\dfrac{F.L.}{B\pi \emptyset t}$

Fig. 3. Method of estimating shear stress in bone adjacent to the threads of a bone pin

CYCLIC BENDING TESTS
(Compression Fatigue)

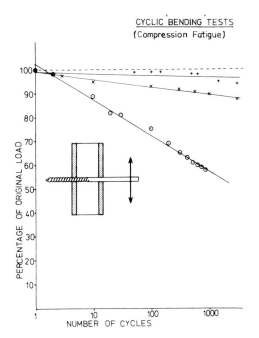

Fig. 4. Cyclic compressive bone loading showing high loads cause progressive failure

+ Original load = 34 Kg :- Compression Stress = 16·3 N/mm²
×   "   " = 89 Kg :-   "   " = 42·7 N/mm²
⊙   "   " = 136 Kg :-   "   " = 65·3 N/mm²
(Note :- Ultimate Compression Strength of Bone > 90 N/mm²)

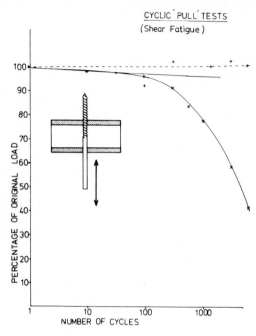

CYCLIC PULL TESTS
(Shear Fatigue)

PERCENTAGE OF ORIGINAL LOAD

NUMBER OF CYCLES

+ Original load = 100 Kg :- Shear Stress = 13·3 N/mm²
X   "   "   = 155 Kg :-   20·6 N/mm²
(Note :-Ultimate Shear Strength of Bone > 80 N/mm²)

Fig. 5. Cyclic shear testing showing rapid failure occurring at 20.6N/mm²

BONE STRESS
(Geometry & Pin Dia)

40 Kg
100 mm
30 mm
Ø
25 mm
5 mm
50 mm
50 mm

	Pin Dia Ø	
	6mm	4 mm
Shear Stress (N/mm²)	15	22
Compression Stress	36	54

	Pin Dia Ø	
	6mm	4 mm
Shear Stress (N/mm²)	4	6
Compression Stress	15	22

Note :-Recomended Max Stress
Normal Bone *
SHEAR : - - - - - 15 N mm²
COMPRESSION : - - 17 N mm²

Fig. 6. Comparison of two examples of fixator mounting, showing differences in deflection and bone stress under limb loading

RESULTS

Based on these calculations, two examples of the effects of applying a vertical load to a limb totally supported by this fixator are shown in Fig. 6. The bone stress and predicted deflection with the limb loaded to 40 Kgf (about 400 N) are shown for two different geometric arrangements, the second of which is much more rigid than the first. Both examples also compare the use of 6 mm and 4 mm bone screws.

The compression stress produced in the bone by a 4 mm screw, subjected to bending, is 50 per cent higher than that produced by a 6 mm screw for the same bending load.

The rigidity of the clamp is very important, both from the point of view of reducing deflection and reducing the stress at the screw/bone interface. As shown in Fig. 2, the bone stress is approximately doubled in the case of a freely rotating clamp in comparison to one which is rigid.

The results of Klip & Bosma (1978) and Denne et al. (1978) show that the safe stress around a bone pin should not exceed 20 per cent of the ultimate strength of the bone. This figure is deduced from measurements of safe load converted to stress levels as shown in Figs. 2 and 3. On this basis the compressive stress should not be allowed to exceed 17 N/mm^2 and the shear stress 15 N/mm^2.

Figure 6 shows that with 6 mm diameter screws the compressive stress in the bone exceeds this recommended figure, and with 4 mm diameter screws both the compressive stress and the shear stress exceed the safe levels, for an axial limb loading of 40 kg.

In the second case, the fixator is attached in a different manner to provide greater rigidity. More widely spaced screws, with shorter effective lengths, are attached to the bone. With 6 mm screws, both compressive and shear stress are within safe limits. With 4 mm screws the compression stress only is exceeded.

DISCUSSION

Rigid external fixation of fractures enables the patient to be mobilised early; but the geometry of the fixation is important to prevent excessive compressive loading at the screw/bone interface, leading to screw-loosening followed by effective failure of the support system.

With adequate rigidity the mobilised patient can apply partial weight-bearing to the limb and indeed any manoeuvres apart from total inactivity will apply some stress to the bone, partly because of the muscle-load component.

The deflections of the limb under load, deduced in Fig. 6, are of the order of millimetres and may be more than occurs in practice. However, bone and soft tissue support may drastically reduce this deflection. If not (as in the case of large grafted defects), efforts to achieve maximum stability by improved geometry or more bone screws may be necessary.

Increased flexibility or weakness in the fixator itself will also increase the stress levels at the bone. With well-spaced screws, compression stress becomes more important than shear stress, but with small diameter screws this also can reach critical levels. Further work is needed to establish the optimum strain configuration at the fracture

to promote early bone growth. A flexible system may induce early callus
at the fracture, but this may put the bone/screw fixation at risk.
Since it is desirable that an external fixator should not be used for
long periods, because of the risk of infection, primary bone union
without callus may take longer to develop than is considered
satisfactory.

CONCLUSIONS

To maintain bone stress levels within the safe limits required under
cyclic loading conditions, a rigid external fixator and larger diameter
bone screws are recommended.
   The geometry of the fixator with respect to the limb is also an
important factor for the surgeon to bear in mind in planning the
operation.

References

Denne, W.A., Buxton, R., Kenwright, J. & Tanner, K.E. (1978): The
   mechanics of Schanz screws and their connection with human tibiae.
   5th Annual Report of Oxford Orthopaedic Engineering Centre, 56.
Evans, M., Kenwright, J. & Tanner, K.E. (1979): Analysis of single-
   sided external fracture fixation. Eng. Med. 8, 133.
Hughes, A.N. & Jordan, B.A. (1972): The mechanical properties of
   surgical bone screws and some aspects of insertion practice. Injury
   4, 25.
Kempson, G.E. (1980): The comparative stiffness of external fixation
   frames. Injury, (in press).
Klip, E.J. & Bosma, R. (1978): Investigations into the mechanical
   behaviour of bone-pin connections. Eng. Med. 7, 43.

17

Influence of paralysis and intra-uterine pressure on the ossification, growth and quality of a developing bone

Z.A. RÁLIŠ

INTRODUCTION

The understanding of the influence of mechanical forces on bone tissue
is especially complicated in the case of developing and growing bones.
Structure, growth, development and shape of such bones is dependent on
the sum total of stimuli and mechanical forces which are normally
present in a developing and growing limb. In studies of developing
bones from paralysed limbs it has to be determined whether any changes
are due to denervation, disuse, lack of normal mechanical and sensory
stimuli, or local circulatory and metabolic changes which might be
present. Efforts to clarify these problems are not only of academic
importance. In two recent reports, in which a number of human
developing paralysed bones and normal controls as well as bones from
rats with experimental myotomy were studied (Ralis et al., 1976; Ralis,
1978), an attempt was made to solve several practical problems.

First, it has been repeatedly reported that children with spina bifida
and paralysed limbs are more liable to fractures of their bones than
normal children, especially after their limbs were further immobilised,
for example by plaster (Burney & Hamsa, 1963; Freehafer, 1974; Gillies &
Hartung, 1938; Golding, 1960; Jeannopoulos, 1954; Katz, 1953; Korhonen,
1971; Sharrard, 1971; Soutter, 1962). Since the reason for this is not
yet fully understood, the assessment of basic morphology of these bones
is clearly of primary importance.

The second problem was to investigate whether the developing paralysed
bones and their subsequent denervation atrophy could be influenced by
some stimuli which would act as substitute for the natural mechanical
forces and impulses of which these bones were deprived. In this
connection, it has been repeatedly shown during dissections of human
material, and also experimentally, that a large group of foot
deformities in spina bifida children is produced not merely due to the
partial paralysis of muscles, but that there is also the effect of
direct external pressure on the paralysed limb intra-utero (Ralis, 1974).
Plenty of evidence of this direct pressure on deformed paralysed limbs
has been found in human and experimental material and these deformities
are called 'paralytic-pressure' deformities (Lendon & Ralis, 1971; Ralis
& Duckworth, 1973). The development, structure and quality of bones
should be studied in two separate spina bifida groups: in one, in which

113

bones are developing in a flail limb deprived of most mechanical stimuli ('true paralytic' deformities), and in the other from limbs showing evidence of direct mechanical pressure ('paralytic-pressure' deformities).

The third interesting problem was to find out why the cross-sectional shape of human tibiae differs in babies and children with spina bifida foot deformities as compared with those from normal children. An understanding of the rules which lead to such changes in shape of a bone cross-section would further contribute to our knowledge about the influence of muscles on developing long bones and the way this process is influenced by paralysis.

Dissected femurs and tibiae in a collection of pathological material from normal and deformed human developing limbs were studied. Conventional and also specialised microscopical techniques were used. These allowed us to assess not only the basic morphological and histological aspects but also to follow the dynamics of bone-remodelling and changes in bone quality and mineralisation.

MATERIALS AND METHOD

Material 1 (Human)

The tibiae from 14 limbs of human foetuses and infants of different ages (12th foetal week - 13th post-natal week) without spina bifida were dissected and compared with those from 17 babies who died with spina bifida and paralysis, aged between 32 foetal weeks and ten post-natal weeks. The latter group was split into three sub-groups: six limbs with no deformities (usually with total paralysis); six limbs with equinus type of deformity (pes equinus and equino-varus) and five limbs with calcaneus type of deformity (pes calcaneus or calcaneo-varus). Most of the babies had been examined neurologically while they were still alive. In about half of them histology and morphometrical analysis of sections of each of the individual leg muscles and the sciatic and femoral nerves had been done previously. External shape and length of the dissected tibiae were assessed and then a block of bone was taken from the exact middle of the shaft. After decalcification, 8 and 14-microns thick histological transverse sections were cut and stained by haematoxylin and eosin Tetrachrome I method for osteoid (Ralis & Ralis, 1975) and in some cases by the PTAIH method for osteoid, boundary bone and bone components (Ralis & Ralis, 1976), and by the Tetrachrome 2 method (Ralis, 1980). These recently developed techniques designed for ordinary 14-micron paraffin bone sections are capable of distinguishing unmineralised osteoid tissue and other features from mineralised bone even after in vitro decalcification. Histophotographs were made by projecting the histological sections from a photographic enlarger directly on to photographic paper (Ralis & Blake, 1976), and the measurements were done from these (see below).

Material 2 (Human)

Complete femurs and tibiae were dissected from 20 babies and children age 21st foetal week - four years, who died with myelomeningocele, various types and degrees of paralysis, and knee and feet deformities,

114

most of which had been assessed and treated during the child's life. This material was split into aetiologically separate 'paralytic' and 'paralytic-pressure' groups. In the latter group were limbs with deformity which could not have been explained by the type of existing neurological deficit, and with some stigma of external pressure found during the post-natal examination. Identical specimens dissected from 26 normal babies of matching age who died for reasons unrelated to the locomotor system served as controls. Uniform blocks representing longitudinal sections through the lower ephysis, epiphyseal plate and metaphysis were taken from each bone. Further double cross-section blocks were taken from each femur in the borderline between the lower and middle third of the bone and from each tibia from the exact middle of the diaphysis. Half of these blocks, which were all fixed in buffered formal-saline, were decalcified in 10 per cent formic acid and half of them were left undecalcified. Sections were taken from the decalcified paraffin embedded blocks and stained in the same way as sections from Material 1. Eighty-ninety microns sections were cut from the undecalcified resin embedded blocks by the sawing microtome 'Leitz 1600'. From these, contact microradiographs were made using the 'Softex' apparatus (Kodak fine resolution film 649-0 and V-6028, 7.5 kV, 4.5 mA, average exposure time 90 min).

Material 3 (Experimental)

In order to explain the differences found in cross-sectional shape of tibiae in babies with various types of foot deformity, and to specify at least some factors responsible, the influence of muscle imbalance produced by experimental myotomy of different muscle groups was studied on growing tibiae in rats. Twelve young wistar white rats (average body weight 90 g) of both sexes were used. Their developing bones were labelled at the beginning of the experiment with a double label of fluorescent bone markers. These are deposited in the newly-mineralised bone. On the first day they were all given an intraperitoneal injection of Alizarin red S, and 24 days later were given an intraperitoneal injection of oxytetracycline (Terramycin Pfizer), both at a dosage of 50 mg/kg body weight and at a concentration of 25 mg/ml. After 60 days the rats were split into three groups: four rats remained as controls; four underwent myotomy of left-foot dorsiflexor (tibialis anterior, long hallux and toes extensors); the remaining four underwent myotomy of foot plantiflexors (triceps surae, long hallux and toes flexors, tibialis posterior). Extensive excision of a musculo-tendinous segment was used in order to avoid healing of the excised tissue. Three animals from each group were sacrificed 21 days, the rest 47 days, post-operatively. Samples for histology were taken and measurements were done separately for each group in the same way as on the human material. In addition, undecalcified ground bone section 80 microns thick were prepared from the mid shaft of the tibia for the fluorescent microphotographs which demonstrate the morphometry of bone remodelling recorded by the bone markers.

MEASUREMENTS

a. *Endochondral Ossification (Material 2, Longitudinal Sections)*

The following measurements were done on sections taken from normal and spina bifida material:

Number of vessels entering the epiphyseal plate through the marrow cavity.
Number of cells representing the thickness of individual zones of the plate (resting, proliferation, hypertrophic cells and provisional calcification).
Columnar arrangement of cells in the plate.
Density of primary, secondary and tertiary trabeculae in the metaphysis, ie numerical proportion of primary bone trabeculae (immediately below the plate), secondary trabeculae (in the level of one height of the epiphyseal plate below the plate) and tertiary trabeculae (in the level of four heights of epiphyseal plate below the plate) to the number of calcified cartilaginous bars in the zone of provisional calcification. These proportions indicate how many of the calcified cartilage bars were actually used as a core for the new metaphyseal trabeculae.

b. *Primary Mineralisation (Material 1 and 2; Longitudinal and Cross-Sections)*

Sections were stained by the author's Tetrachrome 1 and 2 methods in which newly deposited osteoid tissue is stained deep blue and mineralised bone bright red. Speed of mineralisation in the metaphysis was assessed in primary trabeculae by calculating how many arcades down below the plate the newly laid osteoid tissue started to change into mineralised bone. The mineralisation process in the diaphysis was assessed by recording of the thickness of endosteal and periosteal osteoid and its extent and distribution along the bone circumference.

c. *Secondary Mineralisation - Diaphysis (Material 1 and 2; Cross-Sections)*

Extent, progress, evenness or defect of subsequent mineralisation was assessed in paraffin sections stained with Tetrachrome 1 and 2 and on microradiographs.

d. *Diaphyseal Cortex-Modelling and Maturation (Material 1 and 2; Cross-Sections)*

The following measurements were made:

Number of large modelling cavities and actively built Haversian systems.
Primary metaphyseal bone-remodelling (ie gradual disappearance of the primary trabeculae containing large remnants of calcified cartilage which are gradually replaced from outside by the newly-formed endosteal cortical bone).
Cortex maturation (ie ratio of the amount of inter-Haversian woven bone and Haversian lamellar bone as studied by the Tetrachrome 2 method and in microradiographs).

116

e. Diaphyseal Bone Growth (Material 1 and 2; Cross-Sections)

The following measurements were made:

Diameter of the shaft, cortical thickness (measured in three different areas separately and expressed as a mean value). Cross-sectional architecture of the shaft (ie the quantitative proportion of the cortical bone, trabecular bone and bone marrow expressed as a percentage of the bone diameter). Measurements were done in three different segments on the same section and the mean values were taken as representative.

f. Sectional Shape of the Diaphysis of the Tibia (Material 1 and 3; Cross-Sections)

The cross-section through the mid-shaft varied in most cases between a fully triangular and a fully circular shape. An attempt was made to measure the differences in shape by dividing the distance between the flat side of an equilateral triangle inside a circle and the circumference of the circle into 100 divisions. The cross-section of a tibia with an ideal triangular shape measured 0 divisions and that of a fully circular shape measured 100 divisions.

g. Dynamics of the Experimental Remodelling of the Shaft (Material 3; Undecalcified Sections)

Fluorescent bone markers are deposited at the time of injection only in the newly-produced bone, eg along the periosteal and endosteal surfaces of the shaft. The distance between these two lines indicated the width and shape of the cortex at the time of injection. Their shift against the endosteal and periosteal circumferences found at the time when the animals were sacrificed demonstrated the pattern of bone-remodelling during that period.

RESULTS

Results are summarised in Tables 1 and 2. Where the findings are based on Material 2, the spina bifida bones were split into two groups with 'paralytic' or 'paralytic-pressure' deformities.

Epiphyseal plate and endochondral ossification were abnormal in spina bifida, the plate being thin with diminished number of cells especially in the paralytic group. The amount of newly-formed primary and secondary metaphyseal trabeculae was also gradually diminishing. In addition, because many of these babies are born by breech delivery (Stark & Drummond, 1970; Ralis, 1975), often with foot presentation, a portion of these irregular plates were found to be further damaged by fractures, tears and fresh bleeding.

The speed of the primary bone mineralisation of the new metaphyseal trabeculae was in the mean values almost normal in the paralytic group, although the span of counts was larger than in controls. In the paralytic-pressure group, however, there were many cases in which this mineralisation was either very fast (ie already starting 1-2 arcades below the plate) or delayed (starting 5-10 arcades below the plate). In the paralytic group, there was also a delay in the primary

Table 1. *Endochondral ossification, primary and secondary mineralisation*

	'normal' bones	spina bifida bones with 'paralytic' deformity	spina bifida bones with 'paralytic-pressure' deformity
a. endochondral ossification number of vessels entering the plate	normal	usually low	variable
cellular population of the plate	normal	usually low	variable
columnar arrangement in the plate	regular	mostly regular	variable
numerical proportion of I. trabeculae	increasing with age	decreasing with age	
II. trabeculae	almost consistent	decreasing with age	
III. trabeculae	slightly declining	slightly declining with age	
b. primary mineralisation speed of mineralisation of I. trabeculae	normal	normal	fast or delayed
thickness of the endosteal and periosteal osteoid	+	++	+
distribution of the periosteal osteoid around the shaft	on medial and posterior surfaces only	on medial, posterior and lateral surfaces	
extent of the cover of the shaft by periosteal osteoid	reclining steeply after 32nd prenatal week	reclining slowly after 32nd prenatal week	
c. secondary mineralisation diaphysis	even	uneven	slightly uneven

mineralisation of the shaft, compared with the paralytic-pressure and normal groups. This was witnessed by the presence of wide osteoid seams on both endosteal and periosteal surfaces. Spina bifida bones showed in general a wider distribution and longer persistence of periosteal osteoid along the surfaces of the shaft than the normal bones. The quality of the secondary mineralisation, as demonstrated by the Tetrachrome methods and microradiography, was found abnormal in most of the spina bifida bones. They showed uneven distribution of bone mineral both in varying density and spread through the cortex. However, these changes were much less evident in the paralytic-pressure group as compared with the purely paralytic group.

Table 2. Diaphyseal cortex modelling, maturation and growth

| | 'normal' bones | spina bifida bones | |
		with 'paralytic' deformity	with 'paralytic-pressure' deformity
d. diaphyseal cortex modelling and maturation			
number of large modelling cavities and developing Haversian systems	+++	+	++
	continuously rising before and after birth	rising before and declining after birth	
degree of primary metaphyseal bone remodelling	+++	+	+
cortex maturation	normal	delayed	delayed
e. diaphyseal bone growth			
diameter of the shaft	normal	diminished	diminished
cortical thickness	continuously rising before and after birth	rising before and declining after birth	
	normal	markedly diminished	diminished
architecture of the shaft	proportional	disproportional	nearly proportional

The spina bifida bones also showed a delay in the modelling of the diaphyseal cortex and its maturation. The number of large remodelling cavities and developing Haversian systems was decreased and removal of the primary metaphyseal trabecular bone with cartilaginous cores was slow. In addition, in spina bifida material the immature woven bone in the cortex persisted and its conversion into mature lamellar bone was very slow. Naturally, such deficient endochondral ossification, mineralisation and delayed maturation of the growing bones in spina bifida limbs results in their diminished bone mass, smaller diameter of the diaphysis and noticeable thinning of the cortex. The bone architecture has also been found grossly changed in the 'purely paralytic' groups in which the largest part of the bone diameter was occupied by bone marrow.

The cross-sectional shape of the tibial diaphysis was different in each of the groups studied. In normal foetuses and babies its shape is a triangular one and in spina bifida and calcaneus type of foot deformity its shape is nearly triangular. However, the cross-section was almost completely circular in spina bifida bones with equino-varus type of foot deformity and tended to be circular in the fully paralysed spina bifida group with no deformities.

These characteristic shape patterns did not change much with age, the only exception being that in the earlier foetal period a normal mid-shaft in the cross-section had a rather domed shape.

The dynamics of the diaphyseal shape remodelling after experimental myotomy were assessed in the labelled rat bones. The deposited Alizarin red S appeared in their cortical bone in sharp lines of bright red fluorescence, and oxytetracycline as sharp lines of bright yellowish-green fluorescence. Analysis of the position of these lines on histophotographs plotted against the time interval has shown significant changes in the pattern of periosteal and endosteal bone apposition and resorption which resulted in lateral shift of the cortex and a transformation of its shape. These changes were dependent on the type of myotomy. This experiment has shown that the growing tibial cortex under normally functioning muscles keeps its shape flat or slightly concave as a result of compression stresses imposed by the working muscles. The cortex under non-working muscles develops a bulging convex shape, presumably due to lack of such stresses and/or imposed tensile strains by the working muscles on the opposite side. At the same time, there is a lateral shift of the 'centre of gravity' of the growing bone in the direction of non-working muscles.

DISCUSSION

With the techniques used we had an opportunity to assess not only the main morphological changes, but also the finer details in the bone quality and mineralisation.

In order to obtain the maximum significance from our findings, it was necessary to arrange the spina bifida material into the closest possible aetiological groups. All of these babies had a certain degree of paralysis in their lower limbs and the majority of them had some type of hip or foot deformity. In previous dissections of spina bifida material (Ralis & Duckworth, 1973; Ralis, 1974) it has been shown that a paralytic limb deformity which is present at birth may be produced in two different ways. In one it develops as a result of partial paralysis (totally paralysed limbs often show no deformities at birth), in which uneven or unopposed muscle pull deviates part of the extremity first into an extreme and later into a pathological position. These 'true paralytic' deformities were among the first which were recognised and classified by John Sharrard (1959, 1962). In the second group another important factor is involved. These are local intrauterine pressures acting on the partially or totally paralysed limb. The high incidence of such pressures in pregnancies with myelomeningocele is due to many factors. These include the diminished amount of circulating amniotic fluid due to accompanying urogenital malformations (Wilcock & Emery, 1970) or hydrocephalus, irregular or rigid position of limbs in large joints such as the extended hip and knee joints, in breech or transverse presentation (Ralis, 1975a), or presence of deformity in the other limb. Paralysis is an additional factor in this process since such a limb cannot easily move away from the mechanical deforming force. We call these malformations, which have also been produced experimentally (Lendon & Ralis, 1971), 'paralytic-pressure' deformities. The deformities are rigid, neurologically atypical and there are often signs of external pressure on the skin in the post-natal period; their surgical treatment is difficult (Ralis, 1974; Ralis, 1978; Ralis & Duckworth, 1973).

Among the 'normal' limbs which served as controls, the ossification process could be disturbed by systemic illness. Variations and irregular ossification of the costo-chondral junction in children can be detected microscopically during the post-mortem examination (Cohen, 1948; Park, 1954; Park, 1964; Emery, 1964; Emery & Kalpaktsoglou, 1967), or as 'Harris's lines' on radiographs of long bones (Harris, 1933) as evidence of this. Conversely, the spina bifida material might also include bones from subjects with systemic disorders and nutritional disturbances such as vitamin C deficiency (McKibbin & Porter, 1967). It is not yet possible to determine exactly which changes in growing bones and soft tissues are caused by the paralysis itself and which by the lack of mobility, abnormal skeletal loading and position, sensory denervation, growth retardation and local blood supply and metabolic disturbances.

The reduced number of primary and secondary metaphyseal trabeculae in most of the spina bifida bones can be explained, according to Wolf's law, by the lack of mechanical stress. Allison & Brooks (1921) reported that cancellous bone ends of dogs' forelegs after resection of the brachial plexus were found 'quite fragile with fewer and smaller trabeculae'.

Most authors agree about the localisation of fractures of these bones in metaphyseal and epiphyseal regions (Gillies & Hartung, 1958; Golding, 1960; Soutter, 1962; Burney & Hamsa, 1963; Korhonen, 1971), and that they often happen without a known cause (Broadley & Schands, 1964; Korhonen, 1971).

Paralysis alone probably has little influence on the speed of early mineralisation of the newly-formed bone trabeculae under the plate; it was in the paralytic-pressure group where the metaphyseal bone showed fast or delayed mineralisation pattern. However, the amount of unmineralised osteoid tissue in the metaphysis, and especially on the cortical bone surfaces, was increased significantly in the paralytic spina bifida group. The unmineralised bone matrix in the epiphysis and metaphysis forms a substantial portion of the bone even in normal children where every surface of newly-formed trabeculae is covered by osteoid tissue. Its further increase would lead naturally to diminished mechanical bone strength in these regions; this has been shown in rickets, eg by Weir, Bell & Chambers (1949).

Changes in the secondary mineralisation as witnessed by wider osteoid seams and uneven stainability of the cortical matrix in Tetrachrome techniques and variable density of the bone mineral in microradiographs, are directly linked with 'pure analysis' as it seems that the pressure exerted on paralysed limbs in utero appears to have a protective effect on it.

In Marotti & Marotti's (1966) experimental observation on dogs there is other evidence about the disturbance of mineralisation in denervated and immobilised growing limbs. Though in these bones there was an overall decrease in appositional bone growth, the authors observed in some animals that the amount of the Achromycin-labelled bone increased in the immobile bones 5-20 times. This could only mean that in these bones there were large areas represented by a primitive mineral similar to that in the calcification front, in which fluorescent bone markers are primarily deposited, and that maturation of this mineral did not progress further. The patchiness and uneven Tetrachrome staining in our material could be given the same interpretation.

The diminished number of large modelling cavities and Haversian systems indicates the lack of remodelling activity which results in a retardation of further growth. The very slow removal of the original metaphyseal bone and the primitive bone architecture are consequences of this poor rebuilding activity.

The diminished cortical thickness, area and diameter all indicate bone thinning and atrophy. Evans (1957) quoted Zschokke's observation that 'bones in the infantile paralysis are lighter, thinner and lag behind the normal bones in growth'. These were the first signs detectable clinically and radiologically and were, therefore, already reported in the literature about spina bifida children (Sharrard, 1971), and in paralysed, tenotomised and immobilised limbs (Whedon & Shorr, 1957; Geiser & Trueta, 1958; Sharrard, 1971).

The finding that tibial cross-sections which are normally triangular are round in spina bifida with total paralysis, or with equino-varus foot deformities, are in agreement with two quotations mentioned by Ascenzi & Bell (1971): Bernhard in 1924 noticed round-shaped tibiae in cases of talipes equinus with resection of the knee joint; Fick, who in 1875 removed anterior leg muscles in young dogs, noticed that the 'characteristic triangular cross-section is lost'. At the time of birth and up to 3½ months of age the tibial shaft was found to be definitely triangular in all normal babies. The statement that 'in the child, before walking begins the tibial section is rounded' (Ascenzi & Bell, 1971) is in disagreement with this. Allison & Brooks (1921) also noticed that after experimental denervation of the limb in dogs the tibia had a circular cross-section shape.

The distribution pattern of the fluorescent markers in growing rat bones, as well as findings of osteoid on some of the endosteal surfaces in normal human femurs and tibiae, revealed that endosteal apposition does take place in long bones during their development. Others have noticed this, eg Owen et al. (1955). This is contrary to the belief that enlargement of tubular bone during its growth is done simply by periosteal aposition and endosteal resorption (Ham, 1969).

Uneven development of different bone walls during the growth was first reported by Duhamel in the 18th century who labelled the bones with madder. Owen et al. (1955) studied this process on tibiae of growing rabbits by autoradiographic techniques and Liskova & Hert (1971) studied the response of the rabbit's tibia on experimental intermittent stresses by Tetracycline labelling. Results of our experimental observations on the influence of myotomy on the tibial shape in rats were, therefore, more or less expected. Since cross-sections of tibiae of growing rats have the same central shape characteristics as the human, one could presume that changes which followed myotomy in rats would be similar to those which occur after myotomy or muscle paralysis in humans. Application of the principle that a flat cortex will remodel into a bulging cortex under the myotomised muscles to our findings on human tibiae means that one has to presume that all muscles around the circular-shaped tibiae were equally paralysed. This happened not only in the spina bifida group without deformity, in which total paralysis is presumed, but also in limbs with equinus and equino-varus foot deformities, which are supposed to be produced by the contraction of the foot plantiflexors and invertors in a partially paralysed limb. On the other hand, in limbs with the calcaneus type of foot deformity the only bulging cortex was the lateral one. This would mean that the only muscles released were the foot dorsiflexors growing on the lateral aspect of the tibial triangle, ie muscles which are supposed to produce the deformity by their contraction. These findings obviously contradict the idea that pure muscle imbalance is the sole factor responsible for the deformity.

These deformities could only have been produced by the foot being pressed in utero from the outside into the deformed position, which would cause relaxation of muscles on the concave side of the deformity. In the course of continuous growth of the limb these muscles would gradually get shorter and tighter, giving the false impression on later clinical examination that, by their active pull, they were responsible for the deformity. Their diminished mass, atrophy and histological changes would, however, reveal the true situation (Ralis & Duckworth, 1973). Evidence of such external mechanical intra-uterine pressure seen during dissections of paralysed limb has already been reported (Lendon & Ralis, 1971; Ralis & Duckworth, 1973; Ralis, 1974). The observations presented here on the cross-sectional shape of spina bifida tibiae thus provide further supporting evidence for the co-existence of intrauterine paralysis and mechanical moulding pressure.

As to the aetiology of common metaphyseal and epiphyseal fractures in children with paralysed limbs, it is apparent that these bones are weakened in several different ways and represent a potential hazard for the child for several different reasons:

a. The amount of primary trabecular bone in the metaphysis is diminishing markedly and progressively with age.

b. The newly-formed bone is not normally and adequately mineralised. This is apparent not only on surfaces of primary metaphyseal trabeculae, but also on endosteal and periosteal surfaces of the cortex where there is an increased amount of osteoid tissue. The secondary mineralisation of the bone matrix is also irregular and deficient.

c. The mechanical properties of the newly-formed cortical bone are probably further weakened by the persistence of primary metaphyseal bone which contains large remnants of brittle calcified cartilage from the epiphyseal plate exhibiting multiple cracks on microradiographs, and also by sluggish maturation of the cortex structure with only slow replacement of the woven bone by mature lamellar bone. In the shaft there is a diminished ratio of trabecular bone mass to cortical bone mass. Thus not only bone osteoporosis and change in the bone mass, but also degradation of its quality, are the typical features in the developing paralysed bones.

d. Apart from the above findings, so far unpublished, there are further changes already reported in clinical and radiological studies such as growth retardation and reduction in the thickness and diameter of the diaphyseal cortex.

Since the pressure exerted upon the paralysed limbs seems to have a protective effect on those processes in the developing bone which - if retarded - would probably significantly weaken it and lead to fractures, it is important to draw some practical conclusions from these observations. The conservative treatment of spina bifida paralysed limbs should follow the general trends of modern paediatric orthopaedic surgery which is consistently turning away from rigid immobilisation, which arrests the growing limb in plaster, sometimes for considerable periods, towards the more physiological treatment which values movement as an essential part of the normal limb development, trying at least from time to time to stretch the limb passively and to move its muscles and joints. Since forcible exercises of immobile joints have been repeatedly accused of causing the fractures there has been some tendency to be careful with physiotherapy of these bones. Importance of muscle activity, movements and ambulation has been recognised before as a factor responsible for the prevention of osteoporosis in paralysed bones, eg by Abramson (1948), Norton & Foley (1959) and Abramson & Delgadi (1961) and also in myopathies (Walton & Warrick, 1954) and experimental tenotomy (Geiser & Trueta, 1958). Although the limbs are paralysed and will probably never be actively used we should try to impose weight bearing on these bones, if possible, or at least passive movements and artificial 'weight bearing' by regularly exerting passive force in the direction of their long axis. It is hoped that such stimulation by mechanical stress could, in clinical practice, have a protective influence against growth retardation and later deterioration of growing paralysed long bones in these children.

CONCLUSIONS

1. There are these substantial differences between normal and developing bones and bones from children with spina bifida and paralysis: endochondral ossification, primary mineralisation, secondary mineralisation, diaphyseal cortex modelling and maturation, bone mass and cross-sectional shape of the diaphysis.

2. The characteristic cross-sectional shape of diaphysis of normal developing human tibiae can be satisfactorily explained by the action of

surrounding muscles. The moulding action of muscles and their influence
on the cross-sectional shape of a developing bone has been confirmed by
experimental myotomy of foot dorsiflexors and plantiflexors in growing
rats.

3. However, analysis of the cross-sectional shape of tibial diaphysis
in babies with spina bifida foot deformities revealed that many of them
were not produced by muscle pull or their paralysis and imbalance, but
by mechanical intrauterine pressure acting on the paralysed limb.

4. In the majority of aspects studied differences were found between
the spina bifida 'paralytic' and 'paralytic-pressure' groups, confirming
that they represent two separate conditions with different aetiology,
morphology and pathogenesis.

5. It was found that for the common fractures in metaphyseal and
epiphyseal regions of long bones in babies and children with spina
bifida, not only their diminished bone mass, diameter and atrophy are
responsible, but there is a whole spectrum of so-far undescribed factors
which lead to changes in the quality and further weakening of the
developing and paralysed bone. These additional factors are: the
diminished number of primary trabeculae produced in the metaphysis,
increased amount of unmineralised osteoid tissue on endosteal and
periosteal surfaces, deficient secondary mineralisation of the bone
matrix, delayed removal of primary metaphyseal bone which is
mechanically unsound, sluggish cortex maturation and development of
its architecture showing decrease in the trabecular cortical bone ratio,
and lack of modelling cavities in the diaphysis.

6. Since there is evidence that bones from paralysed and deformed
limbs which were developing under additional mechanical pressure have
deteriorated less than bones with paralysis but without such pressure,
it is suggested that, to prevent their further atrophy and fractures,
this positive role of outside pressure on growing paralysed and
motionless bones should be exploited. This could be done in the
physiotherapy of these limbs by artificial 'weight-bearing', eg by
periodical passive pressure in the direction of the long axis of the
bone.

Acknowledgement - This research project was supported by the National
Fund for Research into Crippling Diseases, Grant No. A/8/1067. The
author would like to thank Mrs Heather M. Ralis and Mrs Glenys Stimpson
for the preparation of the manuscript.

References

Abramson, A.S., (1948): Bone disturbances in injury to spinal cord and
    cauda equina (paraplegia). Their prevention by ambulation. J. Bone
    Jt. Surg. 30A, 982.
Abramson, A.S. & Delagi, E.F. (1961): Influence of weight-bearing and
    muscle contraction on disuse osteoporosis. Archs. Phys. Med. 42, 147.
Allison & Brooks (1921): Bone atrophy. An experimental study of the
    changes in bone which result from nonuse. Surg. Gynec. Obst. 33, 250.
Ascenzi, A. & Bell, G.H. (1971): Bone as a mechanical engineering
    problem. In 'The biochemistry and physiology of bone', ed G.H. Bourne,
    Vol. 1, p. 311. New York: Academic Press.

Broadley, P.H. & Schands, A.R. (1964): Pathological fractures in
    crippled children's hospital. Pediatr. Clin. North Amer. 12, 161.
Burney, D.W. & Hamsa, W.R. (1963): Spina bifida with myelomeningocele.
    Clin. Orthop. 30, 167.
Cohen, J. (1948): Normal variation of the costochondral junction. Archs.
    Pathol. 45, 246.
Emery, J.L. (1964): The assessment of the duration of illness in
    children unexpectedly dead. Med. Sci. Law 4, 39.
Emery, J.L. & Kalpaktsoglou, P.K. (1967): The costochondral junction
    during later stages of intrauterine life, and abnormal growth patterns
    found in association with perinatal death. Archs. Dis. Child 42, 1.
Evans, F.G. (1957): 'Stress and strains in bones. Their relation to
    fractures and osteogenesis'. Springfield, Illinois: Charles C. Thomas.
Freehafer, A.A. (1974): The treatment of myelmeningocele patients with
    paralytic hip deformities by iliopsoas transfer. Paraplegia 2, 295.
Geiser, M. & Trueta, J. (1958): Muscle action, bone rarefaction and bone
    formation. J. Bone Jt. Surg. 40B, 282.
Gillies, C.L. & Hartung, W. (1938): Fracture of the tibia in spina
    bifida vera. Radiology 31, 621.
Golding, C. (1960): Spina bifida and epiphyseal displacement. J. Bone
    Jt. Surg. 42B, 387.
Ham, A.W. (1969): 'Histology', 6th ed. Philadelphia: J.B. Lippincott.
Harris, H.A. (1933): 'Bone growth in health and disease', p. 239.
    Oxford: Oxford University Press.
Jeannopoulos, C.L. (1954): Bone changes in children with lesions of the
    spinal cord or roots. N. Y. J. Med. 54, 3219.
Katz, J.F. (1953): Spontaneous fractures in paraplegic children. J.
    Bone Jt. Surg. 35A, 220.
Korhonen, B.J. (1971): Fractures in myelodysplasia. Clin. Orthop. 79,
    145.
Lendon & Ralis (1971): Normal posture and deformities of lower limbs in
    rat foetuses with experimentally produced spina bifida. Develop. Med.
    Child Neurol. 13, Suppl. 15, 50.
Liskova, M. & Hert (1971): Reaction of bone to mechanical stimuli: Part
    2: periosteal and endosteal reaction of tibial diaphysis in rabbit to
    intermittent loading. Folia Morphol. (Prague) 19, 301.
Marotti, G. & Marotti, F. (1966): Topographic-quantitative study of
    bone tissue formation and reconstruction in inert bones. In 3rd
    Europ. Calc. Tiss. Symp., ed H. Fleisch et al., pp. 89-93. Berlin:
    Springer.
McKibbin, B. & Porter, R.W. (1967): The incidence of vitamin C
    deficiency in meningomyelocele. Develop. Med. Child Neurol. 9, 338.
Norton, P.L. & Foley, J.J. (1959): Paraplegia in children. J. Bone Jt.
    Surg. 41A, 1291.
Park, E.A. (1954): The influence of severe illness on rickets. Archs.
    Dis. Child 29, 369.
Park, E.A. (1964): The imprinting of nutritional disturbances on the
    growing bone. Pediatrics 33, 815.
Ralis, Z.A. (1974): The role of mechanical intrauterine pressure in
    pathogenesis of paralytic limb deformities. J. Bone Jt. Surg. 56B,
    383.

Ralis, Z.A. (1975a): Birth trauma to muscles in babies born by breech delivery and its possible fatal consequences. Archs. Dis. Child 50, 4.

Ralis, Z.A. (1975b): Traumatising effect of breech delivery on infants with spina bifida. J. Pediatr. 87, 613.

Ralis, Z.A. (1978): Ossification and growth of long bones in babies and infants with spina bifida. A preliminary report on histometric and microradiographic studies. Kinderchururgie 25, 359.

Ralis, Z.A. (1980): in preparation.

Ralis, Z.A. & Blake, P.D. (1976): The use of histophotography in bone histology and morphometry. Med. Lab. Sciences 33, 63.

Ralis, Z.A. & Duckworth, T. (1973): Morphology of the congenital vertical talus. J. Bone Jt. Surg. 55B, 428.

Ralis, Z.A. & Ralis, H.M. (1975): A simple method for demonstration of osteoid in paraffin sections. Med. Lab. Technol. 32, 203.

Ralis, Z.A. & Ralis, H.M. (1976): Phosphotungstic acid-iron-haematoxylin (PTAIH) method for osteoid, boundary bone and bone components in paraffin section. Microscopica Acta (Basel) 78, 407.

Ralis, Z.A., Ralis, H.M., Randell, M., Watkins, G. & Blake, P.D. (1976): Changes in the shape, ossifications and quality of bones in children with spina bifida. A clinico-pathological and experimental study. Develop. Med. Child Neurol. 18, Suppl. 37, 29.

Sharrard, W.J.W. (1959): Congenital paralytic dislocations of the hip in children with myelomeningocele. J. Bone Jt. Surg. 41B, 622.

Sharrard, W.J.W. (1962): The mechanism of paralytic deformity in spina bifida. Develop. Med. Child Neurol. 4, 310.

Sharrard, W.J.W. (1971): 'Paediatric orthopaedics and fractures'. Oxford: Blackwell.

Soutter, F.E. (1962): Spina bifida and epiphyseal displacement. J. Bone Jt. Surg. 44B, 106.

Stark, G. & Drummond, M. (1970): Spina bifida as an obstetric problem. Develop. Med. Child Neurol. 12, Suppl. 22, 157.

Walton, J.N. & Warrick, C.K. (1954): Osseous changes in myopath. Br. J. Radiol. 27, 1.

Weir, J.B., Bell, G.H. & Chambers, J.W. (1949): The strength and elasticity of bones in rats on a rachitogenic diet. J. Bone Jt. Surg. 31B, 444.

Whedon, G.D. & Shorr, E. (1957): Metabolic studies in paralytic acute anterior poliomyelitis. II Alterations in calcium and phosphotes metabolism. J. Clin. Invest. 36, 966.

Wilcock, A.R. & Emery, J.L. (1970): Deformities of the renal tract in children with meningo-myelocele and hydrocephalus, compared with those of children showing no such central nervous system deformities. Br. J. Urol. 42, 152.

Owen, M., Jowsey, J. & Vaughan, J. (1955): Investigation on the growth and structure of the tibia of the rabbit by microradiographic and autoradiographic techniques. J. Bone Jt. Surg. 37B, 324.

18

The role of the periosteum in bone remodelling and deformity

G.R. HOUGHTON AND G.D. ROOKER

INTRODUCTION

The morphology of an immature long bone differs from the adult bone in
many important respects. The bone grows in length from the growth
plates, but the fibrous periosteum grows interstitially throughout its
length (Warwick & Wiles, 1934; Lacroix, 1948).

Immature periosteum is relatively thick and loosely attached to the
underlying diaphyseal and metaphyseal bone, but very strongly attached
around the perichondral ring at the level of the growth plate and
epiphysis. Muscles and tendons are attached directly to the periosteum
rather than the underlying cortical bone. In adult bones the periosteum
is thin, adherent to the underlying cortex, and muscle and tendon
fibres pass through it to gain direct access to the underlying cortical
bone via Sharpey fibres.

The different growth patterns between periosteum and bone means that
there is differential growth between the periosteum and the underlying
cortical bone except at three points: at either end of the long bone
where the periosteum is attached to the perichondral ring, and at the
so-called 'null point' of periosteal growth which is furthest away from
the most active growth plate and nearest to the least active growth
plate (Lacroix, 1948). This 'null point' of growth between the
periosteum and the underlying cortical bone differs for each individual
long bone, but in the tibia occurs at about 35 per cent of the tibial
length above the lower growth plate, 35 per cent of tibial growth being
contributed to by the growth plate at the distal end of the bone
(Fig. 1).

In an experiment on chicken radii, Crilly (1972) showed that
circumferential division of the periosteum of the diaphysis stimulated
longitudinal bone growth and that an increase in length following such
stimulation was permanent. He also showed that an equivalent length of
incision longitudinally-placed in the periosteum did not have this
effect. It was thus postulated that the strong fibro-elastic periosteal
sleeve was being stretched between the separating bone epiphyses, thus
acting as a check on longitudinal bone growth.

Circumferential division of this sleeve allows mechanical release of
the growth plates and thus gives rise to a stimulation of longitudinal
bone growth. Transplanted bones and bones in culture chambers show the

same phenomenon (Harkness & Trotter, 1978; Houghton & Dekel, 1979).

Fracture or osteotomy will also disrupt the periosteal sleeve and in both instances a growth stimulation is the rule (Edvardsen & Syversen, 1976; Goldthwaite - quoted by Chandler, 1937).

Greenstick fractures in children only partially disrupt the periosteal sleeve and growth stimulation is not a recognised complication of such fractures. However, a greenstick fracture of the upper metaphysis of the tibia in children is often complicated by the development of a persistent valgus deformity of the tibia (Cozen, 1953; Jackson & Cozen, 1971; Weber, 1977). We have designed an experimental model to investigate the possibility that this deformity develops because of hemicircumferential periosteal damage, with medial growth plate stimulation only and thus the development of angular deformity.

MATERIAL AND METHOD

Twenty-four six-week-old New Zealand white rabbits, with a mean weight of 1301 g, were chosen as the experimental animal. The animals were divided into six groups of four and each group had a surgical procedure carried out about the right upper tibia (Fig. 2). The left leg acted as a control and a sham operation dividing skin, soft tissue and disrupting underlying muscle was carried out. The tibiae were then radiographed at weekly intervals with the lower limbs fixed rigidly in a jig in neutral rotation. Directly comparable radiographs were thus taken with a margin of error to within 1°. Varus/valgus angulation was measured by estimating the angle between the growth plate and the diaphysis of the tibia: the plate-shaft angle (PS angle). One animal from each group was sacrificed at two weeks in order to carry out a histological study of the growth plate and periosteum. One animal from the group with periosteal division above the pes anserinus sustained accidental growth plate trauma at the time of operation and was therefore excluded from the series. Details of this method and technique have been given by Houghton & Rooker (1979).

RESULTS

The varus/valgus angulation at the upper tibia was assessed by plotting the PS angle against time for each pair of legs in each group of animals (Fig. 3). In the three groups with incision of the pes anserinus alone, osteotomy of the fibula and lateral hemicircumferential division of the periosteum, there was no development of angular deformity. During normal growth the PS angle appeared to fluctuate, the fluctuation was symmetrical bilaterally. Hemicircumferential periosteal division through and above the pes anserinus developed a significant valgus deformity, but this had corrected by the end of the experimental period. Hemicircumferential division of the medial periosteum below the pes anserinus, however, gave rise to a valgus deformity which persisted right up to the end of skeletal growth.

Histological examination of the growth plates of the animals showed no variation in width from the medial to the lateral side of the upper tibial growth plate nor from the experimental and control tibiae in any group. In those animals which had undergone periosteal division, it was noted at two weeks that the periosteum was adherent to the underlying

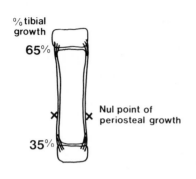

% tibial growth

65%

Nul point of periosteal growth

35%

Fig. 1. The null point of periosteal growth lies nearer the less active growth plate of any long bone

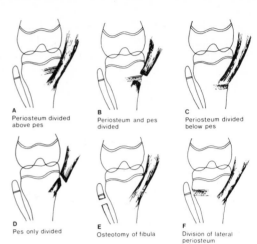

A
Periosteum divided above pes

B
Periosteum and pes divided

C
Periosteum divided below pes

D
Pes only divided

E
Osteotomy of fibula

F
Division of lateral periosteum

Fig. 2. Surgical procedures performed about the right knee

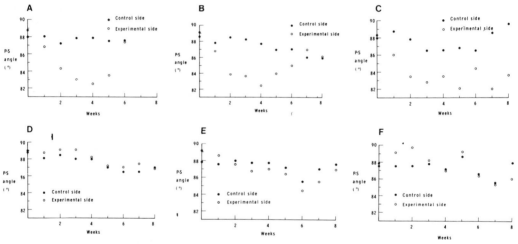

Fig. 3. The P.S. angle in the six experimental groups

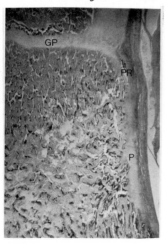

Fig. 4. Adherence of periosteum to underlying metaphyseal bone (G.P. = growth plate, P.R. = perichondral ring, P = periosteum at the site of attachment to underlying bone)

cortical bone (Fig. 4), but this could not be demonstrated in the animal
that had undergone periosteal division below the pes anserinus.

DISCUSSION AND CLINICAL APPLICATION OF FINDINGS

From these experiments it appears that medial hemicircumferential
division of the upper tibia stimulates the medial side of the growth
plate only with development of angular deformity. Lateral periosteal
release with an intact fibula, however, did not give rise to angular
deformity probably due to the tethering effect of the fibula.

If circumferential periosteal incision is carried out near a growth
plate, there is stimulation of growth from each end of the bone, but
during the periosteal repair phase the periosteum becomes adherent to
the underlying bone and there is growth retardation at the adjacent
growth plate (Crilly, 1972). The stimulation persists from the growth
plate remote from the site of incision. Thickening and adherence of the
periosteum at the site of previous incision is believed to tether the
adjacent growth plate and thus check growth. The site of tethering
becomes the new 'null point' of periosteal growth so that the remote
growth plate is thus relatively unrestrained and growth stimulation
persists. From our results, it would seem that remodelling of angular
deformity when the periosteum is divided above and through the pes
anserinus, is due to a unilateral periosteal tethering effect. This
remodelling does not occur if the periosteum is divided below the pes
anserinus. This phenomenon may be due to the unique anatomical
arrangement at the upper tibia. The pes anserinus is a strong group of
tendons attached in the immature animal to the underlying periosteum.
If the periosteum is divided below the muscle, the muscle tends to drag
it proximally and thus release tension on the medial growth plate.
Growth plate 'release' is thus prolonged in this instance and angular
deformity is permanent. In addition, periosteal healing after this
latter procedure appears to occur without histological evidence of
tethering to the underlying cortical bone.

Explanations for the development of a persistent valgus deformity in
greenstick fractures of the upper tibia in children include: fibular
tethering (Taylor, 1963), unilateral tibial delayed union (Pollen,
1973), angulation of the upper tibia due to unchecked pull of lateral
musculotendinous structures (Weber, 1977), and damage to the lateral
growth plate (Goff, 1960). We have recently operated upon such a
fracture and found that the fracture occurred just below the pes
anserinus and that this tendon together with the periosteum is pulled
proximally into the fracture site. It is now our practice to repair the
periosteum after this fracture and to hold the fracture reduced with
percutaneous wire fixation. We believe that the severe complication of
valgus deformity following this injury is due to medial growth plate
stimulation secondary to unilateral periosteal damage and that, if the
periosteum is repaired, the stimulation will not occur. The animal
experiments support this view.

References

Chandler, F.A. (1937): Local overgrowth. J. Am. Med. Ass. 109, 1411.

Cozen, L. (1953): Fracture of the proximal portion of the tibia in children followed by valgus deformity. Surg. Gynec. Obstet. 97, 183.

Crilly, R.G. (1972): Longitudinal overgrowth of chicken radius. J. Anat. 112, 11.

Edvardsen, P. & Syversen, S.M. (1976): Overgrowth of the femur after fracture of the shaft in childhood. J. Bone Jt. Surg. 58B, 339.

Goff, C.W. (1960): 'Surgical treatment of unequal extremities'. Springfield, Illinois, Charles C. Thomas.

Harkness, E.M. & Trotter, W.D. (1978): Growth of transplants of rat humerus following circumferential division of the periosteum. J. Anat. 126, 275.

Houghton, G.R. & Dekel, S. (1979): The periosteal control of long bone growth. Acta Orthop. Scand. 50, 635.

Houghton, G.R. & Rooker, G.D. (1979): The role of the periosteum in the growth of long bones. J. Bone Jt. Surg. 61B, 218.

Jackson, D.W. & Cozen, L. (1971): Genu valgum as a complication of proximal tibial metaphyseal fractures in children. J. Bone Jt. Surg. 58B, 339.

Lacroix, P. (1948): Le mode de croissance du perioste. Archs Biol. 59, 378.

Pollen, A.G. (1973): 'Fractures and dislocations in children'. Edinburgh and London: Churchill Livingstone.

Taylor, S.L. (1963): Tibial overgrowth: a cause of genu valgum. J. Bone Jt. Surg. 45A, 659.

Warwick, W.T. & Wiles, P. (1934): The growth of periosteum in long bones. Brit. J. Surg. 22, 169.

Weber, G. (1977): Fibrous interposition causing valgus deformity after fracture of the upper tibial metaphysis in children. J. Bone Jt. Surg. 59B, 290.

19

The structure of cortical bone determined by X-ray diffraction

S.A. JACKSON

INTRODUCTION

There have been many studies of the physical properties of bone. In
particular its anisotropic, piezoelectric and elastic properties have
been investigated (Fukada & Yashuda, 1957; Bassett & Becker, 1962; Lang,
1970). These studies have assumed that the crystallites of bone are all
uniformly oriented in a homogenous, regular structure. However, by
examining almost any X-ray diffraction photograph of laminar bone, the
arcing of the (002) diffraction ring (as shown in Fig. 1) indicates that
the crystal c-axes, which are coincident with the long axis of the
crystal, are distributed about one general direction. Since the
physical properties of a material such as bone are bound to be dependent
upon its overall crystalline structure, it is important that details of
this structure be determined as accurately as possible before the
results of physical tests can be fully interpreted. It is generally
accepted that bone mineral crystals have their c-axes aligned on average
with the collagen fibres axes (Stuhler, 1938; Engstrom & Zetterstrom,
1951; Engstrom, 1972). Thus a study of the crystallite orientation
enables the fibrous structure of bone to be determined. X-ray
diffraction provides a rapid technique for measuring the crystallite
orientation both qualitatively and quantitatively.

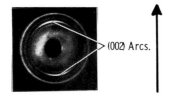

Main Axis of Fibre
Orientation.

(002) Arcs.

(Long Axis of Femur)

*Fig. 1. Typical X-ray diffraction
photograph of laminar bone, showing
(002) diffraction ring. The major
axis of orientation is indicated*

MATERIALS AND METHODS

Both primary and secondary type samples of cortical bone were chosen for
examination since they exhibit a well defined histological structure.
The primary sample, characterised by a regular laminar appearance, was
taken from the mid-femoral region of a Red Devon Ox, aged 2-3 years.

The secondary type sample, characterised by systems of osteons, was taken at post mortem from the mid-femoral region of a 65-year-old man. Both samples were untreated and cut approximately 70 microns thick as shown in Fig. 2, using a 'Metals Research' macrotome. The transverse section was examined using polarised light microscopy to characterise the histology type.

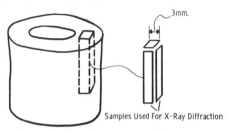

3mm.

Samples Used For X-Ray Diffraction

Fig. 2. Cutting and location of the cortical bone samples from the mid-femoral section

X-ray diffraction of the samples was performed using a stepping goniometer, which measured the full width intensity of the (002) diffraction ring in 9° steps. The X-ray beam (Cu. unfiltered) was collimated to 2 mm at the sample to reduce errors due to local histological variation. The background subtracted was taken as the mean of intensity readings at either side of the (002) ring. To express orientation in three dimensions a representation known as a pole figure was used.

The pole of a set of planes in a crystal is the point where the normal to the planes intersects an enclosing sphere. A pole figure of a particular set of planes is a stereographic projection of such a sphere on which equal intensities of all poles are contoured. Thus the peaks on a pole figure represent the directions of maximum distribution of the poles of a set of crystal planes. Since the (002) planes of bone mineral are perpendicular to the c-axis, which is aligned on average with the collagen fibres, the (002) pole figure defines the fibrous orientation of the bone sample quantitatively. In order to obtain an accurate representation of the (002) pole figure it is necessary to plot many points on the stereographic projection. This is achieved by rotating the specimen about its long axis and thus examining a different plane within the sample, hence producing poles at a different position on the projection. The use of two mutually perpendicular samples, examined normally and with ±30° rotation, allows complete coverage of the projection in 30° steps of longitude. This has proved sufficient to build up a composite pole figure of the whole sample. Because sample rotation causes a change in diffracting volume and X-ray path length, a correction factor was measured from an identically-shaped slab of compacted bone powder and applied to the results.

RESULTS

Pole figures for both the primary and secondary type bone samples are shown in Figs. 3 and 4 respectively. Whilst sample location and histological variation do affect the orientation pattern, the pole figures presented are typical of several samples taken from the same area of the same bone. The contour indexing is arbitrary.

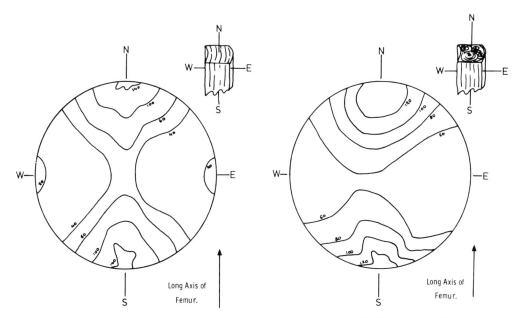

Fig. 3. The (002) pole figure of primary type bone

Fig. 4. The (002) pole figure of secondary type bone

DISCUSSION

The pole figure of primary type bone shows one major axis of orientation which is aligned on average with the long axis of the femur. The contours of the pole figure show that this type of laminar structure has a planar orientation of fibres. This finding is consistent with a fibrous spread within the laminations, but not from one lamination to the next.

Secondary type bone also exhibits one major axis of orientation which is aligned on average with the long axis of the femur. However, the pole figure contours tend to follow lines of latitude, indicating that the degree of preferred orientation has a rotational symmetry about the main fibre axis. Since the osteon which is the predominant feature of secondary type bone has rotational symmetry, it is feasible that the laminar orientation is similar to that of primary type bone, with the symmetrical distribution of orientation produced by the histological structure.

This work has determined the three-dimensional orientation of bone mineral crystals quantitatively. It has been shown that bone is anisotropic in its fibrous structure, with a degree of preferred orientation which can be measured from the pole figures. It is hoped that pole figures will help in the interpretation of future tests on the physical properties of bone.

Acknowledgements - I would like to thank Dr A.G. Cartwright, Dr D. Lewis and Mr J. Tucker for their help and encouragement.

References

Bassett, C.A.L. & Becker, R.O. (1962): Generation of electric
  potentials by bone in response to mechanical stress. Science 137,
  1063.
Engstrom, A. & Zetterstrom, R. (1951): Studies on the ultrastructure of
  bone. Exp. Cell Res. 2, 268.
Engstrom, A. (1972): Aspects of the molecular structure of bone. In
  'The biochemistry and physiology of bone', Vol. 1., ed G.H. Bourne,
  pp. 237-257. London: Academic Press.
Fukada, E. & Yashuda, I.I. (1957): On the piezoelectric effect of bone.
  J. Phys. Soc. Japan 12, 1158.
Lang, S.B. (1970): Ultrasonic method for measuring elastic coefficients
  of bone and results on fresh and dried bovine bones. I.E.E.E. Trans.
  Biomed. 17, 101.
Stuhler, R. (1938): Über den Feinbau des Knochens. Eine Röntgen-
  Feinstruktur-Untersuchung. Fortschr. Gebiete Rontgenstrahln. 57, 231.

20

Quadriceps muscle strength and fibre size during the treatment of osteomalacia

A. YOUNG, R.H.T. EDWARDS, D.A. JONES AND D.P. BRENTON

INTRODUCTION

Vitamin D deficiency has profound effects on the mechanical properties of bone. It also impairs the function of skeletal muscle, altering the forces acting on the bones.

The weakness has a predominantly proximal distribution and may even be the presenting symptom (Skaria et al., 1975). In ancient Indian literature, the author Vagbhatta (circa 500 A.D.) remarked on the combination of 'excessive and constant pain of the hip bones and great loss of strength' (translation by Professor B.C. Katiyar). In 1916, Agnes Scott published a vivid description of Indian women with osteomalacia, including the observation that 'to get up from a sitting to a standing position, the patient climbs up her own legs in a way similar to that of a child suffering from pseudo-hypertrophic muscular atrophy'. More recently, several medical authors have made a particular point of the muscular consequences of the disease (eg Dent, 1956; Smith & Stern, 1967; Schott & Wills, 1976). Nevertheless, the cause of osteomalacic 'myopathy' remains unknown.

This report describes measurements of quadriceps muscle strength and fibre size in a group of 12 patients with osteomalacia receiving treatment with vitamin D or one of its metabolites. An abstract based, in part, on the data reported here has previously been published (Young, Brenton & Edwards, 1978).

PATIENTS

Twelve patients (11 female) were studied (Table 1). Six were Indian women with nutritional osteomalacia, four were women with gluten-sensitive enteropathy and two had post-gastrectomy osteomalacia. Most had clinically apparent proximal muscle weakness.

METHODS

Strength

Quadriceps strength was measured with the patient seated in an adjustable, straight-backed chair with the pelvis secured by an adjustable lap-strap, the lower leg dependent and the knee flexed to 90°

(Edwards et al., 1977b). The force exerted during a maximal, voluntary, isometric contraction of the quadriceps was transmitted to a strain gauge by an inextensible strap looped around the ankle. The value of each maximal voluntary contraction (MVC) was measured as the greatest force held for one second. The strength of the quadriceps was taken to be the best of three MVC trials. The validity and repeatability of this procedure has been discussed elsewhere (Young, 1980).

Table 1. Details of patients, including plasma biochemistry and isometric quadriceps strength (MVC). (Normal MVC values are those of Edwards et al.,]977b). Calcium values are corrected to specific gravity 1.027 or to albumin 46 g/l (Berry et al., 1973).

patient no.	cause of osteomalacia	race	sex	age yr	Ca mM/l	P mM/l	alkaline phosphatase iu/1	KAu/100ml	MVC % of mean normal
1	nutritional	Ind	F	20	2.06	0.64		61	40
2	nutritional	Ind	F	23	1.64	1.45	83		67
3	nutritional	Ind	F	30	2.70	0.71		75	37
4	nutritional	Ind	F	39	1.79	0.88		91	33
5	nutritional	Ind	F	46	2.18	0.80		11	32
6	nutritional	Ind	F	60	2.34	0.65		42	14
7	gluten-sensitive enteropathy (GSE)	Cauc	F	47	2.18	0.64	400		35
8	GSE	Cauc	F	52	2.37	0.86	348		43
9	GSE	Cauc	F	60	2.39	1.44	188		22
10	GSE	Cauc	F	71	2.38	0.69	271		44
11	gastrectomy	Cauc	F	65	2.43	1.09	136		45
12	gastrectomy	Cauc	M	70	1.81	0.99	249*		28

*includes excessive liver phosphatase

Except for those cases where it was only possible to measure the strength of one quadriceps (eg, because of pain or because of risk of fracture through a Looser zone), the results reported were obtained for each patient's stronger leg. They were compared with the corresponding values obtained for the stronger leg of normal subjects of the same body weight (Edwards et al., 1977b).

Muscle Biopsy

Needle-biopsy samples were taken from the lateral quadriceps at the junction of the middle and distal thirds of the thigh (Edwards, Young & Wiles, 1980).

Microscopy

After preliminary orientation of the biopsy (Edwards et al., 1973), transverse sections were examined with standard histochemical techniques (Dubowitz & Brooke, 1973). Type I and type II fibres were identified by their reaction for myosin ATPase after pre-incubation at pH 9.4 and pH 4.3 (Hayashi & Freimau, 1966; Brooke & Kaiser, 1969).

The 'lesser fibre diameter' (Dubowitz & Brooke, 1973) was measured for 100 fibres of each type and a mean cross-sectional area was calculated for both fibre types in each biopsy, assuming a circular cross-section. Combining this with the frequency of each fibre type, it was possible to calculate an overall mean fibre area (MFA) for each biopsy.

Treatment

Four patients with nutritional osteomalacia (nos. 1, 2, 5 and 6) were treated with oral 1α-hydroxycholecalciferol (1-5 μg/day). The other patients were treated with vitamin D_2 or D_3 in doses ranging from 500 to 10 000 units/day, according to their physician's opinion of their radiological and biochemical progress. Patients 7-10 were also put on a gluten-free diet.

Ethics

The patients gave their informed consent before participating in the studies described. The procedures were carried out with the approval of the Research Ethics Committee of the Royal Postgraduate Medical School and Hammersmith Hospital, and the Committee of Ethics of Clinical Investigations at University College Hospital.

RESULTS

Before Treatment

All 12 patients were weaker than normal subjects of the same body weight. The degree of weakness was unrelated to the cause of osteomalacia, the degree of hypocalcaemia or hypophosphataemia, and the serum parathormone level.

Needle-biopsy specimens from the patients' quadriceps muscles contained significantly less adenosine triphosphate (ATP) and phosphoryl creatine (PC) than found in normal muscle by Edwards et al. (1975), but there was no correlation between the severity of weakness and the degree of depletion of muscle ATP and PC.

Other investigations (not reported in detail here) suggested essentially normal electromechanical activation: (1) a normal electromyogram was obtained for each of the six patients tested, (2) only one patient's quadriceps showed an unduly rapid loss of force during prolonged tetanic stimulation, (3) in all 12 patients, quadriceps stimulation at low frequencies (3-20 Hz) and high frequencies (30-100 Hz) gave no indication of the selective, low-frequency, force loss associated with failure of excitation-contraction coupling (Edwards et al., 1977a).

None of the measurements of strength was considered to have been limited by pain. The patients' behaviour was carefully observed during the tests and they were also asked specifically about pain. Moreover, treatment relieved pain more rapidly than it increased strength and, in the few patients in whom a temporary increase in pain followed the start of treatment, there was no corresponding decrease in MVC.

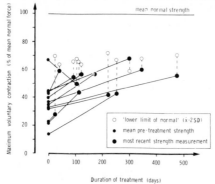
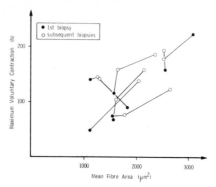

Fig. 1. Changes in quadriceps strength during treatment of 12 patients with osteomalacia. Each patient's strength measurements have been expressed as a percentage of the mean value for normal subjects of the same body weight

Fig. 2. Comparison of quadriceps strength and fibre size in eight patients receiving treatment for osteomalacia due to gluten-sensitive enteropathy (four patients) or nutritional deficiency (four patients)

During Treatment

The effects of treatment on quadriceps strength were observed in the patients followed for at least three months and in patients 8 and 12, followed for shorter periods (Fig. 1). During treatment, all but one of the patients gained strength. Patient no. 2 appeared to become weaker, but, since she was still hypocalcaemic after 105 days of treatment with 1α-hydroxycholecalciferol, her compliance with treatment must be suspect.

The recovery of isometric quadriceps strength appeared to have a time course measured in weeks, months or even years and in only two cases did quadriceps strength return to within 2 s.d. of the mean normal value within the period of study (Fig. 1). The normal subjects were all Caucasian; but, in a group of 15 symptom-free young adult Indian women, all ten who had normal plasma values for calcium, phosphorus and alkaline phosphatase also had a quadriceps strength within the 'normal' range ($\bar{x}$ = 87 per cent of mean 'normal' value) - Newham, Isenberg, Young, Wiles & Edwards (unpublished observations).

Changes in quadriceps strength during treatment were compared with the changes in muscle fibre size in eight patients (Fig. 2). Five patients underwent one follow-up study and three had two follow-up studies. The time intervals between first and last biopsy ranged from 27 to 300 days (mean = 115 days). Gains in strength were usually accompanied by increases in the mean cross-sectional area of the biopsied muscle fibres. The decrease in the strength of patient no. 2 was matched by a reduction in muscle fibre size.

The first and last biopsies from the same eight patients were compared with respect to the values of the ratio MFA II/MFA I (Table 2). The

140

degree of preferential type II fibre atrophy in some of the pre-
treatment biopsies was dramatic. In only one case did the ratio
MFA II/MFA I fail to increase with treatment – it remained constant in
the patient whose initial value (0.97) was highest. The difference
between the two sets of ratios was statistically significant (P ≃ 0.01)
(two-tailed, Wilcoxon two-sample test).

Table 2. Changes in the relative sizes and numbers of type I and type II
fibres during treatment of osteomalacia

patient no.	MFA II/MFA I		frequency of type II fibres (%)		days of treatment
	first biopsy	last biopsy	first biopsy	last biopsy	
1	0.75	0.94	36	38	121
2	0.85	0.92	46	43	105
5	0.97	0.97	56	52	27
6	0.43	0.54	43	33	58
7	0.30	0.77	54	49	170
9	0.32	0.54	46	40	111
10	0.80	0.91	22	20	28
11	0.28	0.53	51	37	300

There was a reduction in the relative frequency of type II fibres from
44 to 39 per cent between the first and last biopsies from the same
eight patients (0.05>P>0.02 in a paired t-test) – see Table 2.

DISCUSSION

Plasma values for creatine phospho inase (CPK) were consistently normal,
in keeping with the absence of any biopsy evidence of extensive
destruction of muscle cells. Even in patients who were so weak that
they were bed-ridden, the reduction in size of the muscle fibres was the
only obvious structural abnormality. This is in agreement with the
findings of Dastur et al. (1975) for 19 patients (gluteus maximus) with
osteomalacia and with those of Skaria et al. (1975) for 17 patients
(ten quadriceps, seven gluteus maximus). A few other authors have also
reported muscle fibre atrophy in individual patients with osteomalacia
(Ekbom et al., 1964; Prineas, Mason & Henson, 1965; Singhal, 1966;
Smith & Stern, 1967) but opinions differ as to the significance of
muscle wasting as a cause for osteomalacic weakness – for example ...
'Uniform generalised wasting proportional to muscle weakness was
observed in every affected patient'(Skaria et al., 1975) and '...muscle
weakness which, as in many instances of osteomalacic myopathy, was often
disproportionate to the muscle wasting' (Schott & Wills, 1976).
Dastur et al. (1975) 'confirmed' the presence of atrophy in their
patients' biopsies by comparison with the size of fibres in biopsies

from normal subjects. However, the appropriateness of their controls is dubious. In the present study, each patient was used as her own control for evaluation of the severity of the muscle fibre atrophy: measurements of MFA made on biopsies taken during treatment with vitamin D were compared with those made on the pre-treatment biopsies from the same eight patients. Comparison of changes in MFA with the increase of quadriceps MVC during treatment made it possible to assess the probable contribution of a reduced mass of muscle (as indicated by MFA) to the patients' initial weakness.

It is possible that the measured rates of recovery of strength observed in this study may seem slow in comparison with subjective clinical experience. This is because even a small increase in strength may result in an enormous increase in the patient's functional ability. For example, it can mean the difference between success and failure in walking or in rising from the toilet unaided. Strength changes occur on a continuous scale whereas functional changes are quantal.

The uniformly slow return of strength argues against the existence of a significant defect in either electromechanical activation or muscle energy metabolism since such a defect might be expected to respond to treatment relatively quickly. Instead, the gains in strength were in proportion to the growth of muscle fibres and were correspondingly slow.

The effect of vitamin D on muscle growth in osteomalacia is slow to become apparent as a measurable increase in strength or fibre size. However the anabolic influence of vitamin D on D-deficient muscle probably starts promptly on the initiation of treatment. Birge & Haddad (1975) demonstrated an increased rate of uptake of tritiated leucine into the diaphragmatic muscle of D-deficient rats within seven hours of the oral administration of cholecalciferol. Augmentation of the diaphragmatic ATP content accompanied the increased amino acid uptake, and the authors postulated that '...ATP concentrations within the cell of the vitamin-deficient animal are reduced to levels which are rate-limiting in the synthesis of protein'. This could apply equally to the patients in this study - their weakness might be indirectly related to their reduced muscle ATP (and PC) content as a result of impaired muscle synthesis. However, Birge & Haddad (1975) also demonstrated that the ATP content of D-deficient rat muscle and its rate of uptake of leucine could be increased by the in-vitro application of 25-hydroxycholecalciferol, but not 1,25-dihydroxycholecalciferol. Yet in this study, three of the four patients treated with 1α-hydroxycholecalciferol showed a strength recovery similar to those treated with cholecalciferol.

It is not clear which metabolite of vitamin D is responsible for the effect on muscle strength. In the osteomalacia of chronic renal failure, 25-hydroxycholecalciferol improves muscle strength (Eastwood et al., 1977) suggesting that 1α-hydroxylation is unnecessary for this effect. Yet, muscle weakness is a cardinal feature of vitamin D-dependent rickets ('pseudomangel rachitis') - a condition due to specific failure of renal 1α-hydroxylation and readily treated with 1α-hydroxycholecalciferol.

It is also hard to explain why, even after prolonged treatment with vitamin D and despite a considerable recovery in muscle fibre cross-sectional area, the patients' quadriceps remained weaker than those of

142

normal subjects.

The pre-treatment muscle fibre hypotrophy was more pronounced in the type II fibres, as is the case in a variety of other disorders (Dubowitz & Brooke, 1973; Edström & Nordemar, 1974; Patten et al., 1974; Young et al., 1975). This would be an additional factor contributing to the initial weakness if type II fibres produce more force per unit cross-sectional area than type I fibres. The post-treatment biopsies, however, gave values for MFA and MFA II/MFA I very similar to those obtained from normal female subjects, ruling out persistence of preferential type II hypotrophy as an explanation for the persisting quadriceps weakness.

On the other hand, the frequency of type II fibres in the patients' biopsies was less after treatment (39 per cent) than before treatment (44 per cent). This change was only a small one and it seems unlikely that it would be adequate to explain the apparently large shortfall in recovery of strength. The reduction in type II fibre frequency becomes more pronounced, however, when the patients' biopsies are compared with those of nine normal Caucasian females (mean age 31, range 16-50 years) in which the mean frequency of type II fibres was 54 per cent (s.d. = 12.1). It is hard to understand why treatment seems to have exaggerated this difference, but this might explain the patients' persisting weakness, especially if it represents an actual loss of muscle fibres rather than an interconversion of fibre types.

It might be possible to establish whether there has been an actual loss of muscle fibres by comparing the ratio of MFA to whole muscle cross-sectional area with the same ratio in normal subjects. Quadriceps cross-sectional area can now be measured from computed axial tomograms (Häggmark, Jansson & Svane, 1978) or from ultrasonograms (Young et al., 1979). However it will still be difficult to find a sufficiently comparable control group. For example, matching for race is complicated by the fact that subclinical osteomalacia is probably common in 'normal' Indian women living in this country (Holmes et al., 1973) and vitamin D-deficiency in Caucasian Britons is usually secondary to some other disease which might have its own effect on muscle.

Not only are the mechanical properties of bone altered in vitamin D-deficiency, but the bones are subjected to altered muscle forces whose return to normal during treatment is slow and may be incomplete.

Acknowledgements - We are indebted to the patients and normal subjects who agreed to participate in this study and to the physicians who invited us to study patients in their care. We also thank Dr J.M. Round and Ms C.A. Maunder-Sewry for muscle histochemistry.

Financial support for this work was provided by the Wellcome Trust, the Muscular Dystrophy Group of Great Britain and the Sir William Coxen Trust.

References

Berry, E.M., Gupta, M.M., Turner, S.J. & Burns, R.R. (1973): Variation in plasma calcium with induced changes in plasma specific gravity, total protein, and albumin. Br. Med. J. 4, 640.

Birge, S.J. & Haddad, J.G. (1975): 25-hydroxycholecalciferol
stimulation of muscle metabolism. J. Clin. Invest. 56, 1100.

Brooke, M.H. & Kaiser, U.K. (1969): Some comments on the histochemical
characterisation of muscle ATPase. J. Histochem. Cytochem. 17, 431.

Dastur, D.K., Gagrat, B.M., Wadia, N.H., Desai, M.M. & Bharucha, E.P.
(1975): Nature of muscular change in osteomalacia: light and electron-
microscope observations. J. Path. 117, 211.

Dent, C.E. (1956): General aspects of calcium and phosphorus metabolism
with especial reference to surgical problems. Proc. Roy. Soc. Med.
48, 715.

Dubowitz, V. & Brooke, M.H. (1973): 'Muscle biopsy: a modern approach'.
New York: Saunders.

Eastwood, J.B., Stamp, T.C.B., de Wardener, H.E., Bordier, P.J. &
Arnaud, C.D. (1977): The effect of 25-hydroxyvitamin D_3 in the
osteomalacia of chronic renal failure. Clin. Sci. Molec. Med. 52,
499.

Edström, L. & Nordemar, R. (1974): Differential changes in type I and
type II muscle fibres in rheumatoid arthritis. Scand. J. Rheumatol.
3, 155.

Edwards, R.H.T., Maunder, C., Lewis, P.D. & Pearse, A.G.E. (1973):
Percutaneous needle biopsy in the diagnosis of muscle disease. Lancet
2, 1070.

Edwards, R.H.T., Jones, D.A., Maunder, C. & Batra, G.J. (1975): Needle
biopsy for muscle chemistry. Lancet 1, 736.

Edwards, R.H.T., Hill, D.K., Jones, D.A. & Merton, P.A. (1977a): Fatigue
of long duration in human skeletal muscle after exercise. J. Physiol.
272, 769.

Edwards, R.H.T., Young, A., Hosking, G.P. & Jones, D.A. (1977b): Human
skeletal muscle function: description of tests and normal values.
Clin. Sci. Molec. Med. 52, 283.

Edwards, R.H.T., Young, A. & Wiles, C.M. (1980): Needle biopsy of
skeletal muscle in the diagnosis of myopathy and the clinical study of
muscle function and repair. New Engl. J. Med. 302, 261.

Ekbom, K., Hed, R., Kirstein, L. & Aström, K.E. (1964): Weakness of
proximal limb muscles, probably due to myopathy after partial
gastrectomy. Acta Med. Scand. 174, 493.

Häggmark, T., Jansson, E. & Svane, B. (1978): Cross-sectional area of
the thigh muscle in man measured by computed tomography. Scand. J.
Clin. Lab. Invest. 38, 355.

Hayashi, M. & Freimau, D.G. (1966): An improved method of fixation for
formalin-sensitive enzymes with special reference to myosin adenosine
triphosphatase. J. Histochem. Cytochem. 14, 577.

Holmes, A.M., Enoch, B.A., Taylor, J.L. & Jones, M.E. (1973): Occult
rickets and osteomalacia among the Asian immigrant population. Quart.
J. Med. 42, 125.

Patten, B.M., Bilezikian, J.P., Mallette, L.E., Prince, A., Engel, W.K.
& Aurbach, G.D. (1974): Neuromuscular disease in primary
hyperparathyroidism. Ann. Intern. Med. 80, 182.

Prineas, J.W., Mason, A.S. & Henson, R.A. (1965): Myopathy in metabolic
bone disease. Br. Med. J. 1, 1034.

Schott, G.D. & Wills, M.R. (1976): Muscle weakness in osteomalacia.
Lancet 1, 626.

Scott, A.C. (1916): A contribution to the study of osteomalacia in India. Ind. J. Med. Res. 4, 140.

Singhal, B.S. (1966): Muscle weakening simulating myopathy in metabolic bone disease. Neurology (India) 14, 194.

Skaria, J., Katiyar, B.C., Srivastava, T.P. & Dube, B. (1975): Myopathy and neuropathy associated with osteomalacia. Acta Neurol. Scand. 51, 37.

Smith, R. & Stern, G. (1967): Myopathy, osteomalacia and hyperparathyroidism. Brain 90, 593.

Vagbhatta (circa 500 A.D.): 'Asthanga Hridaya Nidan', ed Y.N. Upadhyaya (1962), p. 276. Varanasi, India: Vidya Vilas Press, The Chourkhamba Sanskrit Series Office, PO Box 8.

Young, A., Jones, D.A., Maunder, C.A. & Edwards, R.H.T. (1975): Needle biopsy studies of weakness and fatigue in patients with myopathy. Clin. Sci. Molec. Med. 49, 4P.

Young, A., Brenton, D.P. & Edwards, R.H.T. (1978): Analysis of muscle weakness in osteomalacia. Clin. Sci. Molec. Med. 54, 31P.

Young, A., Hughes, I., Russell, P., & Parker, M.J. (1979): Measurement of quadriceps muscle wasting. Ann. Rheum. Dis. 38, 571.

Young, A. (1980): The assessment of impaired muscle function by dynamometry. In 'Disease evaluation and patient assessment in rheumatoid arthritis', ed T.E.W. Feltkamp & J.K. van der Korst. Alphen aan de Rijn, The Netherlands: Stafleu's Sci. Publ.

21

Collagenous tissue morphology: a study of a substructure in rat-tail tendons

L.J. GATHERCOLE AND J.S. SHAH

INTRODUCTION

Fibres of collagenous tissues such as tendons and ligaments, which in vivo work in tension, are crimped. Crimps have been shown to influence low tension stress-strain behaviour of these tissues (Diamant et al., 1972; Dale & Baer, 1974; Baer et al., 1975; Torp et al., 1975a,b; Shah et al., 1977, 1978, 1979). When viewed under a polarising microscope, a crimped collagen fibre exhibits a characteristic pattern of extinction and transmission bands (the 'band pattern') along its length. From the analysis of the variations of the band pattern with rotation of fibres about different axes (Diamant et al., 1972), low angle X-ray diffraction (Gathercole & Keller, 1975) and transmission electron microscopy of thin sections (Dlugosz, Gathercole & Keller, 1978), it is evident that crimps with a characteristic crimp length in the range 10-150 μm are planar. Crimp sites are identifiable in the fibrils of diameter ∿200 nm and in transmission electron microscopy of 10 nm thin sections. It is however not clear how crimped fibrils, which are like zig-zag ribbons, come together to form circular/elliptical cross-sections. Kastelic et al. (1978) have recently shown that rat-tail tendons have a multicomposite structure and are made up of subunits termed as fascicles. They concluded further that each fascicle is an array of crimped collagen fibrils with a crude cylindrical symmetry.

We report here a study by optical polarisation microscopy (PM), scanning electron microscopy (SEM) and low angle X-ray diffraction (LAXD) to evaluate the morphology of the substructures of rat-tail tendons (RTT). The main conclusion of this study regarding crimp arrangement within tendon subunits are different from those of Kastelic et al. (1978).

MATERIALS SELECTION

Rat-tail tendons connect vertebrae to the sacrococcygeal group of muscles. In this study tendons were examined from the dorsal and ventral part of the tails of Wistar rats in the age range 3-12 months. Tails were removed and preserved at -25°C until further use. Two incisions (a longitudinal and tangential) were made through the dermis-epidermis layers to enable tendons to be removed by a very gentle pull from the exposed ends, while avoiding disturbance of the internal organisation. In accordance with the findings of Kastelic et al. (1978) it was observed that tendons consist of subunits. We avoid using 'fascicle' as a name for the subunit because the detailed structure of a fascicle is different from that evaluated in this paper. The number of subunits varied from tendon to tendon and was usually in the range 1-4. At excision the subunits normally adhered to each other. The multiplicity of subunits, if present, was recognisable in the band pattern (Fig. 1). Cross-sections of these tendons also showed that they consisted of multiple units of circular/elliptical cross-sections. It was also possible to tease apart subunits using forceps, on application of a relatively small force. Such composite tendons were not subjected to further study. The objective was to study the structure of subunits by examining the morphology of the simplest tendons (single tendons) which consisted of one subunit. Thus, chosen tendons were of smooth cylindrical form at separation from the tail. Their cross-sections were circular/elliptical with a (major) diameter in the range 50-300 µm. Hydrated (native) specimens after PM were fixed for 30 min in 10 per cent tris-buffered glutaraldehyde at pH 3.5 or 7.5. The fixed specimens were sequentially permeated in 50 per cent and 100 per cent hexylene glycol. The above procedure improves optical transmission through the specimen. (The refractive index of hexylene glycol matches closely to that of collagen, Kastelic et al., 1978.) Specimens treated as above will be referred to as the treated specimens.

METHODS

Polarisation Microscopy (PM)

To study the band pattern, each native or treated specimen was mounted in a cell with transparent windows. This was filled with physiological saline or hexylene glycol (Shah et al., 1979). The mounted specimen could be rotated about its own axis in the cell. The cell was placed on the rotating stage of a Zeiss Ultraphot II microscope. The variations of the band pattern were observed with rotations of the specimen about its own axis and also about the axis of the microscope.

Low Angle X-Ray Diffraction (LAXD)

Diffraction patterns of treated specimens were recorded by a Rigaku-Denki low-angle camera, as previously described (Gathercole & Keller, 1978). Divergence of the collimated X-ray beam was 0.2° and the specimen-to-film distance was 200 mm. The orientation of the specimen with respect to the X-ray beam (ie the angle of inclination of the crimp plane with respect to the plane of incidence on the specimen) was determined by PM of the specimen mounted across the aperture of the collimator-plates.

Examination of Cross-Sections

This was carried out by SEM and optical microscopy. For SEM, specimens were freeze-dried and coated with gold-palladium. They were examinaed in a Cambridge Stereoscan S2 microscope. For optical microscopy, specimens were embedded in Spurr (1969) resin and cross-sections of thickness of about 2 μm were cut to examine them in an optical microscope.

RESULTS

For the description and discussion of results we need to define a notation for the orientation of the specimen. The orientation of the specimen was identified by the orientation of the crimp plane with respect to a plane which was perpendicular to the path of light or X-ray beam* (ρ) and the orientation of the fibre axis with respect to the axis of polarisation in the light beam (θ). ρ varies from $0°$ to $360°$ as one rotates the specimen about its own axis. Thus $\rho = 0°$ or $180°$ or $360°$ whenever the crimp plane is perpendicular to the beam. Angle θ is varied when a specimen is rotated around the axis of the beam (ie when the stage is rotated in PM).

Polarisation Microscopy

Variations of beam patterns of native specimens with various rotations were identical to those observed by Diamant et al. (1972).

In all treated specimens however, an intensely dark longitudinal line, disrupting the lateral continuity of (bright) bands was visible at a specific orientation ρ_L between $0°-90°$ or $90°-180°$ (Fig. 2) and at an angle $90° + \rho_L$. The most common position for the appearance of the line was $\rho_L = 40° - 45°$. As the line defines the lateral discontinuity of the band pattern, with skew bands in each specimen, it is suggestive of a longitudinal discontinuity and/or shearing within each specimen. It was noted that in some specimens the location of the dark line in the band pattern after treatment was the same as that of a faint line of different contrast in the band pattern of the native state. The intensity contrast of these longitudinal lines in the band pattern of native specimens was very weak and variable from specimen to specimen.

The variation of the band pattern on changing angle θ was different in treated specimens from that in the native specimens. In the treated specimens extinction bands always remained narrow and did not merge to form dark bands at orientation $\theta = \theta_0$ (where θ_0 is the crimp angle) as they did in native specimens. A slight decrease in the intensity of the bright bands was however observed with rotation of $\pm 5°$ from the position of the narrowest bands.

Crimped fibril bundles were visible in the treated specimens, because of increased transmission of light through them. They often exhibited 'antiphase' superposition of crimps (ie superimposed fibrils were often crimped in the opposite direction). The observations of the variation of bands and visualisation of 'antiphase' crimps are in agreement with the observations of Kastelic et al. (1978).

Examination of the cross-sections in PM showed a diametral division (Fig. 3a,b) of the cross-section, suggesting the existence of two fibril bundles in semicircular/elliptical halves. SEM of specimens also confirmed the existence of the subdivision and a doublet in the specimens.

---

* This angle is designated as β by Diamant et al. (1972). We prefer the notation more commonly used to describe rotation of the specimen in X-ray diffraction.

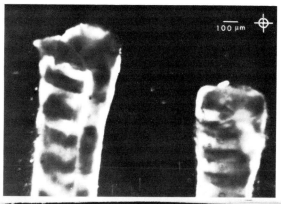

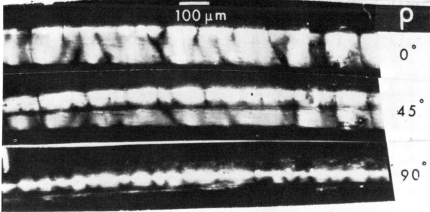

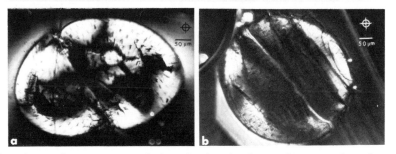

Fig. 1. (top) Band patterns of (native) single and **composite** (two unit) tendons. These demonstrate multiplicity of subunits, if present

Fig. 2. Typical band pattern variations of a treated specimen at orientations (a)ρ = 0°; (b)ρ = 45° and (c)ρ = 90°. Note the presence of a dark line in b and c

Fig. 3. (above) Cross-sectional views of single tendons. These are polarizing optical micrographs of embedded sections showing diametral division across an elliptical and a circular cross-section respectively

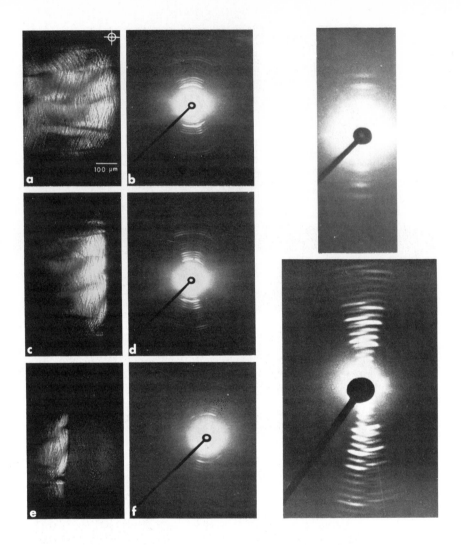

Fig. 4. Variations of LAXD patterns with sampling of central to peripheral volumes of a treated specimen. b,d,f are LAXD patterns in orientation ρ = 0° obtained by different positioning of the specimen. Note the presence of 'cross' pattern of reflections in all positions. The position of the specimen relative to the final collimator aperture is shown in optical polarizing micrographs a,c,e respectively. Note the presence of several crimp apices along the lateral diameter of the collimator in a

Fig. 5. Typical LAXD pattern in the orientation ρ = 90°. The reflections occur along the meridian. Line broadening and azimuthal spreading over a few degrees is evident

Fig. 6. LAXD pattern of a bunch of fibrils stripped from a single tendon in orientation ρ = 0°. It shows a sharp 'cross' pattern of reflections typical of crimps. Also note the absence of multiplicity

150

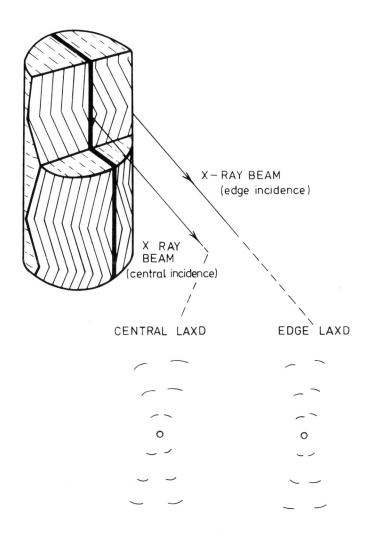

Fig. 7. *Doublet model of the tendon subunit showing the arrangement of crimps in the central longitudinal plane in a partial cut away view, as proposed by this study. The exposed central plane is in the orientation* ρ = 0°

In all specimens it was possible to identify a crimp plane. Figure 4b
is a typical diffraction pattern of a treated specimen in the
orientation $\rho = 0°$. This is characteristic of crimps (ie it exhibits
the 'cross' pattern of orders of 68 nm reflections) but contains more
multiple sets of reflections than previously recorded by Gathercole &
Keller (1975, 1978). The complexity of the pattern cannot totally be
accounted for by sampling of more than one crimp along the axis of the
specimen enclosed in the collimator aperture area and variations in the
crimp sharpness (Gathercole & Keller, 1978). The pattern therefore
suggests the sampling of a multiple number of crimps across the lateral
diameter of the collimator also. The polarisation micrograph of the
specimen (Fig. 4a) in fact confirms the presence of several crimp
apices. Some of these are displaced longitudinally in relation to each
other. Figures 4d and 4f are LAXD patterns of the same specimen
obtained by increasing lateral shift of the specimen with respect to the
collimator centre. Thus, an increasingly peripheral portion of the
specimen is sampled by the X-ray beam (respectively Figs. 4d,f). The
pattern becomes less complex with increasing shift. It should be noted
that in spite of azimuthal and radial overlaps the crimp angle is
discernible as the angle between the most intense set of 68 nm order
reflections in all three patterns (Figs. 4b,d,f). This therefore
indicates that the orientation of the crimp plane is the same in the
peripheral and central portions of the specimens.

Figure 5 is a typical LAXD of a specimen in the orientation of $\rho = 90°$.
The reflections here occur along the meridian (although line broadening
and azimuthal spread over a few degrees is evident). This feature has
been previously shown to be due to the fact that crimps are confined to
planes in the orientation $\rho = 0°$ (Gathercole & Keller, 1975). This
demonstrates that crimped fibrils in our specimens also have their crimp
planes parallel to the plane $\rho = 0°$. This interpretation was confirmed
by taking LAXD of fibril bunches stripped from a specimen. The pattern
(Fig. 6) in the orientation $\rho = 0°$ shows extremely well-defined radial
offsets of reflections, corresponding to the two branches of a crimp.
Unlike Fig. 4b, multiplicity of crimps is absent.

DISCUSSION

LAXD patterns show that all single tendons as entities contain crimped
fibrils. Within the confines of experimental accuracy in recording the
patterns, it is possible to define a unique crimp plane for a single
tendon as a unit entity.

The observations of PM and SEM suggest the existence of a plane
dividing the single tendons internally into two halves, along which
relative displacement of the fibril bundles can take place. To confirm
this, native specimens were asymmetrically strained by gripping opposite
ends off centre and stretching. In PM, enhanced subdivision was seen
after stretching. The internal division could also be made visible by
acid swelling. Furthermore, existence of the doublet was confirmed in
each subunit of composite tendons by observing the band patterns of
treated composite tendons and of the subunits teased from the composites.

Therefore from these combined observations we deduce that rat-tail tendons consist of subunits. Single tendons and subunits from composite tendons have a definable crimp plane. A subunit has an inner doublet characterised by a plane of easy shear along which the two halves can be displaced relative to each other. The above conclusions, in our opinion, are valid even if all our specimens were strained during removal and preparation. This is deduced from the consistent production of longitudinal discontinuity. Deliberate shearing experiments confirm that the halves of a doublet can be displaced to make the discontinuity visible. The doublet structure, in which relative displacement of fibril bundles is possible, can readily explain all our observations, namely: (1) visualisation of 'out of phase crimps' in treated specimens, (2) skewness of extinction bands across fibre diameter, (3) appearance of a line of discontinuity on shearing and on transparentisation, (4) complexities of LAXD patterns (at $\rho = 0°$), particularly those obtained by sampling the fibrils in the central volume. The existence of doublets also explains variations of sampling encountered by Gathercole & Keller (1978) in their LAXD patterns.

The model doublet (Fig. 7) we believe represents an inherent level of collagen organisation in rat-tail tendon because: (1) It exists in all subunits of tendon examined. (2) It is not easy to separate the native doublet into two intact individual halves. (3) It is a substructure of the largest dimensions for which a single plane of crimps is definable by the criteria of LAXD and PM.

The generality of the above statement for all collagenous soft tissues needs to be tested rigorously, but recently, Shah, Palacios & Palacios (1980 - submitted for publication), have seen the existence of doublets in 16-day-old embryonic chick tendons, which also show crimped structure.

The findings on the morphological details of the substructure of tendons presented here are different from the conclusions of Kastelic et al. (1978). In terms of diametral dimensions their fascicles and our doublets fall in the same range. The fascicle, however, does not have a unique crimp plane because it is, in conception, a cylindrically-symmetric array of zig-zag collagen fibrils. Consequently LAXD pattern of a fascicle should show a continuous azimuthal arcing of 68 nm order reflections. Furthermore, the pattern should not alter with the orientation (provided the diameter of the X-ray beam is not too small compared to the diameter of the fascicle). Unfortunately Kastelic et al. (1978) did not record variations of diffraction patterns with orientations. In this study, continuous arcing of 68 nm reflections over a large range of azimuths was not observed. Instead, overlaps of discrete azimuthal offsets was recorded. The difference on LAXD between orientations $\rho = 0°$ and $\rho = 90°$ also cannot be explained by the cylindrically symmetrical structure of the fascicle.

The doublet as a superstructure of crimped fibrils raises many questions regarding its origin, its function, its effect on the mechanical behaviour of tendons and the nature of constituents between the two halves. Variations in the doublet structure, particularly the causes of complexities in the LAXD pattern, also need to be investigated.

Acknowledgements - The authors wish to thank Professor Keller for encouragement in publication of this work. Financial support from the Arthritis and Rheumatism Council and the Medical Research Council (to

LJG) is also acknowledged.

References

Baer, E., Gathercole, L.J. & Keller, A. (1975): Structure hierarchies in
tendon collagen: an interim summary. In 'Structure of fibrous
biopolymers',Colston Papers No. 26, ed E.D.T. Atkins & A. Keller,
p. 185. London: Butterworths.
Dale, W.C. & Baer, E. (1974): Fibre buckling in composite systems: a
model for the ultrastructure of uncalcified collagen tissues. J.
Mater. Sci. 9, 369.
Diamant, J., Keller, A., Baer, E., Litt, M. & Arridge, R.G.C. (1972):
Collagen: ultrastructure and its relation in mechanical properties as
a function of ageing. Proc. Roy. Soc., London B180, 293.
Dlugosz, J., Gathercole, L.J. & Keller, A. (1978): Transmission electron
microscope studies and their relation to polarising optical microscopy
in rat tail tendon. Micron 9, 71.
Gathercole, L.J. & Keller, A. (1975): Light microscopic waveforms in
collageneous tissues and their structural implications. In 'Structure
of fibrous biopolymers', Colston Papers No. 26, ed E.D.T. Atkins & A.
Keller, p. 153. London: Butterworths.
Gathercole, L.J. & Keller, A. (1978): X-ray diffraction effects related
to superstructure in rat tail tendon collagen. Biochim. Biophys.
Acta 535, 253.
Gathercole, L.J., Keller, A. & Shah, J.S. (1974): The periodic wave
pattern in native tendon collagen: correlation of polarising with
scanning electron microscopy. J. Microsc. 102, 95.
Kastelic, J., Galeski, A. & Baer, E. (1978): The multicomposite
structure of tendon. Connect. Tiss. Res. 6, 11.
Shah, J.S., Jayson, M.I.V. & Hampson, W.G.J. (1977): Low tension studies
of collageneous fibres from the ligaments of the lumbar spine. Ann.
Rheum. Dis. 36, 139.
Shah, J.S., Jayson, M.I.V. & Hampson, W.G.J. (1978): Morphology and
mechanical behaviour of collagen fibres from the ligaments of the
human spine and other tissues. Proc. Conf. 'Tendons and ligaments'
Leeds (1978), ed V. Wright. London: Biological Eng. Soc.
Shah, J.S., Jayson, M.I.V. & Hampson, W.G.J. (1979): Mechanical
implications of crimping in collagen fibres of human spinal ligaments.
Eng. Med. 8, 95.
Spurr, A.R. (1969): A low viscosity epoxy resin embedding medium for
electron microscopy. J. Ultrastruct. Res. 26, 31.
Torp, S., Arridge, R.G.C., Armeniades,C.D. & Baer, E. (1975a): Structure
property relationships in tendons as a function of age. In 'Structure
of fibrous biopolymers', Colston Papers No. 26, ed E.D.T. Atkins & A.
Keller, p. 197. London: Butterworths.
Torp, S., Baer, E. & Friedman, B. (1975b): Effects of age and of
mechanical deformation on the ultrastructure of tendon. In 'Structure
of fibrous biopolymers', Colston Papers No. 26, ed E.D.T. Atkins & A.
Keller, p. 223. London: Butterworths.

22

Mechanical factors in the preservation of the joints

JOHN GOODFELLOW

INTRODUCTION

Osteo-arthritis was for long distinguished from other forms of arthritis on the basis that it was the result of 'wear and tear'. In support of this idea, it could be shown that the disease was commoner in old people than in young and it was suggested, too, that it affected most commonly the so-called 'weight-bearing' joints. The appearances of femoral heads removed, for instance, at total hip replacement surgery, confirm that in its advanced stages abrasive wear of the opposed articular surfaces certainly does play a part. However, the theory that some people's joints simply wear out from prolonged use has had to be discarded since it will not fit all the facts. One of the most telling of these facts was reported by Harrison, Schajowicz & Trueta (1953), who noticed that in the human hip joint those areas of articular surface which first showed deterioration were not the areas through which most of the load passed but areas which were little if ever used. In the quarter of a century which has elapsed since the publication of that paper, attention has turned away from mechanically based theories for osteo-arthritis towards theories based upon supposed biochemical lesions of the articular cartilage. Expressed in their simplest form, these theories propose a primary deterioration in the properties of the materials which make up the joint which then leads to secondary mechanical failure of the joint. In this paper I shall approach the problem from a different angle, enquiring instead how it is that most animal joints, most of the time, avoid deterioration of their articular surfaces rather than why some of them sometimes fail.

I regard the skeleton as a structure having a mechanical purpose. I think that the function of an animal limb is to transmit load from one end of it to the other and that this is true for each skeletal component which goes to make up the limb. For instance, each component unit of the bony cortex of a diaphysis needs to resist all stresses, compressive, tensile and shear which develop within the bone. If every such component in a diaphysis performs this function, and only this function, then the mechanical purpose of the diaphysis is fulfilled.

At the plane of a synovial joint cleft the situation is quite different (Fig. 1). If we assume that the articular surfaces are frictionless, then no shear stresses can develop at them. Since they do

155

not adhere, no tensile stress develops and so only normal compressive stress can develop at the articular surfaces. The soft tissues can only develop tensile stress and so it follows that, across the joint cleft, all loads are transmitted as compression at the articular surfaces and tension in the soft tissue sleeve. The function of the ideal articular facet is therefore twofold. First, to resist the compressive component of applied force, developing stress normal to its surface, and second (a kind of negative function) to minimise shear stresses at that surface as nearly as possible to zero. If these are its functions, then its failure must be evidenced by their opposites. Articular surfaces fail, in one quality, if the frictional resistance between them rises. They fail in their second quality if they cannot sustain the compressive forces applied to them. This would be evidenced by their interpenetration under load.

The function of the structures immediately beneath the articular surface must be to resist the compressive force applied to the surface. The articular cartilage, the subchondral bone plate and the trabeculated material immediately beneath have all together one function, to resist the compressive force applied at the articular surface. They transmit that component of load from the articular surface to the diaphysis. I refer to the articular cartilage, the subchondral bone and the trabecular bone beneath, as in one breath, to draw attention to the fact that they are all structurally interdependent and that damage to one component must threaten the function of the others. I regard the whole intra-capsular part of a bone (the part co-extensive more or less with the developmental epiphysis) as a unit, quite different from the diaphysis with which it blends (Fig. 2).

By treating the epiphyses as integrated structures we avoid the argument whether in this or that form of arthritis it is the articular cartilage or the bone beneath which fails first. Failure of the cartilage inevitably prejudices the load-bearing function of the bone beneath, just as failure of the subchondral bone must result in collapse of the overlying cartilage. We can leave the discussion of which happens first to another occasion, for there is fairly universal agreement that any arthritis which is evidenced by primary destruction of the cartilage and/or of the subjacent bone, is, indeed, osteo-arthritis.

MAGNITUDE OF JOINT FORCES

Several features of the design of animal skeletons affect the magnitude of the forces which the 'epiphysis' (in terms of the above definition) must withstand. Load transmission across joints is conveniently expressed in the form of couples. Since the lever arms through which force is applied to the limb can be as long as the bones are long and since the intrinsic joint couple (due to ligaments and muscles) has to act about a lever arm which is no longer than the bones are broad, it follows that the articular surfaces must expect to bear a multiple of the body's weight, even under static circumstances (Fig. 3). While it may appear to be bad design, on the credit side, this system of load transmission allows muscle force to be employed to attenuate the peaks of dynamic loading.

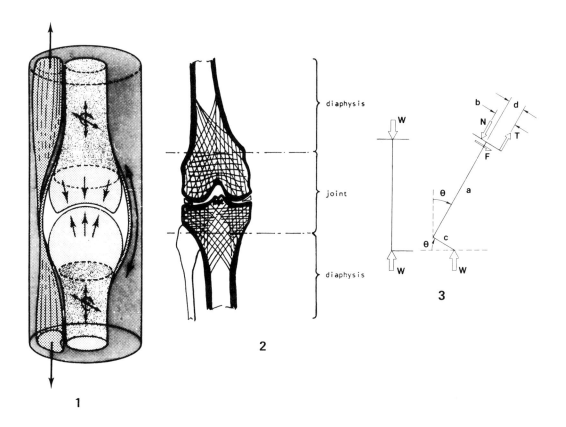

Fig. 1. A simplified model of a limb. The symbols suggest: (a) that in the diaphysis the shear, tension and compression stresses are continuously distributed throughout the bone material, and (b) that at the plane of a joint cleft the articular surfaces develop only compression stress and the soft tissues develop only tension stress

Fig. 2. The contrasting structure of the diaphysis and the epiphysis reflect their different mechanical functions

Fig. 3. Equilibrium of the tibia

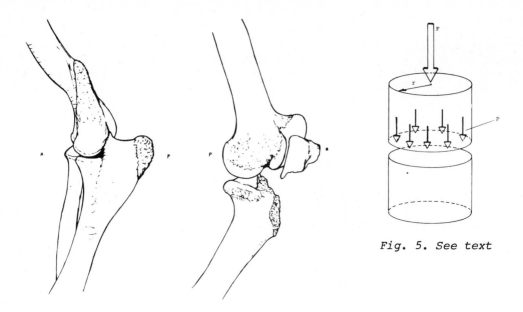

Fig. 5. See text

Fig. 4. (a) The humero-ulnar and (b) the tibio-femoral joints of the giraffe. The very long bones are equipped at their ends with equivalently long 'outriggers' for the attachment of the muscles and ligaments

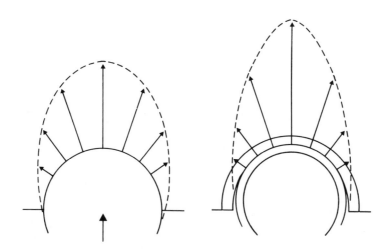

Fig. 6. (a) Pressure distribution at curved articular surfaces. (b) This model is more like the natural joint in having a 'soft' layer between the two surfaces to represent the effect of articular cartilage

There are several design features of the skeleton which diminish the magnitude of the compressive force at the articular surfaces. Among the more obvious are the tubercles, trochanters, knobs and bosses with which the expanded ends of the limb bones are provided. The tendons and ligaments which attach to these 'out-riggers' have the line of their action displaced away from the midline of the limb and enjoy, thereby, somewhat longer lever arms (Fig. 4).

ARTICULAR SURFACE PRESSURE

The most important reason for the trumpet shape of the limb bones is to enable their epiphyses to offer large areas of contact to one another. Each unit of the area of the compression-bearing epiphysis experiences force per unit area, pressure under which it must not fail. Figure 5 demonstrates in the simplest way that the surface area of the joint's facets is the *main* determinant of the shape of an animal joint. The force applied at any particular joint is dependent upon the overall mass of the animal and the dimensions of the lever arms of its limbs and the magnitude of this force may be considered as one of the design specifications which the joint has to meet. The materials of which the joint is constructed are standard. They are similar in big animals and small ones; similar in the large and in the small joints of the same animal. Faced with a great range of expected loads and only standard materials, the design problem can only be resolved by transmitting loads at the same pressure in all joints. The minimum area required for the articular surfaces of any animal joint could therefore be worked out on the basis of the simple formula in Fig. 5 which relates the force to be transmitted to the strength of the joint tissues and the areas of surface contact.

EFFECT OF CURVED SURFACES

Unfortunately it is not so simple ... joints have to be mobile, so the articular facets of animal joints are usually curved rather than flat. If they were flat the pressure would be distributed almost evenly over them. However, when a convex surface is thrust into a matched concave one, the pressure distribution is not even but takes the form of a distribution curve like that shown in Fig. 6(a). If the articulating facets each had a hard core and a relatively soft covering then the pressure distribution at their surfaces could be even less advantageous (Fig. 6(b)). Curved articular surfaces therefore present problems. First, if the maximum pressure to be sustained by any unit of the articular surface is to lie within a certain biologically compatible range, then it is necessary to employ curved articular surfaces much larger than would be required for flat surfaces. But there is another even more pressing reason to avoid pressure gradients within joint contact areas, a reason which is related to the way in which articular cartilage sustains compressive load.

PRESSURE GRADIENTS AND ARTICULAR CARTILAGE

Much has been learnt about the load-bearing characteristics of articular cartilage from indentation experiments (Kempson et al., 1971). Load, applied over a restricted area of the cartilage, induces steep pressure gradients in response to which there is flow of the water content of the cartilage. The result is a local change in the shape of the cartilage - an indentation. Alteration in its shape must result in deformation and increased tension in some part of the collagen network, which may then rupture. Benninghoff's (1925) split lines are the result of the ultimate in indentation experiments.

At the other end of the spectrum of possibilities, is the circumstance in which the compression force is applied equally over the whole articular surface of the cartilage. Under such hydrostatic pressure, provided that there was no flow of fluid into bone, there could be no flow of water within the cartilage, no change in its shape and therefore no increase in the tension of its collagen mesh. Ideally, no matter how great the hydrostatic pressure applied, the collagen could not be ruptured. In order to satisfy the requirements of animal economy and to protect the articular cartilage from the damaging effects of flow within it, the synovial joint ought therefore to be designed to transmit its loads with the least possible pressure gradients at the articular surfaces.

THE ISO-BARIC JOINT SURFACE

Some features of articular surface shape which may serve to minimise pressure gradients are shown in Fig. 7(a). The curvatures of the model joint surfaces are slightly incongruous when unloaded. As load increases (Fig. 7(b)) the compliance of the materials of which they are made allows the components to become more congruous until, somewhere within the expected load range, they eventually match exactly (Fig. 7(c)). Initial incongruity of joint surfaces can therefore have an 'iso-baric' effect. During the regime of light loading an increase in the magnitude of the load results in an increase in the dimensions of the contact areas. The average pressure within those contact areas therefore rises less steeply than the rate of increase of load and could even remain constant.

It is however during the regime of heavy loading, that is after the compliance of the components has allowed complete congruity to be established, that the benefit of the joint's initial incongruity may be most valuable. As the model joint in Fig. 7(c) suggests, it is theoretically possible to arrange the shape of the epiphysis so that the compressive component of load is carried across the articular surface at uniform pressure. Whether this ideal circumstance is ever achieved in human joints is unknown. We have, in fact, very little information about the average pressures which develop within contact areas at human joints and almost nothing is known about the pressure gradients within them. It has been shown, however, both in the human hip (Greenwald & Haynes, 1972) and in the human and animal knee (Goodfellow & O'Connor, 1975), that the areas of contact do increase with load and that the articular surfaces of these joints are designed upon the principles of the model in Fig. 7.

The menisci of the human knee are of great interest in this context since, in the practice of orthopaedic surgery, large numbers of survival experiments have been performed in man to test the theory that joint

160

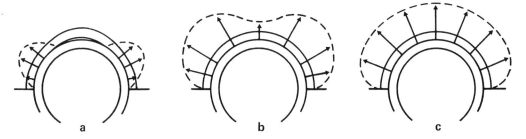

Fig. 7. Effect of initial incongruity on pressure distribution at curved joint interfaces, as the load applied increases from (a) to (b) to (c)

surface congruity matters. The next chapter of this book describes some of the results of these fortuitous experiments.

In the hip joints of man and other animals, it is now known that initial incongruity of this kind is typical of healthy joints under light loading and that the compliance of the materials (bone and cartilage) so exactly matches their shape, that within the physiological range of loading, complete congruity is achieved (Bullough, Goodfellow & O'Connor, 1973). This fine balance of geometric shape and material properties contrasts strongly with what is seen in thousands of femoral heads removed every day at surgery. These demonstrate a very different pattern of loading.

It is a commonplace of engineering practice that a bearing changes its shape as it deteriorates, Indeed change of shape is the normal criterion used as evidence for its deterioration. It is however less usual to encounter a bearing in engineering practice which first changes its shape and then, as a consequence, deteriorates. Without doubt such a sequence does occur at animal articulations. Osteo-arthritis, indistinguishable in every way from the 'primary' form of this disease, regularly results from almost any distortion of the articular surfaces, whether caused by trauma, infection or disordered development and this raises the question whether other cases of osteo-arthritis, less obvious in their aetiology, have a similar cause. Could it be that changes in the precise shape of the articular surfaces is the final common pathway by which many causes effect the same result? The shape of the articular surface in a living animal has no more permanence than does the outline of the branches of a tree seen on the horizon. If the shape is much the same from year to year despite the fact that its components are in constant flux, it is because some control mechanism keeps it so. This is readily demonstrated by the way in which a change in the mechanical environment of a joint can result in a change in the shape of its articular surfaces (Goodfellow & Mitsoo, 1977).

In considering the mechanical function of synovial joints I have drawn attention to some of the constraints which determine the design of successful joints and also some of the processes by which design features, such as the precise shapes of the joint surfaces, may be maintained once they are incorporated into the successful design. The problem of understanding the healthy function of joints may have to be solved before we can uncover their modes of failure.

References

Benninghoff, A. (1925): Form und Bau der Gelenkknorpel in ihren
  Beziehungen zu Funktion. II Der Aufbau des Gelenkknorpel in seinem
  Beziehungen zu Funktion. Z. Zellforsch. 2, 783.
Bullough, P.G., Goodfellow, J. & O'Connor, J. (1973): The relationship
  between degenerative changes and load-bearing in the human hip. J.
  Bone Jt. Surg. 55B, 746.
Goodfellow, J. & Mitsoo, A. (1977): Joint surface incongruity and its
  maintenance. J. Bone Jt. Surg. 59B, 446.
Goodfellow, J.W. & O'Connor, J.J. (1975): The transmission of loads
  through the hip and knee: an hypothesis on the aetiology of
  osteoarthritis. J. Bone Jt. Surg. 57B, 400.
Greenwald, A.S. & Haynes, D.W. (1972): Weight-bearing areas of the human
  hip joint. J. Bone Jt. Surg. 54B, 157.
Harrison, M.H.M., Schajowicz, F. & Trueta, J. (1953): Osteoarthritis of
  the hip: a study of the nature and evolution of the disease. J. Bone
  Jt. Surg. 35B, 598.
Kempson, G.E., Freeman, M.A.R. & Swanson, S.A.V. (1971): The
  determination of a creep modulus for articular cartilage from
  indentation tests on the human femoral head. J. Biomech. 4, 239.

23

The clinical consequences of deformities about the knee joint

W. WAUGH

INTRODUCTION

The primary causes of the pathological changes in osteoarthritis (OA) and rheumatoid arthritis (RA) are uncertain; but, in the knee, mechanical factors play an important part in the destructive processes which ultimately lead to the disorganisation of the joint.

OA and RA must be considered separately because of the fundamentally different pathological lesions involved. In OA the primary lesion is in articular cartilage, whereas in RA inflammatory changes in the synovial membrane are generally believed to precede the articular cartilage and bony lesions. Furthermore, in the latter stages of each disease, the characteristic deformity is different: in OA a varus deformity is most commonly seen, whereas in RA a valgus deformity is more usual. RA and OA are frequently present together since OA changes will follow RA after the latter condition is quiescent.

The importance of angular deformities at the knee and their relation to osteoarthritis was not appreciated until the early 1960s when the results of tibial osteotomy were reported (Jackson & Waugh, 1961). The operation was carried out initially simply to correct a bow-leg or knock-knee deformity in patients with osteoarthritis, in the hope that this would reduce the 'strain' on the joint and so relieve pain. It was only when seeking an explanation for the apparent success of the operation that we arrived at the concept that a varus deformity was associated with excessive loading of the medial side of the joint and that this produced OA changes localised to the medial tibio-femoral compartment, whereas the lateral tibio-femoral compartment remained relatively normal. Tibial osteotomy was considered to produce its effect by transferring load to the more normal side of the joint (Jackson, Green & Waugh, 1969). Twenty years ago, this was a new concept which went some way to justify what seemed to be a logical form of treatment for the OA knee.

OSTEOARTHRITIS

OA and Deformity

Although the primary cause of the articular cartilage lesion in OA is

163

unknown, a varus or valgus deformity can cause degenerative changes in one or other tibio-femoral compartment. For example, malunion of a fracture of the shaft of the femur is most commonly associated with a varus deformity at the fracture site and medial compartment OA is likely to develop during the course of ten to 15 years. Malunion of a fracture of the tibia may also have similar consequences. Disorders or injuries of the lower femoral or upper tibial epiphyses may produce a deformity by premature fusion on one side and overgrowth on the other.

It is also important to appreciate that lesions of primary articular cartilage may be localised to either the medial or lateral side of the joint. When this occurs, loss of height of the cartilage produces an alteration in geometry which inevitably results in an angular deformity. Such lesions may be produced by a fracture damaging the articular surface, by osteochondritis dissecans or they may follow a meniscectomy.

The Relevance of Meniscectomy

In 1948, Fairbank drew attention to radiographic changes which followed meniscectomy and suggested that the menisci had an important weight-bearing function in the knee. At this time meniscectomy was frequently performed and generally regarded as an innocuous procedure. Fairbank's work seemed to receive relatively little recognition and the long-term outcome of meniscectomy was not questioned for many years. In 1968, Woodyard reported the results in 50 patients who had had meniscectomies between 1929 and 1939 at the Wingfield-Morris Orthopaedic Hospital, Oxford. Forty-seven (92 per cent) had radiographic evidence of OA (the changes being graded severe in 27 per cent). In 1968, Jackson reported a larger series of 382 patients who had had meniscectomies five years or more previously at Harlow Wood Orthopaedic Hospital. He found that degenerative changes were present in 21 per cent of the knees on the side of the joint from which the meniscus had been removed, compared with 5 per cent in the opposite knee (which was used as a control). In the following years a number of papers appeared which reported the long-term results which may follow meniscectomy (Tapper & Hoover, 1969; Appel, 1970, and Johnson et al., 1974). Difficulties of definition make it hard to estimate the true incidence of OA following meniscectomy, but it seems likely that about 25 per cent of patients will develop OA ten or more years after the operation.

Seedhom, Dowson & Wright (1974) described an experiment in which two cadaveric knees were compressed in an Instron machine, before and after removing the menisci. They calculated that the stress on articular cartilage at heel-strike might be between 1.4 and 2.4 N/mm^2 normally and that without menisci the figure would be about 5 N/mm^2. Shrive, O'Connor & Goodfellow (1978) came to similar conclusions, but their figures indicated that the magnitude of load-bearing showed considerable variance. In human cadaveric knees (with some degenerative changes) and in healthy pigs' knees, the menisci were thought to bear between 45 per cent and 75 per cent. When a meniscus is removed, excessive load-bearing on that side of the joint results in loss of articular cartilage in that compartment of the knee, which is sufficient to produce an alteration in the normal coronal tibio-femoral angle. For example, after a medial meniscectomy a varus deformity will develop which will

164

lead to progressive deterioration in the joint. This applies also to a lateral meniscectomy which may be followed by a lateral compartment osteoarthritis.

Medial and Lateral Tibio-Femoral Compartment OA

Medial compartment OA is more common than lateral compartment OA. Gait analysis in Nottingham has demonstrated that a medial plateau load of between 60 per cent and 80 per cent is to be expected in knees within the normal range of coronal tibio-femoral angles (between 5° - 10° of valgus). This might suggest 'relative overloading' of the medial side of the knee, but Kettelkamp & Chao (1972) have reported that the average area of contact on the medial plateau is 1.6 times greater than the area of contact on the lateral plateau, so the load per unit area would consequently seem to be of the same order on each side of the joint. However, Maquet et al. (1975) reported different findings in a somewhat similar experiment in which he used greater loads (2.2 - 2.5 kN). He found that the medial and lateral contact areas were almost the same, which perhaps does suggest that there may be relative overloading of the medial side of the joint. This might go some way to explain the common occurrence of medial compartment OA compared with lateral. Furthermore, the contact area is decreased after meniscectomy so that the load per unit area will be increased.

  Medial compartment OA seems to be more common in short stocky men who often have restricted internal rotation of the hip joint and there may be, in these circumstances, an abnormal rotational strain on the medial side of the knee.

  Lateral compartment OA may follow lateral meniscectomy, fracture of the lateral tibial condyle or osteochondritis dissecans, but in the absence of these factors it is difficult to explain the cause of primary involvement of the lateral compartment. The condition is certainly rare in men. In a recent review of 100 tibial osteotomies at Harlow Wood Orthopaedic Hospital, 75 were for medial compartment OA. Of the 25 knees with lateral compartment OA, all were in women. There has been a similar finding in patients having knee replacement operations: in 342 operations, 91 were for OA and the remainder for RA. Only 25 of the OA knees had valgus deformities and all were women. Although patients having operations for OA represent a highly selected group it seems that medial compartment OA is a good deal more common than lateral compartment OA and when the latter does occur, women are much more commonly affected. An explanation is needed to account for this sex difference. Perhaps the greater coronal tibio-femoral valgus angle which is normally found in women, and is related to the increased width of the female pelvis, may be a factor - or there may even be an inherent difference in the bone structure of the female knee.

Load Distribution in the Knee

Orthopaedic surgeons use radiographs of the whole leg taken with the patient standing to give an indication of angular deformity and the possible distribution of load. The mechanical axis is drawn from the centre of the femoral head to the centre of the ankle (Fig. 1). In a normal knee, with a coronal tibio-femoral angle of 7° of valgus, the

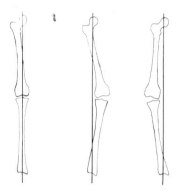

Fig. 1. This diagram shows a
mechanical axis drawn in a normal
knee (left), in a valgus (centre)
and in a varus knee (right)

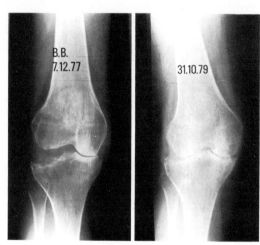

Fig. 2. (a) This radiograph shows a
valgus knee in which the patient
has compensated for a valgus
deformity by transferring load to
the medial side of the joint
(indicated by the sclerosis in the
medial femoral and tibial condyles).
(b) The knee subsequently relapsed
into valgus

Mrs. BB. A standing radiograph of her right knee
on 7.12.77. shows collapse of bone on the lateral
side of the knee which suggests that initially she
must have had valgus deformity. In spite of this there
is a pattern of sclerosis in the medial femoral and
tibial condyles which indicates considerable loading
of this side of the joint; at the same time the coronal
tibio-femoral angle is 0° of varus. Gait analysis confirmed that the medial plateau load was 99 percent.
She must, therefore, have achieved a remarkable
balancing feat. It seemed unlikely that she could
maintain this indefinitely and by 31.10.79 her knee
was becoming more painful and radiographs confirmed that there was now a valgus deformity with a reduction of the medial plateau load to 52 percent.

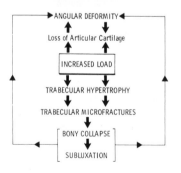

Fig. 3. This diagram shows the 'vicious circle' produced by an angular
deformity which leads to the destruction of the joint

line would pass through the centre of the knee and static analysis would suggest that the load would be equally distributed between each side of the joint (Maquet, 1976). When there is a varus deformity, this line passes medial to the centre of the knee and the assumption is made that a greater share of the load will be taken through the medial compartment. A method of gait analysis (Johnson & Waugh, 1979) confirms that this is true in varus knees. In valgus knees, however, the medial plateau load may be greater than 50 per cent with a valgus angle of, say, 15°. Furthermore, a graph of the medial plateau load (as a percentage of the total load) against the knee angle shows that the former approaches 100 per cent where there is a severe varus deformity, but the load does not reach 0 per cent when the knee is in a similar degree of valgus. It seems that some patients with valgus knees may develop a compensatory mechanism which decreases the lateral plateau load and this may be because they are able to place their foot in a position on the floor which brings the tibia vertical during the stance phase. This may offer an explanation for the comparative rarity of lateral compartment OA and lend support to Hagstedt's (1974) suggestion that patients with this deformity present with symptoms at a much later stage than those with varus medial compartment OA. Figure 2 shows an example of compensation in a patient with RA - see legend for the case-history.

Bone responds to the increased loading associated with a deformity by trabecular hypertrophy and the increase in strength so produced provides adequate compensation, but as time passes microfractures develop and lead to collapse of bone.

Increased deformity now leads to further increase in loading so a vicious circle develops (Fig. 3). The collateral ligaments on the convex side of the deformity only become stretched late in the process since bony collapse produces relative shortening on the concave side of the joint. Ultimately, the tibia may slide laterally on the femur. This direction may be determined by the action of the iliotibial band or the popliteus muscle; medial subluxation is rarely seen in either valgus or varus knees. This final stage is associated with attenuation and disappearance of the cruciate ligaments so that the whole top of the tibia presents a continuous sloping articular surface.

THE RHEUMATOID KNEE

RA is considered to be primarily a disease of synovial membrane and articular cartilage lesions follow from this. Frequently, both tibio-femoral compartments are involved so it is not so easy to explain the subsequent deformity, although the uni-compartment involvement can occur. In contrast to OA, the RA knee more often presents with a valgus deformity and at present there is no certain explanation of this. The disease is more common in women, but it would be facile to suggest that the greater tendency to valgus is responsible for the deformity.

When a painful effusion develops early in the disease, the patients hold their knees in a flexed posture and, if the inflammatory response is not controlled by medical treatment, a contracture of the posterior structures may develop so that the ability to extend the knee fully will be permanently lost. This flexion deformity increases progressively for dynamic reasons. It may be that, in this situation, imbalance between the medial and lateral hamstrings (in favour of the latter) will lead to valgus angulation. A more important factor may involve the action of the iliotibial band on the lateral side. The influence of this structure (which has its proximal origins in the gluteus maximus muscle, as well as in the tensor fascia femoris) on the knee joint is little understood. But when there is a flexion contracture, it is easy to imagine that it could produce abduction at the knee and also external rotation of the tibia. This could explain triple deformity of flexion-valgus-external rotation which is commonly seen. Another interesting observation has been made by Freeman (1980) who points out that in the varus knee the bony collapse of lateral femoral condyle is a more obvious feature. He suggests that this may be due to pressure from the patella (which is often more laterally placed than normal in these knees) and presumably this would be more likely to occur in the presence of a flexion contraction.

Although the flexion-valgus-external rotation deformity is frequently seen in RA, it has not been possible to establish any association between flexion and valgus in a group of 251 knees who had replacement operations for RA. A possible reason for this may be that many patients classified as having RA, were, in fact, suffering from secondary OA.

It is also important to look at the knee joint in relation to the rest of the body, and, in particular, to the hips and feet. In RA, there is often a destructive arthritis of one hip which may lead to the shortening of that leg. This produces a 'long-leg arthropathy' on the opposite side with a flexion-valgus deformity of the knee. The triple knee deformity is also frequently associated with a fixed valgus deformity of the foot. The latter condition is likely to produce valgus and external rotation of the knee, but it is not always possible to know whether the knee deformity follows the foot or vice versa.

The effect of a deformity of one knee on the other knee needs also to be considered. For example, a valgus deformity on one side may be followed by a varus deformity on the other, producing the 'wind-swept appearance'. It is difficult to know why this should happen in a particular patient since it is certainly not invariable: it is perhaps more common to see severe bilateral valgus or varus deformities (rather than valgus in one knee and varus in the other).

Severe destruction of either the medial or lateral side of the knee associated with a grotesque deformity is sometimes seen. It may be that some patients are able to tolerate such gross abnormalities because of the powerful analgesic and anti-inflammatory drugs which are prescribed for them. In particular, corticosteroids may produce osteoporosis so that the bones are less able to resist the forces to which they are subjected. To this extent, the bizarre changes which are seen may be partly iatrogenic in origin.

Many different factors must operate in each patient so that it is probably unwise to look for a single cause to explain the findings in an individual knee. An extreme example of the result of several factors operating to produce extensive destruction of the joint is illustrated in a case history (see Fig. 4 and legend).

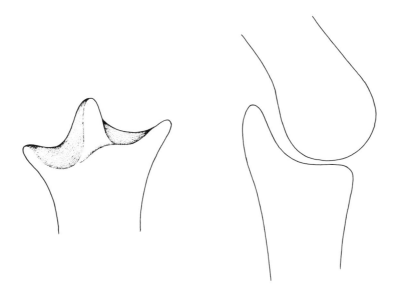

Fig. 4. This diagram shows very severe bony destruction in a knee as seen at operation

Mrs. MB. had suffered from RA for many years and radiographs of her right knee showed posterior subluxation of the tibia with considerable collapse of both tibial condyles. The important factors in her case were the large dose of steriods which she had been taking for a long time and also that her patella had been removed previously. Her left knee had also been arthrodesed and this presumably increased the stress on her right knee as when, for example, she tried to rise from a chair or go up steps, and this is likely to have contributed to the bizarre changes which occured

CONCLUSION

Whatever the cause of the initial deformity the mechanical factors described in OA will operate in RA and often to a spectacular extent. The bone in RA is soft as a result of the disease process and becomes even softer when steroid drugs have been used. The picture in RA is also complicated because, when the disease is burnt out, OA changes supervene.

Speculation about the reasons for the development of deformity in RA and OA knee raises many questions which cannot yet be answered. Nonetheless, it is important to recognise the gross changes which are brought about by abnormal load-bearing associated with excessive valgus or varus angulation. If not corrected, such deformities will lead to bony collapse, subluxation and destruction of the joint. Tibial osteotomy in OA might prevent this, but most patients present with articular changes which are so far advanced that they are not reversible. The importance of restoring the normal coronal tibio-femoral alignment after knee replacement operations is now well recognised and it is certainly likely that mechanical failure will occur if this is not achieved. Malalignment of only a few degrees of varus may result in progressive wear (and ultimately loosening) on the medial side of the polythene tibial component. Careful clinical and radiological observation, together with gait analysis, may allow correction before bony destruction occurs.

References

Appel, H. (1970): Late results after meniscectomy in the knee joint. Acta Orthop. Scand. Suppl. 133, 1.

Fairbank, T.J. (1948): Knee joint changes after meniscectomy. J. Bone Jt. Surg. 30B, 664.

Freeman, M.A.R. (1980): 'Arthritis of the knee'. Berlin: Springer.

Hagstedt, B. (1974): High tibial osteotomy for gonarrthrosis. University of Lund.

Jackson, J.P. & Waug W. (1961): Tibial osteotomy for osteoarthritis of the knee. J. Bone Jt. Surg. 43B, 4.

Jackson, J.P. (1968): Degenerative changes in the knee after meniscectomy. Br. Med. J. 2, 525.

Jackson, J.P., Green, J.P. & Waugh, W. (1969): High tibial osteotomy for arthritis of the knee. J. Bone Jt. Surg. 51B, 88.

Johnson, F. & Waugh, W. (1979): Method for routine clinical assessment of knee joint forces. Med. Biol. Eng. Comput. 17, 145.

Johnson, R.J., Kettelkamp, D.B., Clark, W. & Leaverton, P. (1974): Factors affecting the late results in meniscectomy. J. Bone Jt. Surg. 56A, 719.

Kettelkamp, D.B. & Chao, E.Y. (1972): A method for quantitative analysis of medial and lateral compression forces of the knees during standing. Clin. Orthop. 83, 202.

Maquet, P.G., Van de Berg, A.J. & Simonet, J.C. (1975): Femoral tibial weight-bearing areas. J. Bone Jt. Surg. 57A, 766.

Maquet, P.G. (1976): Biomechanics of the knee. New York: Springer.

Seedhom, B.B., Dowson, D. & Wright, V. (1974): The load-bearing function of the menisci. In 'The knee joint'. Int. Congr. Ser. No. 324, Amsterdam: Excerpta Medica.

Shrive, N.G., O'Connor, J.J. & Goodfellow, J.W. (1977): Load-bearing in the knee joint. Clin. Orthop. 131, 279.

Tapper, E.M. & Hoover, N.W. (1969): The late results of meniscectomy. J. Bone Jt. Surg. 51A, 517.

Woodyard, J.E. (1968): A long-term survey after meniscectomy. Orthopaedics: Oxford, 1, 22-39.

24

The effect of intra-articular hydrocortisone on the rheumatoid knee: an electrogoniometric assessment

D.H. BOSSINGHAM, A.K. McQUEEN AND A.G. MOWAT

INTRODUCTION

Intra-articular corticosteroid injections for patients with rheumatoid arthritis have been widely used for nearly 30 years, but good objective measures of their efficacy are lacking. Measurement of synovitis and effusion, using a tape measure, is unreliable (Kirwan et al., 1979) but thermography does demonstrate reduction in inflammation (Bird, Ring & Bacon, 1979).

Patients with rheumatoid arthritis affecting the knee have been shown to use less of their available range of flexion during walking than patients with comparable joint disease from osteoarthrosis (Mukherjee et al., 1975). Our study set out to discover whether the gait abnormality was correctible, and to observe its relationship to the pain reported by the patient.

METHOD

Twelve patients (6m:6f) with rheumatoid arthritis, of mean age 47.5 years (range 26 - 68) and having mean disease duration of five years (1-12 years) were selected because of predominant synovitis affecting one knee. Each patient was assessed before injection and then at regular intervals after injection. The affected knee was aspirated to dryness and 50 mg hydrocortisone acetate injected.

Semi-objective measurements were made: for pain, using a visual analogue scale, stride length and walking time using a standard distance.

Gait measurement was carried out using an electrogoniometer similar to that described by Johnston & Smidt (1969). Measurements of stance flexion and swing phase flexion were made from the tracings. An average from three gait cycles was used for each measurement.

RESULTS

All patients improved their pain score and walking time and these values correlated closely P<0.001.

Interpolated points for improvement in pain (Fig. 1) show a rapid rise reaching a maximum at day seven, whilst a similar graph for stance phase flexion (Fig. 2) shows a more gradual rise to a maximum at day 25. These two graphs fail to show any statistical correlation. Improvement in pain score and gait performance was apparent until day 70 for the group considered as a whole.

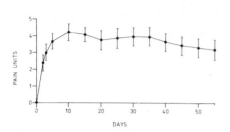

Fig. 1. *Improvement in pain against time (interpolated points)*

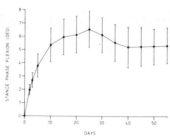

Fig. 2. *Improvement in stance phase flexion against time (interpolated points)*

Values for stance phase and swing phase flexion showed good correlation throughout ($r = 0.58$ for 140 measurements). Two patients however remained consistently away from the regression line and no reason for this is apparent.

A single-blind study to compare the effect of joint aspiration and injection of 2 ml isotonic saline as a placebo against joint aspiration and injection of hydrocortisone was carried out. Seven female patients with rheumatoid arthritis were studied in this way. Overall the group showed no improvement after placebo but after hydrocortisone there was improvement in pain ($P<0.008$) and stance phase flexion ($P<0.04$), swing phase flexion also improved but this did not reach statistical significance.

CONCLUSIONS

This electrogoniometer offers a simple method of observing gait changes in rheumatoid arthritis secondary to drug treatment. The abnormal gait resulting from rheumatoid arthritis affecting the knee is altered towards a more normal pattern by intra-articular hydrocortisone. The latent period between maximum improvement in pain and function may be due to improvement in muscle power, especially that of the quadriceps, which results in turn from pain relief.

References

Bird, H.A., Ring, E.F.J. & Bacon, P.A. (1979): A thermographic and clinical comparison of three intra-articular steroid preparations in rheumatoid arthritis. Ann. Rheum. Dis. 38, 36.

Johnston, R.C. & Smidt, G.L. (1969): Measurements of hip joint motion during walking: evaluation of electrogoniometric method. J. Bone Jt. Surg. 51A, 1083.

Kirwan, J.R., Byron, M.A., Winfield, J., Altman, D.G. & Gumpel, J.M. (1979): Circumferential measurements in the assessment of synovitis of the knee. Rheum. Rehab. 18, 78.

Mukherjee, A., Deane, G., Grew, N. & Morris, J.R.W. (1975): Kinematic assessment of arthritic knees. In 'Orthopaedic engineering', ed J.D. Harris & K. Copeland. London: Biological Engineering Society.

25

Mechanical factors and osteoarthrosis with special reference to the knee joint

B.B. SEEDHOM, T. TAKEDA AND V. WRIGHT

INTRODUCTION

It is a rather popular but an old-fashioned view that osteoarthrosis is
a wear process, similar to that occurring in mechanical bearings (Leidy,
1849). Cartilage degeneration has also been attributed to fatigue
(Weightman, 1976) as well as to habitual disuse (Trueta, 1963;
Goodfellow & Bullough, 1967). In habitually disused cartilage, the
metabolites do not circulate in the cartilage matrix as they would when
the joint is subjected to normal cyclic loading (Linn & Sokoloff, 1965).
An example of a habitually disused area has been described by Goodfellow
et al. (1976) who studied the 'odd' medial facet of the patella. This
facet does not normally come into contact with the femur until an angle
of flexion of 135° has been reached. This is much larger than the knee
flexion angle during ambulation and most sedentary activities. The
degeneration observed in this facet rarely advances beyond overt
cartilage fibrillation. Goodfellow et al. therefore attributed the
surface degenerative changes observed in this facet to habitual disuse:
'The cartilage of this facet is certainly out of contact when standing,
walking, running and probably out of contact during the hours of
sleeping.'
Our work is about the mechanism that triggers fibrillation and further
degenerative changes, leading to denudation of the bone from cartilage
and subsequent deformation of bone. We have looked first at the
patellar surface of the femur. The patello-femoral surfaces seem to
take the brunt of attack by osteoarthrosis. Osteoarthrotic lesions have
been observed in the patellar surface of the femur as early as in the
second decade of life by Meachim & Emery, 1974. They classified the
degree of degeneration and described the topography and the location of
the lesions in relation to anatomical features of the femur (Emery &
Meachim, 1973). However, attempts were not made to find out: (1) whether
these lesions occur randomly or if they were localised; (2) whether the
areas in which they are observed are stressed or unstressed; (3) if they
are stressed, what was the magnitude of the stress during normal human
activities.
This paper reports preliminary work which has attempted to answer
these questions and is aimed at a clearer understanding of the rate of
mechanical stress in the development of osteoarthrosis.

Experimental work was carried out on the patello-femoral compartment of 39 human cadaveric knees. On the basis of this work, a hypothesis was proposed to describe possible relation between stress and the degenerative lesions observed in the patello-femoral compartment. The hypothesis was then tested in the tibio-femoral compartment.

EXPERIMENTAL WORK

The experiment was carried out on 39 unembalmed cadaveric knees (Table 1 for age and sex distribution). The apparatus and details of the technique used are described fully elsewhere (Seedhom et al., 1979).

Table 1. *Distribution of knee specimens by sex and age*

age (years)	16-25	26-35	36-45	46-55	56-65	66-75	76-85	86-95	unknown
male	1	3	-	3	7	4	1	1	4
female	-	-	-	-	6	2	3	-	4

The pattern of contact area between the femur and the patella was studied and established in relation to the angle of flexion of the knee, rather than any anatomical features of the joint. To do so, a small quantity of casting material (polymethyl methacrylate or silicone rubber) was introduced between the femur and the patella. The patella was then replaced on the femur and, in order to maintain it in its natural position, a small tension was applied along the quadriceps femoris tendon. After the casting had set and was removed, other castings were obtained at different angles of flexion. Replicas of the femur and patella were made and each of the contact castings was placed on the replica in turn. These castings had holes where the patello-femoral contact occurred, and so it was possible to outline each contact area on the replicas of both the femur and the patella.
A contact area map was then obtained from a photograph of each replica with the corresponding angle of flexion indicated on each contact area. For each specimen, after the contact map was obtained, any lesion observed on the patellar surface of the femur was outlined on its contact map. This was done with the help of three records: a drawing of the femur outlining the shape of the lesion, a colour slide of the joint, and the replica itself which retained the roughnesses on the articular surface. Before carrying out the experiment, the majority of the lesions on the articular surfaces were first stained (to show them clearly) using the Indian ink technique developed by Meachim (1972). With the help of the three records mentioned above, each of the lesions was accurately outlined on its respective contact map, and was also divided into regions which were shaded according to the degree of severity of degeneration of the cartilage. Typical contact maps are shown on the left of Fig. 1 for three specimens over a range of joint angles. On the right, each specimen is shown with the cartilage lesion and the nearest contact area with its corresponding angle of flexion.

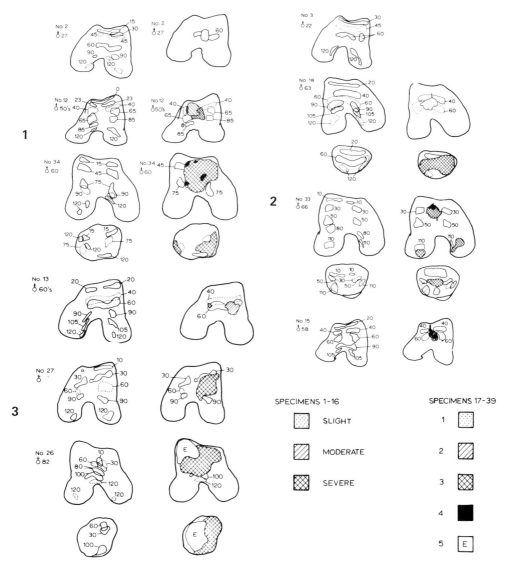

Fig. 1. (top left) Patellofemoral contact areas according to angle of knee flexion and osteoarthrotic lesions observed in the specimens mapped with the nearest contact areas. Key to shading for specimens 17-39 is as follows: (1) areas showing minimal fibrillation, (2) areas which showed darkly stained linear markings resembling ravines formed by deep vertical splitting of the cartilage, (3) areas of overt fibrillation, (4) areas of full thickness cartilage loss, and (5) areas showing eburnation

Fig. 2. (top right) Lesions occur in areas corresponding to contact between femur and patella at the range of flexion 40°-80°. On the left are drawn the contact maps for four joints. On the right are shown the lesions with the nearest contact areas

Fig. 3. (above) These specimens may have been subject to excessive lateral pressure, but the lesions still occur in areas corresponding to patellofemoral contact at the range of flexion 40°-80°

RESULTS AND DISCUSSION

Incidence of Osteoarthrotic Lesions and their Location

Out of the 39 specimens, 35 had lesions on the patellar surface of the femur. The lesions were found to be localised, occurring almost every time at contact areas corresponding to 40°-80° of flexion of the knee. The contact maps were arranged in an ascending order of the degree of degeneration of the cartilage, and it was noted that the lesions start at this contact region and spread from there. Figure 2 shows a sample of four specimens. Where a joint might have been subjected to excessive lateral pressure, the lesion location moved laterally; but it still occurred in the contact region, corresponding to the same part of the range of flexion 40°-80°, as can be seen from the sample of specimens shown in Fig. 3.

Do the Lesions occur in Stressed or Unstressed Areas?

On examining graphs of the loads acting in the patello-femoral joint during various ambulatory activities, it was clear that the peak loads occurred in the range of flexion 40°-80°, as Fig. 4 shows. Thus it appears that the lesions occur in areas of cartilage that experience the greatest loads during level walking, walking up or down a ramp, and during ascending or descending stairs. Therefore the lesions occur in stressed areas.

Patello-Femoral Stresses and their Duration

Before drawing any conclusions regarding the relationship between loads and stresses occurring and the lesions observed in the patello-femoral joint, it was important to examine the actual magnitudes of stresses arising in the joint during various activities. In a previous study (Seedhom & Tsubuku, 1977) data were published concerning patello-femoral stresses, which were determined under physiological loads (Table 2).

Table 2. Patello-femoral stresses in various ambulatory activities

activity	stress
level walking	$1 \ MN/m^2$
walking up ramp	
walking down ramp	$4-6 \ MN/m^2$
climbing stairs	
descending stairs	

It was assumed that the majority of individuals in the Western world load the knee mainly during ambulatory activities, of which level walking is the most predominant. Thus it seems that, perhaps for 90 per cent or more of the period during which the knee joint is exercised, the average stress arising at the peak loads in the patello-femoral joint is not high ($1 \ MN/m^2$). This stress is lower than that occurring in the hip, or in the tibio-femoral compartment in the region covered by the menisci (Seedhom, 1979; Seedhom & Hargreaves, 1979). However, the patello-

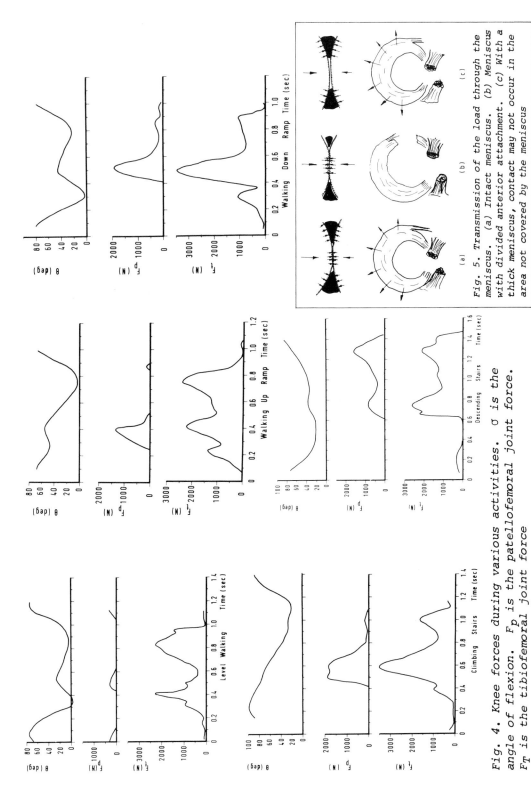

Fig. 4. Knee forces during various activities. σ is the angle of flexion. Fp is the patellofemoral joint force. FT is the tibiofemoral joint force

Fig. 5. Transmission of the load through the meniscus. (a) Intact meniscus. (b) Meniscus with divided anterior attachment. (c) With a thick meniscus, contact may not occur in the area not covered by the meniscus

177

femoral compartment is also subjected to much higher stresses (4-6 MN/m^2) for much shorter periods (10 per cent or less, of knee exercise or loading time); that is, during ambulatory activities other than level walking.

The Relationship between Stress and Patello-Femoral Osteoarthrosis

The following hypothesis describes a possible way in which mechanical stress might be responsible for initiating the degenerative changes observed in the patellar surfaces of the femur. It is proposed that articular cartilage becomes conditioned to the stresses to which it is subjected. Thus, if articular cartilage is subjected for most of the time to a low stress it will be conditioned both chemically and hence mechanically to transmit this low stress. If then it was subjected to a high stress for a much shorter period, the cartilage may not be able to transmit it without sustaining some damage. If the rate of damage is greater than the rate of repair, then further degeneration of the cartilage may occur.

It was interesting to test this hypothesis against the popular view that many people have sedentary occupations, and that for most of the time their joints are hardly stressed at all. However, a closer look at sedentary activities shows that, even while sitting at a desk or at a work-table, people are seldom still for long. They frequently lean forward and backward and also flex and extend the knee. Less frequently they have to get in and out of their chairs with or without the aid of the arms. During such movements the patello-femoral joint is loaded cyclically. The frequency of loading, however, is certainly lower than that during walking and will depend mainly on the degree of restlessness of the individual. Preliminary estimates have been made of the loads and stresses acting on the patello-femoral joint during sitting (unpublished data).

At about 60° flexion when extending the knee, a load of about 200 N acts on the patello-femoral joint. The corresponding average stress is about 0.5 MN/m^2. During a sudden extension (a jerk) the load can be about 500 N and the corresponding average stress 1 MN/m^2. In getting out of a chair the load acting on the knee in the region of flexion 40°-80° is 600-1200 N with an average (four subjects) of 900 N (Ellis et al., 1979, unpublished data). The corresponding average stress is 2.2 MN/m^2.

At 110° of flexion and above, during extension of the knee whilst sitting, the load acting is about 650 N and the corresponding average stress is 3-4.5 MN/m^2 (since the maximum available area of contact is about 150-200 mm^2). Higher stresses occur when getting out of a chair.

Thus it seems that in sedentary occupations the area where the lesions occur is stressed in a similar fashion as it is during the ambulatory activities; that is, subjected to a low stress for most of the time and to a much higher stress for only a small part of the time. On the other hand the areas of contact corresponding to angles of flexion more than 100° sustain stresses which are high for most of the time. It is interesting to note that the incidence of lesions in these latter areas is much lower (five specimens in 39) than in the areas corresponding to the range of flexion 40°-80° (35 specimens in 39). This is consistent with the hypothesis proposed and as such is a possible explanation of

178

the localisation of the lesions.

The Hypothesis and Tibio-Femoral Osteoarthrosis

It was interesting also to test the hypothesis to see if it applies in the tibio-femoral compartment. In this compartment the load is shared between the areas covered by the menisci and the areas of articular cartilage which are in direct contact. When a meniscus is removed following an injury, the load is transmitted on a much smaller area, and consequently the stresses are greatly increased. It has been observed that degeneration changes occur in about 25 per cent of the knee compartments from which menisci have been removed (Fairbank, 1948; Saugman-Jensen, 1963; Jackson, 1968). The degenerative changes in the form of loss of joint space may legitimately be regarded as an accelerated wear process due to the increased stress in the knee following meniscectomy. Whilst the above is somehow consistent with the hypothesis proposed, a very pertinent question arises: why do these degeneration changes occur only in 25 per cent of the cases?

An attempt to explain this may require a closer look at the load transmission in the knee. Consider a meniscus such as that shown in Fig. 4(a). The meniscus closely packs the space surrounding the region of contact between the femoral and tibial condyles. When a load is applied to the joint, the femoral and tibial condyles approximate and try to 'squeeze' the meniscus radially outward. Due to the geometry of the condyles and the meniscus, as well as the presence of synovial fluid, the mensicus would simply slip out under these conditions if it were not for its powerful attachments to the tibia. These attachments enable the meniscus to resist the extruding forces. Although a tensile stress will develop along its circumference and as a consequence, it will expand a little, it will also be compressed in the direction of the load and thus transmit some load through its structure. The rest of the load acting would be transmitted on the areas of direct contact between the condyles. When a meniscal attachment is divided due to trauma (as illustrated in Fig. 4(b)) and the joint is loaded, the meniscus presents no resistance to the extruding forces and it becomes redundant. The load would then be transmitted solely on the areas of direct contact between the femur and tibia with the possible consequences discussed above.

However, there are cases in which the meniscus may be of a sufficient thickness such that initially, under no load, it separates the surfaces of the femur and tibia that would otherwide be in direct contact, as illustrated in Fig. 4(c). When a load is applied it would be transmitted solely by the menisci until its magnitude is sufficient to bridge the gap between the femur and the tibia. Thereafter some of the load would be transmitted on the area of direct contact between the femur and the tibia. In such cases the stress in this area can be extremely low as has been shown by Seedhom & Hargreaves (1979). When knees with thick menisci were loaded by 1400-1600 N (which is only slightly lower than that occurring during level walking) the stress on the area of direct contact was 0.01-0.5 N/mm^2. (The range of stress in this area extends to 2.73 N/mm^2, for other knees.)

It seems that in a knee with thick menisci the areas of direct contact

are subject to a low stress during level walking. Only during faster
and strenuous activities will higher stress act in these areas.
Degenerative changes, in the form of fibrillation and pronounced surface
roughness, can be observed frequently on the areas of the tibial
condyles that are not covered by the menisci. This is consistent with
the proposed hypothesis. An individual who is not physically active may
possibly have such a lesion, if his knees have thick menisci. Further,
if he sustains a meniscal injury and his meniscus had to be removed, the
loads acting on his joint will be transmitted on a greatly reduced area
of a poor quality cartilage. In such a case it is highly likely that
degeneration changes will accelerate and become more readily
distinguishable on radiographs.

Yet knees which do not have thick menisci, or which belong to active
individuals, will be more highly stressed on the areas of direct contact,
and very likely will have healthier cartilage in these areas. Following
a removal of a meniscus from such a knee the average stresses during
level walking will increase from 1.5-2.0 MN/m^2 to 5 MN/m^2. Whilst this
is a considerable rise in the stress, it is still not as great a rise
as would occur in knees with thick menisci. Following meniscectomy, the
stress in these joints would rise from 0.3 MN/m^2 to 5 MN/m^2. The
cartilage may adapt to moderate increase in stress, but perhaps not so
readily to ten or 20-fold increases.

The above may partly explain why, in a non-athletic population, only
25 per cent of knees develop degeneration changes following meniscectomy.
It may be that many of these individuals have thick menisci and the
increase in stress following meniscectomy is so great that the cartilage
cannot adapt to it.

CONCLUSIONS

A study of joint contact regions, and the stresses arising in the
patello-femoral compartment has shown that the osteoarthrotic lesions
frequently observed in this joint are localised, and occur mainly in
contact areas which correspond to 40°-80° of knee flexion. The areas
where these lesions occur were found to correspond to the contact areas
which occur when the peak loads are transmitted in various ambulatory
activities. The stress arising were on two distinct levels: a low
stress (1 MN/m^2) for about 90 per cent of the time during which the knee
is exercised, and a high stress (4-6 MN/m^2), for about ten per cent of
that time. A hypothesis is proposed, which suggests that because of
this mode of stressing, the cartilage adapts chemically and mechanically
to transmit the low stress to which it is subjected for most of the
time. When it is subjected to the higher stress, even for much shorter
periods, it cannot transmit it without sustaining some damage. The
results of studies carried out on the tibio-femoral compartment seem to
be consistent with this hypothesis.

References

Fairbank, T.J. (1948): Knee changes after meniscectomy. J. Bone Jt.
    Surg. 30B, 666.
Goodfellow, J.W. & Bullough, P.G. (1967): The pattern of ageing of
    articular cartilage of the elbow joint. J. Bone Jt. Surg. 49B, 175.

Goodfellow, J.W., Hungerford, D.S. & Zindel, M. (1976): Patello-femoral joint mechanics and pathology: I. Functional anatomy of the patello-femoral joint. J. Bone Jt. Surg. 58B, 287.

Jackson, J.P. (1968): Degenerative changes in the knee after meniscectomy. Br. Med. J. 2, 525.

Leidy, J. (1849): On the intimate structure and history of the articular cartilages. Am. J. Med. Sci. 34, 277.

Linn, F.C. & Sokoloff, L. (1965): Movement and composition of interstitial fluid of cartilage. Arth. Rheum. 8, 481.

Meachim, G. (1972): Light microscopy of Indian ink preparations of fibrillated cartilage. Ann. Rheum. Dis. 31, 457.

Meachim, G. & Emery, I.H. (1974): Quantitative aspects of patello-femoral cartilage fibrillation in Liverpool necropsies. Ann. Rheum. Dis. 33, 39.

Saugman-Jensen, J. (1963): 'Meniscus injuries of the knee joint.' Copenhagen: Knaeets Minisklaesioner.

Seedhom, B.B. & Tsubuku, M. (1977): A technique for the study of contact between visco-elastic bodies with special reference to the patello-femoral joint. J. Biomech. 10, 252.

Seedhom, B.B. (1979): Transmission of the load in the knee joint with special reference to the role of the menisci, Part 1: anatomy, analysis and apparatus. Eng. Med. 8, 207.

Seedhom, B.B. & Hargreaves, D.J. (1979): Transmission of the load in the knee joint with special reference to the role of the menisci, Part II. Eng. Med. 8, 220.

Sokoloff, L. (1968): 'The biology of degenerative joint disease', p. 69. Chicago: University of Chicago Press.

Trueta, J. (1963): Studies in the etiopathology of osteoarthrosis of the hip. Clin. Orthop. 31, 7.

Weightman, B. (1976): Tensile fatigue of human articular cartilage. J. Biomech. 9, 193.

26

Bone stress in Paget's disease

P.B. GUYER

INTRODUCTION

Osteitis deformans was first described by Sir James Paget (1877),
following 20 years' observation of a patient who had been under his care.
Of this patient he said: 'He suffered little on account of his disease,
and followed all the pursuits of a country gentleman.' This was so
until the patient developed the complication of sarcomatous change in
the left forearm which was affected by the bone disease, and from this
he subsequently died.

Current interest in the possibility of bone stress being significant
in the pathogenesis of the disease stems from epidemiological work
carried out from Southampton (Barker et al., 1977; Gardner, Guyer &
Barker, 1979; Guyer & Chamberlain, 1980). Arising from these
epidemiological surveys, 1864 patients with osteitis deformans have now
been seen in the United Kingdom, and the present observations are based
upon this series of patients.

METHODS

Epidemiological studies to establish the prevalence of the disease have
now been carried out in 31 centres in the United Kingdom (Barker et al.,
1980). These have been based upon an examination of films covering the
lumbar spine, pelvis and femora in patients of both sexes aged 55 years
or more. One thousand films were selected sequentially from the stored
films of the X-ray departments in each centre. Any patient who was
found to have Paget's disease also had all other available X-rays
examined for evidence of the disease, and these films were analysed in
detail for the anatomical distribution of the bone disease.

RESULTS

The survey comprised two elements, an initial study of 1225 patients and
a subsequent study of 639 patients. From Table 1 it can be seen that
the skeletal involvement in the series is very closely comparable.
Table 2 summarises the analysis of the bone distribution, the findings
being presented as a percentage of the number of X-rays examined which
showed the disease. From this it can be seen that the innominate bone
is most commonly affected, followed by the lumbar and sacrum spine. The

shoulder girdle is much less commonly affected, and the skull slightly
less than the shoulder girdle. In the initial series of 1225 patients
there was a tendency for the right side of the body to be affected to a
greater extent than the left - in the pelvis the right/left ratio was
226:150 for males, and 133:129 for females. In the femur the ratio was
69:61 and 74:48 for males and females respectively, and in the shoulder
girdle 60:58 and 108:91.

Table 1. Comparison of two series of patients showing similar anatomical
distribution of Paget's disease: skeletal distribution (percentage
figures)

Initial 1225 Patients		Subsequent 639 Patients
85	pelvis	81
47	lumbar spine	36
29	femora	23
27	skull	25
21	dorsal spine	19
11	cervical spine	18

Table 2. Highest frequency of skeletal involvement in the lower half of
the trunk   (1864 patients - percentage figures)

pelvis	76	skull	28	scapula	22
lumbar spine	33	femur	25	cervical spine	13
sacrum	29	dorsal spine	24	ribs	3

Table 3. Distribution of Paget's disease in the spine, based on a
detailed examination of 400 patients, showing preference for the upper
cervical, low dorsal and mid lumbar vertebrae

cervical		dorsal		lumbar	
vertebra	number diseased	vertebra	number diseased	vertebra	number diseased
1	12	1-6	6	1	101
2	9	7	5	2	116
3	4	8	8	3	161
4	3	9	9	4	173
5	4	10	11	5	83
6	4	11	16		
7	6	12	14		

Within the spine (Table 3) there was a definite preference for certain
vertebrae, with the first, second and seventh vertebrae being most
frequently affected in the cervical region. In the dorsal region the
lower vertebrae become progressively more frequently involved, and in
the lumbar region there was a strong preference for involvement of the

third and fourth lumbar vertebrae, each being involved twice as often as the fifth lumbar vertebra.

There was a clear trend for the disease to advance with age, as shown by Fig. 1, in which the percentage of the skeleton affected is plotted against the ages of the patients.

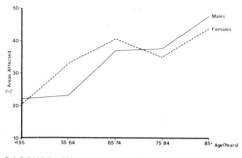

Fig. 1. Increasing extent of skeletal involvement with age based upon a detailed analysis of 400 patients. (Reported from Clin. Radiol. 1978: 29, 421-426, by permission)

DISCUSSION

The observations that the disease process almost always starts close to a synovial joint, that the lower limb girdle is affected more than twice as frequently as the upper limb girdle, the uneven distribution through the vertebral column, the tendency towards right-sided preference for the disease, and the increase in extent with age, all suggest that bone stress may play a part in the pathogenesis of osteitis deformans (Guyer & Clough, 1978).

The nature of this stress is undetermined. The very frequent involvement of the pelvis suggests that transmitted weight may be a factor, possibly in some way associated with movement at the hip joint, since there is a preference for right-sided involvement of the pelvis. However, the distribution within the spine suggests that here other factors may be operational. In a case-controlled study we have found that the distribution of disc degeneration within the lumbar spine is closely similar to that of Paget's disease (Guyer & Shepherd, 1980) and it may therefore be that the factors concerned with disc degeneration may also be significant in Paget's disease in the spine. Whilst it has been suggested that patients who are overweight are more prone to disc degeneration (Sutton & Grainger, 1975) it seems possible that movement at the intervertebral discs is also significant. This concept of vertebral movement being significant would also account for the preference for the upper cervical vertebrae rather than elsewhere within the cervical region, and also for the preference for the lower, rather than the upper region of the dorsal spine.

Previous authors have noted that there is a preference for right-sided involvement of the skeleton (Dickson, Camp & Ghormley, 1945; McKusick, 1966). Within our series this preference was only really notable in the male pelvis, although the same tendency did exist to a much smaller extent in other areas.

From these data it appears that bone stress is significant in the pathogenesis of osteitis deformans. Concentration of an absorbed environmental factor in bone may sensitise it to stress, and a combination of significant levels of both factors may be needed to produce the appearance of Paget's disease of bone.

184

References

Barker, D.J.P.B., Clough, P.W.L., Guyer, P.B. & Gardner, M.J. (1977):
  Paget's disease of bone in 14 British towns. Br. Med. J. 1, 1181.
Barker, D.J.P.B., Chamberlain, A.T., Guyer, P.B. & Gardner, M.J. (1980):
  Paget's disease of bone: the Lancashire focus. Br. Med. J. 280, 1105.
Dickson, D.O., Camp, J.D. & Ghormley, R.K. (1945): Osteitis deformans.
  Radiology, 44, 449.
Gardner, M.J., Guyer, P.B. & Barker, D.J.P.B. (1978): Radiological
  prevalence of Paget's disease of bone in British migrants to
  Australia. Br. Med. J. 1, 1649.
Guyer, P.B. & Chamberlain, A.T. (1980): Paget's disease of bone in two
  American cities. Br. Med. J. 280, 985.
Guyer, P.B. & Clough, P.W.L. (1978): Paget's disease of bone. Clin.
  Radiol. 29, 421.
Guyer, P.B. & Shepherd, D.F.C. (1980): Paget's disease of the lumbar
  spine. Br. J. Radiol. 53, 286.
McKusick, V.A. (1966): 'Heritable disorders of connective tissue', 2nd
  edn. St. Louis: Mosby.
Paget, J. (1877): On a form of chronic inflammation of bone. Medico.
  Chir. Trans. (London) 60, 37.
Sutton, D. & Granger, R.G. (1975): 'A textbook of radiology', 2nd edn.,
  p. 261. Edinburgh: Churchill Livingstone.

27

The relationship between the tensile properties of human articular cartilage and age

G.E. KEMPSON

INTRODUCTION

Osteoarthrosis is often referred to as 'a disease of aging', a statement which is supported by the statistical evidence that the prevalence of the condition increases markedly with increasing age, reaching a maximum in the seventh decade. This raises the question whether changes occur in the structure of joints with age which could predispose to the development of osteoarthrosis.

Some of the earliest degenerative changes in osteoarthrosis occur in the articular cartilage. These early changes are characterised by fibrillation of the cartilage in which the mesh of collagen fibres is disrupted. At this stage the cartilage matrix is no longer an integral structure and the mechanical properties of the tissue have deteriorated considerably. One of the pressing questions relating to the pathogenesis of osteoarthrosis is the sequence of events leading to the initial fibrillation of cartilage.

Evidence exists which strongly suggests that mechanical factors can play a role in the development of osteoarthrosis. The most convincing evidence is that of McDevitt & Muir (1976) who showed that, as the result of sectioning the anterior cruciate ligament of the right knee of dogs, the animals developed degenerative changes in the articular cartilage as early as three weeks post-operatively, which progressed to 'osteoarthrosis'. Control tests revealed that the only result of sectioning the cruciate ligament was to produce mechanical instability in the knee joint.

Figure 1 shows a chart which indicates the possible routes by which mechanical factors may lead to osteoarthrosis. It is clear that if the mechanical properties of articular cartilage were to deteriorate with increasing age the probability of mechanical damage occurring to the cartilage would increase.

This investigation was performed to determine the relationship, if any, between the tensile properties of human articular cartilage and age.

MATERIALS AND METHODS

Articular cartilage was obtained from the femoral condyles of 24 human knee joints in the age range 8 to 91 years. All the joints were

obtained from routine post-mortem examinations with a cause of death
which was unlikely to have affected the articular cartilage, and stored
at -20°C prior to testing. The methods of excising the cartilage from
the joint surface and the preparation of miniature dumbell-shaped
tension specimens, 200 μm thick, 10 mm long - with a central parallel-
sided gauge length 0.5 mm wide by 3 mm long - have been described
previously (Kempson et al., 1973 and Kempson, 1975). Specimens were
excised from three regions on each of the two femoral condyles, namely
the patellar groove, the central condylar region and the posterior
region. The specimens were prepared from the superficial and fourth
layers (800 μm below the surface), and they were oriented with their
central axes parallel to the predominant direction of the collagen
fibres in the superficial zone (Kempson et al., 1973). Only specimens
which were normal, according to the Indian ink test of Meachim (1972),
were tested.

Each specimen was excised and tested in tension, in a plane parallel
to the articular surface, using a materials testing machine (Instron
1115). The test was performed at a constant rate of extension of 5 mm/
min and the specimen was immersed in Ringer's solution. Measurement of
the tensile force applied to the specimen was made continuously by a
load cell (Instron 2511-102) and plotted on a chart recorder.
Measurements of the extension of the 3 mm gauge length were made at
predetermined intervals of force using a photographic technique.
Corresponding values of force and extension, together with measurements
of the original dimensions of each specimen, were used to determine
corresponding values of nominal tensile stress and strain and hence to
plot a stress versus strain curve for each specimen up to and including
fracture. Values of tensile stiffness were determined from the gradient
to the stress versus strain curve at two stress levels, namely 5 MN/m^2
and 10 MN/m^2.

RESULTS

Figure 2 shows the relationship between the tensile fracture stress of
82 specimens from the superficial layer of the medial femoral condyles
and age. The experimental points were fitted by the best straight line
using a least squares analysis. It can be seen that the tensile
strength of the superficial layer decreased markedly with increasing
age. The correlation coefficient was -0.59, with a statistical
significance of $P \ll 0.001$.

Figure 3 shows the relationship between tensile strength and age for
specimens from the fourth layer (800 μm below the articular surface)
corresponding to the superficial layer specimens of Fig. 2. The tensile
strength of the fourth layers also decreased with increasing age. The
correlation coefficient was -0.59, $P \ll 0.001$.

Figure 4 shows the relationship between the tensile stiffness at a
stress of 10 MN/m^2 and age for all superficial layer specimens from the
medial femoral condyles. The results show that, like the tensile
strength, the stiffness at this relatively high stress decreases with
increasing age. The correlation coefficient was -0.3, $P = 0.01$.

Figure 5 shows results corresponding to Fig. 4, but at the lower
stress of 5 MN/m^2. In this case the decrease in tensile stiffness with

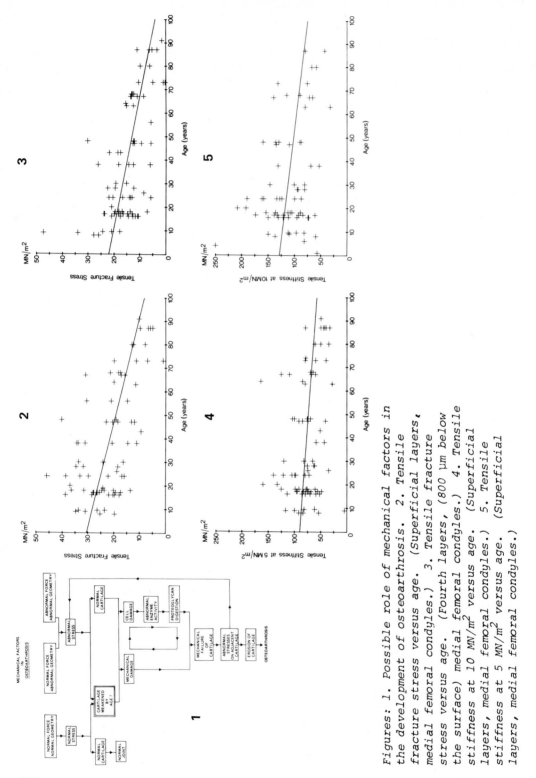

Figures: 1. Possible role of mechanical factors in the development of osteoarthrosis. 2. Tensile fracture stress versus age. (Superficial layers, medial femoral condyles.) 3. Tensile fracture stress versus age. (Fourth layers, (800 μm below the surface) medial femoral condyles.) 4. Tensile stiffness at 10 MN/m² versus age. (Superficial layers, medial femoral condyles.) 5. Tensile stiffness at 5 MN/m² versus age. (Superficial layers, medial femoral condyles.)

age was less marked than that at the higher stress. The correlation coefficient was -0.29, <P<0.01.

DISCUSSION

Earlier results of investigations into the relationship between the tensile properties of human articular cartilage from the femoral condyles of the knee joint and the structure of the tissue have shown that both the tensile fracture stress and the stiffness at high stress levels are strongly dependent on the content of both collagen in the matrix (Kempson et al., 1973) and on the integrity of the collagen fibre mesh (Kempson et al., 1976). The deterioration in the tensile properties of cartilage with increasing age, which was demonstrated in this study, could reflect either a decrease in the quantity of collagen present in the matrix with increasing age or a change in the structural organisation and integrity of the collagen mesh.

The first suggestion is unlikely since it has been shown that, on a wet weight basis, the content of collagen in cartilage from the human femoral head does not decrease with age (Venn, 1978). The second suggestion, that the organisation and integrity of the collagen mesh deteriorates with age, has not been fully investigated. However, the hypothesis that the physical properties of the collagen mesh deteriorates with age as the result of mechanical fatigue was examined by Weightman (1976). The results showed that the fatigue resistance of cartilage from the femoral head decreased with age, but the decrease in measured strength with age was more rapid than that predicted from the fatigue curves of younger specimens. It was concluded that another mechanism, distinct from fatigue, was responsible for the additional decrease in strength.

Recent results from the author's laboratory (unpublished material) have shown that when human articular cartilage is treated with leucocytic elastase the tensile strength and stiffness are reduced considerably without any significant release of collagen or disruption of the integrity of the specimens. Elastase cleaves the N-terminal, and probably the C-terminal, non-helical ends of the tropocollagen molecule, thereby disrupting the major intra- and intermolecular covalent cross-links. It is tempting to suggest that modification of cross-links within and between tropocollagen molecules may occur with increasing age, with consequent changes in the tensile properties.

The result shown in Fig. 5, that the tensile stiffness at 5 MN/m^2 decreased less markedly with age than did the fracture stress or the stiffness at 10 MN/m^2, reflects the fact that the tensile stiffness in the initial part of the stress versus strain curve depends partly on the properties of the collagen fibres and partly on the resistance to re-alignment of these fibres under tension offered by the proteoglycan gel (Kempson et al., 1976). This resistance is strongly dependent on the total proteoglycan content which, on the femoral head, has been shown to increase slightly with age. Any changes in the properties of the collagen fibres would, therefore, be compensated by an increase in the proteoglycan content with the result that the tensile stiffness at low stress would be less dependent on age than that at high stress where the proteoglycan does not significantly influence tensile stiffness

(Kempson et al., 1976).

It is clear from this investigation that more information concerning age-related changes in the structure of the cartilage matrix and in particular the collagen fibre mesh, is urgently needed.

CONCLUSIONS

Tension tests of specimens of cartilage taken from the superficial and fourth layers of the femoral condyles of the human knee joint in planes parallel to the articular surface have shown that: (1) the tensile fracture stress of both layers decreased markedly with increasing age, (2) the tensile stiffness at 10 MN/m^2 decreased with increasing age, (3) the tensile stiffness at 5 MN/m^2 decreased less markedly with age than either fracture stress or stiffness at 10 MN/m^2.

References

Kempson, G.E., Muir, H., Pollard, C. & Tuke, M. (1973): The tensile properties of cartilage of human femoral condyles related to the content of collagen and glycosaminoglycans. Biochim. Biophys. Acta 297, 456.

Kempson, G.E. (1975): Mechanical properties of articular cartilage and their relationship to matrix degradation and age. Ann. Rheum. Dis. 34, Suppl. 2, 111.

Kempson, G.E., Tuke, M., Dingle, J.T. & Barrett, A.J. (1976): The effects of proteolytic enzymes on the mechanical properties of adult human articular cartilage. Biochim. Biophys. Acta 428, 741.

McDevitt, C.A. & Muir, H. (1976): Biochemical changes in the cartilage of the knee in experimental and natural osteoarthritis of the dog. J. Bone Jt. Surg. 58B, 94.

Meachim, G. (1972): Light microscopy of Indian ink preparations of fibrillated cartilage. Ann. Rheum. Dis. 31, 457.

Venn, M.F. (1978): Variation of chemical composition with age in human femoral head cartilage. Ann. Rheum. Dis. 37, 168.

Weightman, B.O. (1976): Tensile fatigue of human articular cartilage. J. Biomech. 9, 193.

28

Trunk stresses in telecommunications engineers

A.S. NICHOLSON, D.A. STUBBS, N.J. SHEPPARD AND P.R. DAVIS

INTRODUCTION

It has been estimated that between 60 and 80 per cent of the industrialised world's adult population experiences back pain at some time during their working lives (Hirsch, 1966; Horal, 1969; Hult, 1954a). The onset of low back pain symptoms has been found to occur most frequently in persons aged between 20 and 30 years of age (Hult, 1954a; Mirabile & Simons, 1972; Nachemson, 1971) with remission intervals of between three months to three years (Hult, 1954a; Rowe, 1968) although the frequency of repeated episodes appears to reach a peak in the fifth decade (Nachemson, 1971).

Many studies have shown that the incidence of low back ailments is greater in occupations involving heavy manual work, and that hard physical work promotes the appearance of degenerative back disease (Anderson & Duthie, 1963; Hult, 1954a,b; Ikata, 1965; Lawrence & Aitken-Swan, 1952; Lawrence, 1969; Magora & Taustein, 1969; Partridge et al., 1965; Stubbs & Nicholson, 1979); further, the length of incapacitation is greater in heavy occupations (Blow & Jackson, 1971; Hult, 1954b; Lawrence & Aitken-Swan, 1952; Partridge et al., 1968). Higher incidences of disc degeneration and greater abnormalities in heavy manual workers than in non-manual workers has been shown radiographically (Hult, 1954a,b; Lawrence, Molyneux & Dingwall-Fordyce, 1966; Partridge et al., 1968; Troup, Roantree & Archibald, 1970).

Jackson (1968) discussed the condition 'wear and tear' in relation to the insults reponsible for trunk injuries. He suggested the expression represents two groups of pathological conditions of primary aetiological significance (a) those in which long-term effects of load handling are superimposed upon other factors and contribute to, or are associated with, the degenerative conditions of the musculo-skeletal system, (b) those in which the forces of insult are greater and produce immediate effects of acute trauma and industrial injury. Similarly, Mehnert (1969), Schmorl (1928) and Troup (1965) considered that degeneration of the spine is hastened by a series of slight injuries or 'minitraumas'. Although there have been attempts to relate the type of mechanical stress on the spine to the quality and location of degenerative changes, the results are so far inconclusive (Farfan, 1977).

A methodology suitable for studying the magnitude of vertebral

191

stresses in work situations has been developed by the Materials Handling Research Unit and used for a number of years (Davis, Stubbs & Ridd, 1977). The technique is based upon observations by Davis (1956), Morris, Lucas & Bresler (1961) and others that during lifting and other manual handling activities there is a close correlation between the magnitude of stress on the trunk and the magnitude of intra-abdominal pressure in male subjects.

In previous studies investigating manual handling in the building and construction industry, Stubbs & Nicholson (1979) found that the occupations defined as involving heavy manual work had significantly higher back injury rates than the 'light' occupations. Davis & Stubbs (1978) found that the workers in these heavy occupations sustain repeated, frequent, high trunk stresses inducing peak intra-abdominal pressures above 100 mmHg (13.3 kPa). From later laboratory studies to establish 'safe' lifting capacities for British male servicemen (Davis & Stubbs, 1977/78), it was considered that the 'safe' value of intra-abdominal pressure was 90 mmHg (12.0 kPa) in the weakest 10 per cent of the population investigated.

METHOD

The Materials Handling Research Unit at the University of Surrey was commissioned by the Post Office Telecommunications Headquarters to carry out research aimed at reducing the number of occupationally caused back injuries in telecommunications engineers.

The first part of the study was a detailed analysis of 'reportable accidents' incurred over a 12-month period from May 1977 to April 1978 (see Davis & Sheppard, 1980). A 'reportable accident' was an incident at work, as a result of which a man was absent from work for three days or more, with a doctor's certificate. Of the 79 occupational groups or 'duty codes' within the industry, 23 had accident rates significantly greater than the overall accident rate (P<0.05). Field observations of these 'top 23' duty codes were then carried out in order to identify factors giving rise to the accidents. Methods included still and cine photography and assessment of the working environment by measuring various physical parameters. When necessary the engineers were questioned in order to gain a fuller understanding of their working methods and activities.

The employer categorised injuries according to a doctor's report. Accidents reported by the employer as 'back injuries' were then separated from the general statistics. Twelve of the top 23 duty codes were found to have back injury rates greater than the mean back injury rate of the top 23. Workers in these 12 high risk occupations were then investigated in a second observation period in order to measure intra-abdominal pressure by means of radio pressure pills while the engineers carried out their normal duties. When those activities found to be inducing high peak intra-abdominal pressures were identified, a third observation period was arranged to study more closely the factors contributing to the stressful activities.

RESULTS

Figure 1 shows the distribution of accident rate per 1000 men at risk

192

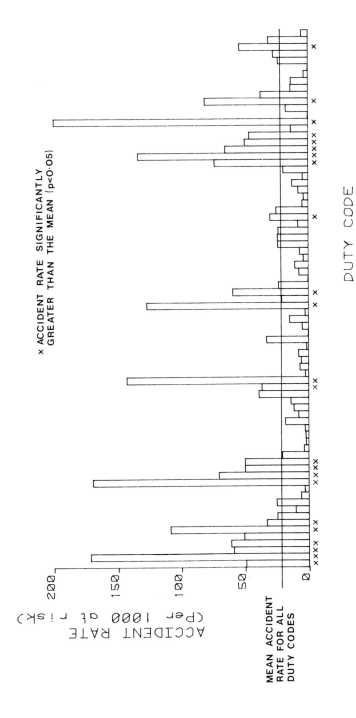

Fig. 1. Distribution of reportable accidents by duty code for Post Office Telecommunications Engineers 1977/78

DUTY CODE	BACK INJURY RATE	ACTIVITY GROUP A			B			C		D	
002	66.7	■	■	■	■	■	■	■		□	
013	51.9	■	■	■	■	■	■	■		□	□
004	26.6	■	■	■	■	■	■	■		□	□
070	25.0	■						■		□	□
006	24.6	■					■	■		□	
061	22.9	■	■	■	■	■	■	■		□	□
034	19.9									□	
001	17.5	■	■	■	■	■	■	■		□	
065	16.8	■	■	■				■		□	□
041	16.2	■	■	■				■		□	□	□
003	15.7	■	■	■	■	■	■	■		□	□	·
014	14.2	■	■	■	■	■	■	■		□	
026	14.2				■	■			□	□		□
072	14.1									□	□	□
053	12.8								□	□	□
008	12.5									□		□
079	12.4							■	□	□	
077	11.3			■		■					
064	10.5							■	□	□	
078	10.4								□	□		□
062	10.3			■	■		■		□	□	
005	10.3				■				□	□	
010	10.1	■							□			□
007	9.5	■		■				■	□	□	
048	9.0				■	■			□	□	□
063	8.6	■							□	□	□
015	8.6	■							□	□	□
039	8.5								□	□	□
071	8.3											□
076	7.0			■		■			□		
052	6.9								□	□	□
058	6.5								□	□	
022	6.2	■										□
060	5.0								□		□
017	4.5									□	□
016	4.4	■							□	□	□
049	4.2								□		□
024	4.0											□
025	3.8								□		
069	3.5										·	□
066	3.5									□	□
032	3.3											□
027	3.1								□	□	□
040	3.0								□	□	□
011	2.8	■										□
044	2.6								□	□	□
023	2.4								□		
059	2.1								□		
009	2.0	■										□
031	2.0								□	□	□
045	1.4											□
057	1.4								□	□	
055	1.3								□	□	□
037	1.1								□	□	□
021	1.1											□
051	1.0									□	
036	1.0								□	□	
018	1.0								□		□
033	1.0											□
080	0.8										
046	0.5											□
028	0											□
050	0								□	□	□
042	0								□	□	□
073	0									□	□
047	0											□
030	0											□
056	0								□	□	□
074	0									□	□
012	0											□
038	0								□	□	□
029	0									□		□
020	0											□
019	0											□
043	0								□	□	□
075	0									□	□
035	0											□
068	0											□

Fig. 2. (opposite) The distribution of activities performed by 'duty code' showing the back injury rates (per 1000 at risk). For definition of groups A, B, C and D, see text.

■ *Activities inducing pressures ≥90 mmHg*
□ *Activities inducing pressures <90 mmHg*

Table 1. Accident rates for all accidents, handling accidents, back injuries and those attributed to handling incidents of telecommunications engineers

Accident category	Accident rate (per 1000 at risk)		
	All duty codes	Top 23 codes	Other 56 codes
All accidents	22.2	46.9*	10.4*
Handling accidents	7.3	16.0*	3.0*
Back injuries	5.6	12.3*	2.3*
Back injuries attributed to handling incidents	3.6	7.8*	1.5*

*Level of significance between occupational groups and all duty codes, P<0.001

Table 2. Back injuries attributed to handling by age within the telecommunications industry

Age group	Number employed	Number of back injuries due to handling	Number per 1000 at risk
16-30[1]	42 141	120	2.8
31-48[2]	39 673	201	5.0
49+[3]	19 117	42	2.2
All personnel	100 931	363	3.6

2>1 and 3: x^2 = 24.9 and 24.9 respectively, P<0.001

Table 3. Accumulated results of intra-abdominal pressure measurements for various activities recorded during field studies

Activity group	Intra-abdominal pressure (mmHg)						Number of observation periods
	mean	s.d.	no≥30	no≥50	no≥90	no≥120	no≥150	
A	74.09*	33.85	323	240	90	31	9	16
B	54.46*	21.07	290	147	24	2	0	15
C	44.43*	13.38	829	225	8	0	0	7
D	20.92*	5.09	13	0	0	0	0	4

*A>B>C>D, P<0.001

per year by duty code, revealing those 23 occupational groups suffering accident rates significantly greater than the mean. Seventeen of the top 23 duty codes involved manual work performed outdoors, where work conditions are less controlled. The accident rates of all accidents, handling accidents, back injuries and back injuries attributed to handling incidents for the top 23 duty codes were compared with the other 56 duty codes, and the whole population of telecommunications engineers (Table 1). The top 23 duty codes suffered significantly greater accident rates than the overall population in all four accident categories ($P < 0.001$). From this analysis, it appears that the top 23, which constitute only 33 per cent of this working population of 100 931 engineers, suffer 69 per cent of all the 2263 three-day-plus accidents.

Table 2 presents the incidence by age group of back injuries attributed to handling. Those under 30 years and over 48 years of age have a significantly lower rate than those between 31 and 47 years of age.

Table 3 shows the accumulated results of intra-abdominal pressure measurements made during 42 periods of field observations. The results from individual field activities were grouped into four categories depending upon the mean values obtained and the relative frequency of the activity. Sufficient observation periods were undertaken in order to minimise individual variability. The data presented in Fig. 2 show the relationship between the back injury rate (per 1000 employees at risk) and the activities performed by duty code. Activity groups A, B and C are each made up of three component activities, group D being split into three sub-groups, each comprising common activities.

Group A consists of activities which are common to most parties working outdoors. The frequency of handling varies from job to job but it is not unusual for each activity to be carried out a dozen times per day. *Group B* activities predominantly involve handling small mechanical aids and other pieces of equipment carried in vehicles. These are moved relatively frequently throughout a day's work. *Group C* consists of largely digging activities and ladder handling, both essential requirements of a large number of duty code activities, particularly for those working outside. Rates of handling in this group are in excess of those in any other group. Activities in *Group D*, although being a component of a large number of duty codes, are carried out infrequently except by some specialist groups.

DISCUSSION

An important observation in this study has been a high incidence of accidents, handling accidents, and back injuries occurring in certain occupations within the telecommunications industry. Although the annual accident rate of 22.2 per thousand is slightly lower than that of 26.0 reported for the building construction industry (from figures available in the Department of Employment Gazette, 1977 and 1978) a comparison between the rates for light and heavy occupations for the two industries reveals a different picture. The 56 duty codes in the telecommunications industry with lower accident rates (Table 1) have rates significantly less ($P < 0.05$) than the light occupations in the construction industry (from Stubbs & Nicholson, 1979), whereas the top

23 codes have rates not significantly different from the heavy occupations in the construction industry. By undertaking a comprehensive analysis of activities performed by duty code with intra-abdominal pressure measured in field situations, the hypothesis that repeated, frequent high trunk stresses give rise to an increased liability to back injury can be tested. The occupational factors causing these trunk stresses can also be identified.

Figure 2 shows that the 12 of the top 23 duty codes suffering higher than average back injury rates carry out the greatest proportion of activities from groups A, B and C, that is activities giving high mean peak intra-abdominal pressures and performed relatively frequently. Ten of these 12 duty codes work out-of-doors throughout the year. They also do heavy lifting and carrying, often with incorrect working postures. These are factors which have been recognised as causes of, or contributors to degenerative back disease (Brown, 1973; Hult, 1954a,b; Kellgren, Lawrence & Aitken-Swan, 1953; Lawrence, 1955; Niemi & Voutilainen, 1957; Saari & Wickstrom, 1978; Stubbs & Nicholson, 1979; Troup, 1965). The finding that the majority of these activities give rise to intra-abdominal pressures greater than 90 mmHg (12.0 kPa), reinforces the argument that these are the hazardous activities.

The next group of 18 duty codes have varied job requirements (Fig. 2). Eight of this group are included in the top 23 codes, although only three of these perform work outdoors with similar job requirements to those discussed above. Only a further three of these 18 codes perform activities with any component of lifting or manhandling. On the whole, a greater proportion of the activities are from group D. The remaining duties are predominantly of a sedentary nature, many of them being clerical. Very few of the activities give rise to intra-abdominal pressures greater than 90 mmHg (12.0 kPa) and the back injury rate is correspondingly low.

It is therefore clear that those duty codes with the highest back injury rates perform the greatest proportion of activities giving peak intra-abdominal pressures greater than 90 mmHg (12.0 kPa), and some greater than 150 mmHg (20.0 kPa). In addition, these activities are performed relatively frequently compared with other duty codes which have low back injury rates.

The finding that back injuries attributed to handling incidents occur most frequently in the 31-45 year age group, and that 93 per cent of the accidents occur after the first year of employment, suggests that a number of these accidents arise from the cumulative effects of load handling over a number of years.

The decline in accident frequency observed in those over 45 years of age may be the result of several factors. Firstly, most of the works supervisors are aged between 40 and retirement age, and although assigned to a particular occupation, are not involved in active work to the same degree as previously. Secondly, by the time these workers have reached this stage of employment, they are very experienced in their work and are less likely to put themselves into dangerous situations. Thirdly, this group could be considered the 'survivor population' since those who have previously incurred serious injuries, especially to the back, may either have left the industry or been re-employed in lighter duties. Therefore, those remaining are less susceptible to injury or accident.

If only the top 23 duty codes are considered, the distribution of back injuries by age differs from the overall population in that the younger age groups have a relatively higher rate of injury and the middle age groups slightly lower. This earlier onset of back morbidity seen in heavy occupations was also observed by Magora & Taustein (1969); Hult (1954a); Anderson et al. (1962) and others. The observation is also reinforced by considerations of the training policy of the industry. All young recruits follow an apprenticeship of several years during which they are carefully supervised, and recruitment to those outside jobs which constitute the bulk of the top 23 codes is largely from more mature men.

A more detailed investigation of one of the tasks in group A, handling manhole covers and joint boxes, revealed that the two most common manoeuvres, removing and replacing, consisted of two fundamental components, the stoop lift and the pull or drag. Both components have been studied independently in the laboratory and it has been shown that lifting weights comparable to that of covers in a stooped posture commonly induces peak intra-abdominal pressures in excess of 100 mmHg (13.3 kPa). A pull or drag has generally been found to give rise to lower pressures. One way to reduce the level of spinal stress is therefore to correct bad working postures. Much attention has been given to this in industry in recent years in the form of kinetic handling courses, but more emphasis needs to be placed on correcting working postures 'on site' where the worker is often aware of the problems himself.

A second method of minimising the amount of stressful handling activities is to use mechanical or materials handling aids. If these are not well-designed, they may be ignored or rejected by workers, especially if they are time-consuming to use. It is noteworthy that one of the activities recognised as causing unacceptable levels of spinal stress was lifting and moving mechanical aids themselves.

CONCLUSION

These findings give considerable support to the hypothesis that there are differential back injury rates for different jobs in industry depending on the frequency of handling and magnitude of the loads, postural requirements and environmental factors. The study has revealed some work components apparently responsible for the acceleration of degeneration of the spinal structures in telecommunications engineers. It is suggested that these fall into two groups, those causing an acute, sudden injury with little sign of previous degeneration, and those causing gradual degenerative changes resulting in a cumulative injury in latter years.

References

Anderson, J.A.D., Duthie, J.J.R. & Moody, B.P. (1962): Social and economic effects of rheumatic diseases in a mining population. Ann. Rheum. Dis. 21, 324.

Anderson, J.A.D. & Duthie, J.J.R. (1963): Rheumatic complaints in dockyard workers. Ann. Rheum. Dis. 22, 401.

Blow, R.J. & Jackson, J.M. (1971): Rehabilitation of registered dock workers - an analysis of back injuries in registered dock workers. Roy. Soc. Med. Proc. 64, 735.

Brown, J.R. (1973): Lifting as an industrial hazard. Am. Ind. Hyg. Ass. J. 34, 292.

Davis, P.R. (1956): Variations of the intra-abdominal pressure during weight lifting in various postures. J. Anat. 90, 601.

Davis, P.R. & Sheppard, N.J. (1980): Pattern of accident distribution in the telecommunications industry. Br. J. Ind. Med. 37, 175.

Davis, P.R., Stubbs, D.A. & Ridd, J.E. (1977): Radio pills; their use in monitoring back stress. J. Med. Eng. Tech. 4, 209.

Davis, P.R. & Stubbs, D.A. (1977/78): Safe levels of manual forces for young males, 1, 2 & 3. Appl. Ergon. 8, 141; 8, 219; and 9, 33.

Davis, P.R. & Stubbs, D.A. (1978): 'A method of establishing safe handling forces in working situations.' DHEW(NIOSH) Pub. No. 78-185. 34.

Department of Employment Gazette (1977/78): Vols. 85 & 86. London: HMSO.

Farfan, H.F. (1977): A reorientation in the surgical approach to degenerative lumbar intervertebral joint disease. Orthop. Clin. N. Am. 8, 9.

Hirsch, C. (1966): Etiology and pathogenesis of low-back pain. Israel J. Med. Sci. 2, 362.

Horal, J. (1969): The clinical appearance of low back pain disorders in the city of Gothenburg, Sweden. Acta Orthop. Scand. Suppl., 118.

Hult, L. (1954a): Cervical, dorsal and lumbar spine syndromes. Acta Orthop. Scand. Suppl., 17.

Hult, L. (1954b): The Monkfors investigation. Acta Orthop. Scand. Suppl., 16.

Ikata, T. (1965): Statistical and dynamic studies of lesions due to overloading on the spine. Shikoku Acta Med. 40, 262.

Jackson, J.M. (1968): Biomechanical hazards in the dockworker. Ann. Occup. Hyg. 11, 147.

Kellgren, J.H., Lawrence, J.S. & Aitken-Swan, J. (1953): Rheumatic complaints in an urban population. Ann. Rheum. Dis. 12, 5.

Lawrence, J.S. & Aitken-Swan, J. (1952): Rheumatism in miners. Part 1 Rheumatic complaints. Br. J. Indust. Med. 9, 1.

Lawrence, J.S. (1955): Rheumatism in coal miners: Part III occupational factors. Br. J. Indust. Med. 12, 249.

Lawrence, J.S., Molyneux, M.K. & Dingwall-Fordyce, I. (1966): Rheumatism in foundry workers. Br. J. Indust. Med. 23, 42.

Lawrence, J.S. (1969): Disc degeneration: its frequency and relationship to symptoms. Ann. Rheum. Dis. 28, 121.

Magora, A. & Taustein, I. (1969): An investigation of the problem of sick leave in the patient suffering from low back pain. Indust. Med. 38, 80.

Menhert, E. (1969): Degenerative Veränderungen durch statische Fehlbelastung beiden Einlegerinnen der Baumwollspinnereien - eine vermedbare Schädigung der Wirbelsäule. Dtsch. Gesundheitswes. 24, 1716.

Mirabile, M.P. & Simons, G.R. (1972): An analysis and interpretation of industrial medical data. J. Occup. Med. 14, 227.

Morris, J.M., Lucas, D.B. & Bresler, B. (1961): Role of the trunk in stability of the spine. J. Bone Jt. Surg. 43A, 327.

Nachemson, A.L. (1971): Low back pain - its etiology and treatment. Clin. Med. 78, 18.

Niemi, M. & Voutilainen, A. (1957): Back troubles among Finnish postmen. In 'International congress on occupational health', Vol. III, p. 141.

Partridge, R.E.H., Anderson, J.A.D., McCarthy, M.A. & Duthie, J.J.R. (1965): Rheumatism in light industry. Ann. Rheum. Dis. 24, 332.

Partridge, R.E.H., Anderson, J.A.D., McCarthy, M.A. & Duthie, J.J.R. (1968): Rheumatic complaints among workers in iron foundries. Ann. Rheum. Dis. 27, 244.

Rowe, M.L. (1968): Low back pain in industry. J. Occ. Med. 11, 161.

Saari, J.S. & Wickström, G. (1978): Load on back in concrete reinforcement work. Scand. J. Work Environ. Health, 4, Suppl. 1, 13.

Schmorl, G. (1928): Über Knorpelknötchen an den Wirbelbandscheiben. Fortschr. Röntgenstr. 38, 265.

Stubbs, D.A. (1975): Trunk stresses in construction workers. Ph.D. Thesis, University of Surrey, England.

Troup, J.D.G. (1965): Relation of lumbar spine disorders to heavy manual work and lifting. Lancet 1, 857.

Troup, J.D.G., Roantree, W.B. & Archibald, R.M. (1970): Survey of cases of lumbar spine disability. A methodological study. Medical Officer Broadsheet, National Coal Board, UK.

29

The thermographic study of skin after wheelchair sitting

ROBIN BLACK, A.F. FILIPPONE AND G. HAHN

INTRODUCTION

A tissue trauma programme has evolved at the Ontario Crippled Children's Centre (OCCC) in response to the pressure sore problem prevalent in the population of patients with spina bifida. These children are paraplegic from birth, and most will be full-time wheelchair users for the majority of their lives. It was felt that this programme should not only deal with pressure sores on a crisis management basis, but establish a programme of education and seating to prevent the occurrence of the first pressure sore (Hahn & Black, 1978). The Rehabilitation Engineering Department made a substantial contribution to this programme through the design and fitting of wheelchair support systems. In conjunction with this activity, it became necessary to implement measurement techniques which would aid in defining each patient's seating needs, and biomechanical risks. Pressure measurement systems have been used in a number of seating programmes (Rogers et al., 1975 and Manley, 1977) to assess the pressures which are developed over bony prominences during sitting. In this author's view, these measurements are important in determining whether the seating system meets specification set in the clinic, but do not necessarily imply that a particular seating system is safe. Earlier studies (P. Brand, personal communications; Goller, 1971; Mahanty & Roemer, in press), have demonstrated that tissue exposed to increased levels of accumulated stress will show increases in temperature even after relief from this stress. Expanding on these principles, thermography has been used in the tissue trauma programme at OCCC to evaluate the patient's tissues after exposure to the stress of wheelchair sitting.

METHOD

It is necessary to highlight temperature gradients and isotherm patterns when studying the stress response of tissue. For this reason the AGA colour photograph has been used to generate real-time images of these changing isotherm patterns. Selected still thermograph pictures were stored photographically on 110 transparency film in microfiche jackets for ease of comparison and review during follow-up examinations. Time lapse cinematography, at a rate of one frame per three seconds, was used to demonstrate pattern changes and to highlight local variations in cooling rates. These films were reviewed at selected rates on an analysis projector to enhance appreciation of both slow and rapid pattern changes with time.

An isotherm area-meter, developed by the Defence and Civil Institute of Environmental Medicine (DCIEM), was used to quantify the temperature changes. This is an analogue device which inspects an adjustable data window and measures the area of each isotherm as a percentage of the total field of view. A microcomputer was used to sample and store these data for subsequent graphic display. These techniques have been used clinically for three years. During this time qualitative methods for their interpretation have been developed.

The quantitative experiments were conducted with able-bodied subjects in the environmental chamber at DCIEM (Black et al., 1979). Several different wheelchair seat configurations were constructed to provide a variety of pressure levels over the ischial tuberosities during sitting trials. Subjects sat for 30 minutes prior to thermographic examination which lasted 30 minutes. The computer sampled data from the area-meter at regular intervals from both the left and right buttock. Simultaneous sampling of both areas was achieved automatically by switching the visual data window from one side to the other just prior to the data retrieval.

RESULTS

Patient Studies

There are many factors which may complicate the interpretation of thermographic data, some of which are external influences such as the stability of the examination room environment and others are side-effects of factors such as level of activity, drugs, circadian rhythms and presence of pathology. It is, therefore, necessary to acquire a thorough history of each patient. The quality of skin cover on the buttocks is inspected and previous pathology and surgery noted.

There are thermal reactions which we classify as dangerous for any patient. If a rapid hyperthermic response is seen, reaching a maximum temperature two or three minutes after sitting, which then proceeds to cool, the level of sitting stress is considered dangerously high but the tissues healthy. This type of reaction was seen with able-bodied subjects sitting on the high stress experimental seats. If a hyperthermic response is present which continues for more than ten or 15 minutes, then the stress is assessed to be too great for the tissue to tolerate, stimulating an inflammatory response. The maximum skin temperature observed was 37°C, but an extended hyperthermal response may sustain this temperature for more than 30 minutes while the area of tissue at this temperature increases.

The most common type of thermal response begins with the whole surface at an elevated temperature of 35 to 37°C, followed by rapid cooling at differing local rates in the first few minutes until a pattern of isotherms is evident. Areas which have the highest temperatures appear to correspond with those tissues exposed to the highest pressure. The skin temperature pattern can be seen thermographically 15 or 20 minutes after the patient has been transferred from the seat, even though there may be no evidence of erythema or inflammation.

Thermography has been used to assist the design of special seating supports. It is not necessarily the aim of the seating design to attempt to have the same pressure across all of the support surface. Some patients may be most suited to a firm contoured seat which takes advantage of body movements to provide regular pressure relief over weight bearing bony prominences, while others may require a very soft support surface due to their inherent immobility.

Quantitative Studies

The quantitative studies with able-bodied subjects confirmed that high levels of pressure applied to healthy tissue produces a hyperthermic response. This is characterized by the skin reaching a peak temperature within the first three to four minutes of pressure relief. Within the first few seconds of pressure relief, those areas which received very high pressures, in excess of 300 mmHg, exhibited no evidence of any local temperature change compared to the unstressed tissues. Those areas of tissue which received lower levels of stress demonstrated a relatively high initial local temperature, but began to cool immediately.

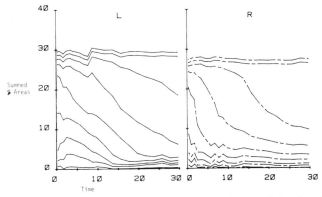

The figure shows quantitative measurements of a subject with a high stress applied to his right ischial tuberosity and a minimal stress to the contralateral side. In the accumulated area plots, the hyperthermic response shows a characteristic concave curve in the initial period of tissue recovery.

DISCUSSION

The tissue trauma programme at OCCC uses a 'design cycle' of patient assessment, prescription of seating, seat fabrication, measurement and evaluation. Thermography plays a major role in this cycle by providing a record of the patient's tolerance to the accumulated stresses of prolonged wheelchair sitting.

Thermographic data have been interpreted primarily by each patient serving as his own control and secondarily by recognising 'unsafe' patterns of response. The isotherms are used to locate sitting stresses and the relative cooling rates of the high and low risk sites provide an indication of the health of the tissues or the safety of the stress.

Quantitative techniques are now being introduced to characterise changes in these isotherm patterns. Our present approach makes use of area measurements. It is expected that with extended experience this analytical technique may only be appropriate for characterising the cooling rates of high risk sites. Other approaches to pattern recognition such as shape definition may extend our ability to interpret these data and facilitate seat design.

Acknowledgements - the authors would like to recognise support from Tent 28 of the Variety Club for making the thermographic equipment available and the Federal Department of Health and Welfare for support of the research programme.

In addition the following individuals have made significant contributions to the programme: Dr M. Milner for guidance within the Rehabilitation Engineering Department; Dr L.D. Reed, Dr S. Livingstone and Mr R.E. Limmer from DCIEM for their collaboration in our Phase I research activities as well as the overall cooperation from DCIEM in our environmental tests.

Thanks are also extended to Miss D. Weiss for her assistance in the preparation of this manuscript.

References

Black, R., Filippone, A.F., Reed, L.D., Livingstone, S.D. & Limmer, R.E. (1979): Seat evaluation by time-lapse and quantitative thermography. Proc. IEEE Conference Digest, Sept. 6, 1979, Toronto, Canada.
Goller, H. (1971): Thermographic studies of human skin subjected to localized pressure. Am. J. Roent. Rad. Ther. Nucl. Med., 113, 749.
Hahn, G. & Black, R. (1978): Ontario Crippled Children's Centre tissue trauma programme. Paraplegia 15, 8689.
Mahanty, S.D. & Roemer, R.B. (in press): Archs. Phys. Med.
Manley, M.T. (1977): The prevention and treatment of pressure sores in the sitting paraplegic. S. Afr. Med. J. 52, 771.
Rogers, J., Edberg, E., Hervey, N. & Rogers, J. (1975): Cushion and pad fitting procedure for the wheelchair confined person. Annual Progress Report, pp . 25-31. Rancho Los Amigos.

30

Biochemical factors in the aetiology and prevention of pressure sores

M. FERGUSON-PELL, J.C. BARBENEL AND J.H. EVANS

INTRODUCTION

Patients vulnerable to pressure sores vary widely in their age, clinical diagnosis and social and economic status. A recent survey of pressure sore prevalence (Jordan & Clark, 1977) has indicated that in the Greater Glasgow Health Board Area approximately 9 per cent of patients receiving professional nursing care in hospital or at home had at least one pressure sore. The majority of these patients (67 per cent) were over 70 years of age. Sixty per cent of those patients with pressure sores were incontinent to some extent.

In the next two decades it is likely that the number of patients having the potential to develop pressure sores will increase dramatically. Norton (1979) quotes an anticipated increase of over 20 per cent in the number of people over 75 years of age between 1976 and 1986, and an increase of 42 per cent in people aged 85 or more by 1996 if current trends continue.

A number of attempts have been made to estimate the cost of pressure sores in monetary terms (Schell & Wolcott, 1966; Newell et al., 1970; Fernie, 1973; McDougall, 1976). Even conservative estimates based on resources allocated in the form of hospital bed occupancy to patients with pressure sores imply expenditure of several hundred million pounds per annum in the UK. Effective measures for prevention and efficient treatment are urgently required in order to conserve scarce clinical resources and to reduce the level of human suffering and additional disablement caused by pressure sores.

In a recent court case (Di Folco versus Glasgow Northern Hospitals Board of Management, Edinburgh Court of Session, 20 Feb. 1975), a patient successfully demonstrated that the pressure sores he developed were the result of an inadequate provision of preventive measures by nursing staff.

The nurse or therapist with the task of specifying a regime to prevent pressure sores often has to face a challenging decision-making problem. Specification of an appropriate care regime will require some of the following factors to be considered: (1) Regular turning of the patient is advisable to reduce periods of ischaemia for tissues over bony prominences and to aid ventilation of vulnerable sites. (2) Observation and documentation of skin condition for vulnerable areas should be

initiated. The skin should be regularly cleansed. The method of
cleansing, in particular whether 'rubbing' or massage should be applied,
is still being disputed. (3) An appropriate support surface has to be
selected. If difficulties with turning the patient, due to burns or
existing pressure sores, are encountered the frequency of turning may
be reduced by using an active support surface such as a ripple mattress
(Bliss & Murray, 1979). The inflation pressure (or hardness) and ripple
frequency for the mattress are often required to be set by the user but
criteria for obtaining the correct settings are often vague. Even
conventional foam mattresses require the correct thickness, density of
foam and mattress cover to be chosen to suit the individual patient.
Bed sheets that are 'tucked in' are thought to produce hammocking,
whereas those that are not are liable to produce possibly injurous
creases. For some patients a sheepskin, synthetic or genuine, may be
appropriate. (4) Accessories such as a suitable wheelchair cushion,
rest chair, sheepskin heel or ankle pads, thick foam bathmats,
inflatable toilet seats, and transferring boards have implications for
some patients in preventing pressure sores.

AETIOLOGICAL FACTORS

The continuing development and evaluation of equipment for patients
vulnerable to pressure sores and techniques for prevention is dependent
in part upon an understanding of the aetiology of sores. Barton (1979)
suggests that there are two types of pressure sore. The first type is
developed following prolonged ischaemia and the second results from
damage to tissue vasculature. Tissue damage resulting from severe or
repetitive insult, for example on operating table or caused by poorly
fitting prosthetic sockets, is likely to fall in the second category.
Pressure sores developed by patients in bed or sitting in wheelchairs
are likely to be of the first type, apart from superficial injuries
resulting from the maceration of tissues exposed to urine, faeces, or
perspiration.
    Occlusion of blood vessels and lymphatics in tissues overlying bony
prominences occurs as tissues are deformed when transmitting body weight
and other forces to the support surface. The spatial distribution of
these forces may be represented as stress components vertical and
horizontal to the plane of the skin. The relationships between stresses
at the skin/support interface and the potentially damaging deformations
in the tissues are unknown and are likely to be extremely complex.
    The duration for which ischaemic conditions can be tolerated is
thought to be inversely related to the amplitude of the associated
normal stress, or pressure, generated in the tissues (Trumble, 1930;
Husain, 1953; Kosiak, 1959; Lindan, 1961; Willms-Kretschmer & Majno,
1969). Reswick & Rogers (1976) have produced suggested guidelines (Fig.
1) for the pressure-time tolerance of tissues. Such guidelines can at
best only be approximate as numerous additional clinical factors are
likely to modify the vulnerability of tissues to ischaemia. Schell &
Wolcott (1966) suggest that the following factors may be implicated in
pressure sore aetiology: (1) *Physical*: pressure, heat, moisture,
friction, shearing force, hygiene. (2) *Nutrition*: general
undernutrition, specific nutritional deficiencies (eg protein, ascorbic

acid). (3) *Anaemia*. (4) *Infection*.

PRESSURE MEASUREMENTS ON HOSPITAL MATTRESSES

A complete evaluation of support surfaces would include the measurement of both the horizontal (shear) and vertical (pressure) components of mechanical stress at the body/support interface. Considerable difficulty has been encountered in the design and development of suitable shear stress sensors (Bennett et al., 1979; Tappin et al., 1980) that are sufficiently small and thin for accurate measurement. The study reported below considered only the differences in pressure over the bony prominences of patients and able-bodied subjects.

Four low-profile (0.3 mm x 10 mm) pressure sensors (Ferguson-Pell et al., 1976) were placed on each trochanter of a group of five healthy volunteers. The volunteer was asked to lie on the mattress/cover/sheet configuration under test. This was supported on a standard King's Fund bed. Readings were taken with the body in a specified posture with the legs extended in line with the trunk and the inter-trochanteric axis vertical. Six readings for each pressure sensor were recorded, repositioning the body afresh on each occasion. The following mattress/cover configurations were tested: (a) Flexible polyether foam (density 32-34 kg/m³) covered with a water-permeable, knitted, two-way stretch cover and a single sheet. (b) As in (a) but fitted with plastic and linen draw-sheets in addition to the single sheet. (c) Flexible polyether foam (density 32-34 kg/m³) covered with a two-way stretch waterproof cover (made from material supplied by Clutsom-Penn, UK No. 31902) and a single sheet. (d) As in (a) but fitted with a non-stretch waterproof nylon cover. No draw-sheet was fitted. This mattress/cover configuration is in widespread use and is used in the analysis below as a standard against which to compare the other mattresses.
(e) 'Polyflotation' mattresses (Talley, UK and Scimedics, USA) 150 mm thick (50 mm more than (a)) with orthogonal cuts made in top surface. Covered by a single sheet only. (f) As in (e) but fitted with plastic and linen draw-sheets in addition to the single sheet. (g) Interior-sprung mattress fitted with a waterproof non-stretch cover and a single sheet.

The grand mean of the readings taken for each mattress configuration was calculated (Table 1). Comparisons between the mattresses tested were made using Student's t-test. The results for each mattress were compared with the 'standard' mattress (d).

The interior-sprung mattress (g) was found to produce a mean pressure that was significantly higher than that for the standard mattress (d) (P<0.001). Significantly lower pressures were developed on mattresses (a) and (b), the polyether mattresses fitted with the two-way stretch water-permeable cover. The two-way stretch waterproof cover was not found to produce a significantly lower pressure for mattress (c), possibly due to its only moderate extensibility.

A comparison between mattresses (a) and (b) indicates a marginally significant difference (P=0.1) due to the presence of draw-sheets. A similar result was obtained comparing mattresses (e) and (f).

The series of pressure measurements was repeated using the electro-pneumatic Pressure Evaluator developed by Reswick & Rogers (1976)

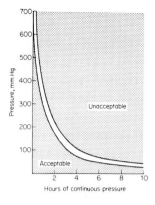

Fig. 1. Suggested guidelines for maximum duration of ischaemia in tissues over bony prominences according to the magnitude of the interface pressure present (after Reswick & Rogers, 1976)

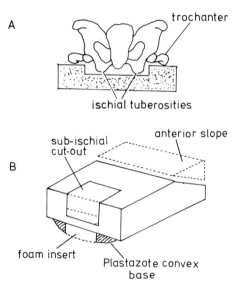

Fig. 2. (a) Pressure relief for the sitting spinal injury patient in tissues over bony prominences is provided by removal of a rectangular section of foam to half the thickness of the block used such that body weight is borne by the trochanteric shelf and the proximal thighs. (b) Other options are available, for example the provision of a convex 'Plastazote' base to take up sag in the wheelchair sling-seat, an anterior slope to simplify transferring, and various sizes and depths of ischial cut-out

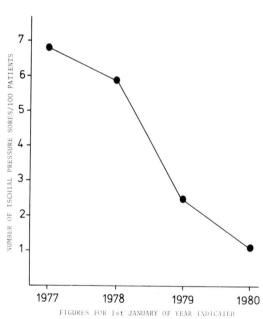

Fig. 3. Reduction in number of admissions for treatment of ischial pressure sores in spinal patients at Philipshill Hospital, Glasgow, following introduction of individual wheelchair cushion fitting programme in January 1976

Table 1. *Variations in mean pressure measured using four low-profile capacitive pressure transducers placed over the trochanters of five healthy subjects according to mattress type*

Mattress type	Mean pressure		Standard deviation	
	mmHg	kPa	mmHg	kPa
A	44	5.8	25	3.3
B	52	6.9	35	4.6
C	57	7.6	33	4.4
D	59	7.8	30	4.0
E	62	8.2	37	4.9
F	69	9.2	45	6.0
G	87	11.6	53	7.0

Table 2. *Variation in mean trochanteric pressure on different mattress/ cover configurations for healthy subjects using an electro-pneumatic Pressure Evaluator*

Mattress type	Mean pressure		Standard deviation	
	mmHg	kPa	mmHg	kPa
A	52	6.9	8	1.1
B	54	7.2	11	1.5
C	55	7.3	9	1.2
D	58	7.7	11	1.5
E	54	7.2	9	1.2
F	55	7.3	9	1.2
G	103	13.7	29	3.8

Table 3. *Pressures developed by a group of nine spinal injury patients on different mattress/cover configurations. Trochanteric pressures were measured using an electro-pneumatic Pressure Evaluator*

Mattress type	Mean pressure		Standard deviation	
	mmHg	kPa	mmHg	kPa
A	97	12.9	29	3.9
B	not tested			
C	105	14.0	32	4.3
D	119	15.8	31	4.1
E	72	9.6	15	2.0
F	not tested			
G	154	20.5	52	6.9

(Talley UK) fitted with a 100 mm diameter sensing pad. The Pressure
Evaluator is designed to measure the peak pressure over the bony
prominence of interest whereas the array of sensors used in the
measurements described above provided a value for the average pressure
over the apex of the trochanters.

The results in Table 2 were obtained for the same group of healthy
volunteers using similar methods to those adopted for measurements made
using the capacitive sensors. Minor differences in pressure between
different support configurations shown by the capacitive sensors were
not detected by the Pressure Evaluator. It is possible that the action
of inflating the electro-pneumatic device substantially perturbs the
region being measured.

An additional limited series of measurements was undertaken using the
Pressure Evaluator with a group of nine spinal injury patients. This
was intended to establish any differences between the interface
pressures developed by patients and the group of healthy subjects (Table 3).

Statistical comparison between the results obtained for the patients
and healthy subjects indicates a significantly higher mean pressure
developed by the patients on the mattress/cover configurations tested.
The overall mean pressure for the healthy subjects on all the mattresses
was 64 mmHg (8.5 kPa) and 109 mmHg (14.5 kPa) for the patients. This
difference is significant at the P<0.001 level. The ranking of the
mattresses according to mean pressure was similar for both patients and
healthy subjects apart from the Polyflotation mattress which ranks more
favourably for the group of patients.

WHEELCHAIR FITTING PROGRAMME

Many of the techniques developed in the evaluation of the hospital
mattresses described above are directly applicable to the problem of
supplying simple effective support surfaces for patients vulnerable to
pressure sores who sit for prolonged periods in wheelchairs.

Based on the principles of the Pressure Clinic established by Rogers
(1974) at Rancho Los Amigos Hospital a similar facility was created by
the authors at Philipshill Hospital in Glasgow. For simplicity of use
in the clinical environment the Pressure Evaluator described above is
preferred to the capacitive device for obtaining readings of interface
pressure beneath the ischial tuberosities of patients sitting on a
wheelchair cushion.

Using the criterion that the pressure beneath the ischial tuberosities
of spinal injury patients should not exceed 40 mmHg (5.3 kPa) for
effective reduction of the risk of pressure sores (Ferguson-Pell et al.,
1980) a group of 150 spinal injury patients have been fitted with
cushions manufactured from blocks of high density polyether foam. The
foam blocks are modified by local removal of material from the region of
the ischial tuberosities in order to obtain an acceptable distribution
of pressure. These modifications are usually in the form of a
rectangular cut-out, half the thickness of the foam block into which the
ischial tuberosities locate (Fig. 2).

The objectives of this procedure are to reduce the sub-ischial
pressure to less than 40 mmHg (5.3 kPa) but while using the simplest
series of modifications to the foam block which meet all the patient's

postural and functional requirements. For a small number of patients this has meant that either a simple plain block of foam or even their existing cushion suffices. For others any one or a combination of the options in Fig. 2 may be required.

The cushions are fitted with two-way stretch covers and patients are discouraged from placing incontinence pads or blankets over the cushion. This ensures that interface pressures are maintained at a satisfactory level.

For a few patients it has been found difficult to reduce interface pressure to the required 40 mmHg level. This is often because they are emaciated with little tissue covering extremely prominent ischial tuberosities or are scoliotic and load one ischial tuberosity excessively. Such patients are provided with a cushion that provides maximum pressure relief and are then asked to increase the frequency of their 'push-ups' thereby reducing the duration of periods of ischaemia. These patients are asked to be particularly vigilant in care of their skin.

The cushion-fitting programme has been operating for four years and the reduction in pressure sore incidence among spinal injury patients associated with Philipshill Hospital has been monitored. In the period December 1975 to December 1978 the proportion of patients admitted with ischial sores compared with the number of patients admitted with pressure sores on other body sites was reduced from 68 per cent to 43 per cent. Figure 3 indicates the reduction in patient admissions with ischial pressure sores as a percentage of all spinal injury patients associated with the hospital. The number of in-patient days per patient per year required for treatment of ischial pressure sores has fallen from 4.8 days in 1976 to 3.1 days in 1979. No other change in patient treatment has been introduced in this period that could account for these improvements.

Although improvements can and should be made in the supply and use of conventional mattresses in order to reduce interface pressures, there are still likely to be patients vulnerable to pressure sores with interface pressures considerably higher than average. In an attempt to identify these patients it is suggested that interface pressure should be introduced as a factor in the active scoring of patients at risk for developing pressure sores. One major difficulty with introducing such measurements would be that of establishing a reliable maximum pressure threshold or pressure versus risk scale for groups of recumbent patients.

Until the physiological significance of interface pressure is more fully understood, the combination of pressure optimisation for the individual and regular turning might produce beneficial results in much the same way as has been achieved in the wheelchair cushion-fitting programme. Even if objective pressures cannot be met in all cases the fact that a measurement has been made helps to identify the patient at risk and should encourage greater vigilance and preferential care.

References

Barton, A.A. (1979): Underlying causes. In 'The prevention of pressure sores'. Proceedings of the conference organised by the Nursing Practice Research Unit and DHSS, Northwick Park Hospital, 25 June 1979.

Bennett, L., Karner, D., Lee, B.K. & Trainer, F.A. (1979): Shear vs
  pressure as causative factors in blood flow occlusion. Archs. Phys.
  Med. Rehab. 60, 309.
Bliss, M. & Murray, E. (1979): The use of ripple beds. Nursing Times,
  Feb. 15, 280.
Ferguson-Pell, M.W., Bell, F. & Evans, J.H. (1976): Interface pressure
  sensors - existing devices, their suitability and limitations. In
  'Bed sore biomechanics', ed R.M. Kenedi, J.M. Cowden & J.T. Scales.
  London: Macmillan.
Ferguson-Pell, M.W., Wilkie, I.C., Reswick, J.B. & Barbenel, J.C. (1980):
  Pressure sore prevention for the wheelchair-bound spinal injury
  patient. Paraplegia, 18, 42.
Fernie, G.R. (1973): Biomechanical aspects of the aetiology of
  decubitus ulcers on human patients. Ph.D. thesis, University of
  Strathclyde.
Husain, T. (1953): Experimental study of some pressure effects on
  tissue - with respect to the bedsore problem. J. Path. Bact. 66, 347.
Jordan, M.M. & Clark, M.O. (1977): Report on the incidence of pressure
  sores in the patient community of the Greater Glasgow Health Board
  Area on 21 January, 1976.
Kosiak, M. (1959): Etiology and pathology of ischaemic ulcers. Archs.
  Phys. Med. Rehab. 40, 62.
Lindan, O. (1961): Etiology of decubitus ulcers: an experimental study.
  Archs. Phys. Med. Rehab. 42, 747.
McDougall, A. (1976): In 'Bed sore biomechanics', ed R.M. Kenedi,
  J.M. Cowden & J.T. Scales, pp. 181-164. London: Macmillan.
Newell, P.H., Thornburgh, J.D. & Fleming, W.C. (1970): The management
  of pressure and other external factors in the prevention of ischaemic
  ulcers. Trans. ASME. J. Basic Eng. 590.
Norton, D. (1979): Extent and nature of the problem. In 'The
  prevention of pressure sores'. Proceedings of the conference
  organised by the Nursing Practice Research Unit and DHSS, at Northwick
  Park Hospital, 25 June 1979.
Reswick, J.B. & Rogers, J.E. (1976): Experience at Rancho Los Amigos
  Hospital with devices and techniques to prevent pressure sores. In
  'Bed sore biomechanics', ed R.M. Kenedi, J.M. Cowden & J.T. Scales,
  pp. 301-310. London: Macmillan.
Rogers, J.E. (1974): Position and seating. In 'Annual report of
  progress', Rehabilitation Center at Rancho Los Amigos Hospital.
Schell, V.C. & Wolcott, L.E. (1966): The aetiology and management of
  decubitus ulcers. Missouri Med. 63, 109.
Tappin, I.W., Pollard, J. & Beckett, E.A. (1980): Method of measuring
  'shearing' forces on the sole of the foot. Clin. Phys. Physiol. Meas.
  1, 83.
Trumble, H.C. (1930): The skin tolerance for pressure and pressure
  sores. Med. J. Austr. Nov. 29, 724.
Willms-Kretschmer, K. & Majno, G. (1969): Ischaemia of the skin. Am.
  J. Path. 54, 327.

Acknowledgements - the work reported was carried out at the
Bioengineering Unit, Strathclyde University, Glasgow (Professors R.M.
Kenedi and J.P. Paul) and at Philipshill Hospital, Busby, Glasgow. The
authors wish to thank Dr I.C. Wilkie and Dr I. Seymour for their
contributions to the work reported. This study was made possible by a
grant from the Scottish Home and Health Department.

The authors:

M.A. Adams (Ch. 4): The Polytechnic of Central London, 115 New Cavendish Street, London, W1, England.

Andrew A. Amis (Ch. 6): Mechanical Engineering Department, Imperial College of Science and Technology, Exhibition Road, London SW7, England.

J.C. Barbenel (Ch. 7, 30): Bioengineering Unit, University of Strathclyde, Wolfson Centre, Glasgow G4 0NW, Scotland.

Edmund Biden (Ch. 9): Department of Engineering Science, Oxford University, Parks Road, Oxford, OX1 3PJ, England.

Robin Black (Ch. 29): Ontario Crippled Children's Centre, 350 Rumsey Road, Toronto, Ontario, M4G 1R8, Canada.

D.H. Bossingham (Ch. 24): Department of Rheumatology, Nuffield Orthopaedic Centre, Headington, Oxford OX3 7LD, England.

P.M. Braiden (Ch. 8): Department of Engineering Science, University of Durham, South Road, Durham DH1 3LE, England.

D.P. Brenton (Ch. 20): Department of Human Metabolism, Rayne Institute, University College Hospital Medical School, University Street, London WC1E 6JJ, England.

P. Brinckmann (Ch. 2): Orthopedic Hospital, University of Munster, Department of Biomechanics, Hufferstrasse 27, D-4400 Munster, Federal Republic of Germany.

Aurelio Cappozzo (Ch. 3): Laboratory of Biomechanics, Istituto di Fisiologia Umana, Università degli Studi, Rome, Italy.

J.D. Currey (Ch. 14): Department of Biology, University of York, York YO1 5DD, England.

P.R. Davis (Ch. 28): Department of Human Biology and Health, and Materials Handling Research Unit, University of Surrey, Guildford GU2 5XH, Surrey, England.

D. Dowson (Ch. 6): Department of Mechanical Engineering, University of Leeds, Leeds 2, England.

R.H.T. Edwards (Ch. 20): Department of Human Metabolism, Rayne Institute, University College Hospital Medical School, University Street, London WC1E 6JJ, England.

J.H. Evans (Ch. 30): University of Strathclyde, Bioengineering Unit, Wolfson Centre, Glasgow G4 0NW, Scotland.

M. Evans (Ch. 16): Oxford Orthopaedic Engineering Centre, Nuffield Orthopaedic Centre, Headington, Oxford OX3 7LD, England.

M. Ferguson-Pell (Ch. 30): University of Strathclyde, Bioengineering Unit, Wolfson Centre, Glasgow G4 0NW, Scotland.

A.F. Filippone (Ch. 29): Ontario Crippled Children's Centre, 350 Rumsey Road, Toronto, Ontario, M4G 1R8, Canada.

W. Frobin (Ch. 2): Orthopedic Hospital, University of Munster, Department of Biomechanics, Hufferstrasse 27, D-4400 Munster, Federal Republic of Germany.

L.J. Gathercole (Ch. 21): University of Bristol, H.H. Wills Physics Laboratory, Bristol BS8 1TL, England.

John Goodfellow (Ch. 9, 22): Nuffield Orthopaedic Centre, Headington, Oxford OX3 7LD, England.

A.E. Goodship (Ch. 13): Department of Anatomy, School of Veterinary Science, Park Row, Bristol England.

P.B. Guyer (Ch. 26): X-Ray Department, Royal South Hants Hospital, Southampton, England.

G. Hahn (Ch. 29): Ontario Crippled Children's Centre, 350 Rumsey Road, Toronto, Ontario, M4G 1R8, Canada.

J.D. Harris (Ch. 16): Oxford Orthopaedic Engineering Centre, Nuffield Orthopaedic Centre, Headington, Oxford OX3 7LD, England.

E. Hierholzer (Ch. 2): Orthopedic Hospital, University of Munster, Department of Biomechanics, Hufferstrasse 27, D-4400 Munster, Federal Republic of Germany.

A. Horsman (Ch. 14): M.R.C. Mineral Metabolism Unit, The General Infirmary, Great George Street, Leeds LS1 3EX, England.

G.R. Houghton (Ch. 18): Nuffield Orthopaedic Centre, Headington, Oxford OX3 7LD, England.

W.C. Hutton (Ch. 4): The Polytechnic of Central London, 115 New Cavendish Street, London W1, England.

S.A. Jackson (Ch. 19): Department of Medical Physics, University Hospital, Queen's Medical Centre, Nottingham NG7 2UH, England.

D.A. Jones (Ch. 20): Department of Human Metabolism, Rayne Institute, University College Hospital Medical School, University Street, London WC1E 6JJ, England.

G.E. Kempson (Ch. 27): Department of Medical Engineering, Level D, Centre Block, Southampton General Hospital, SO9 4XY, England.

J. Kenwright (Ch. 16): Nuffield Orthopaedic Centre, Headington, Oxford OX3 7LD, England.

S. Khodadadeh (Ch. 11): Oxford Orthopaedic Engineering Centre, Nuffield Orthopaedic Centre, Headington, Oxford OX3 7LD, England.

L.E. Lanyon (Ch. 12, 13): Department of Anatomy, School of Veterinary Science, Park Row, Bristol, England.

A.K. McQueen (Ch. 24): Nuffield Department of Orthopaedic Surgery, Nuffield Orthopaedic Centre, Headington, Oxford OX3 7LD, England.

M. Martens (Ch. 15): Katholieke Universiteit Leuven, Academisch Ziekenhuis Pellenberg, Weligerveld 1, B-3041 Pellenberg, Belgium.

P.A. Medlicott (Ch. 5): Accident Service, John Radcliffe Hospital, Oxford OX3 9DU, England.

J.H. Miller (Ch. 6): Accident and Orthopaedic Division, Royal Infirmary, Glasgow G4 0SF, Scotland.

R.J. Minns (Ch. 8): Bioengineering Laboratory, Department of Medical Physics, Nuffield Ward, Dryburn Hospital, Durham DH1 5TW, England.

A.G. Mowat (Ch. 24): Department of Rheumatology, Nuffield Orthopaedic Centre, Headington, Oxford OX3 7LD, England.

A.S. Nicholson (Ch. 28): Materials Handling Research Unit, Institute of Industrial & Environmental Health and Safety, University of Surrey, Guildford GU2 5XH, Surrey, England.

J.A. O'Connor (Ch. 13): Department of Anatomy, School of Veterinary Science, Park Row, Bristol, England.

John O'Connor (Ch. 9): Department of Engineering Science, Oxford University, Parks Road, Oxford OX1 3PJ, England.

Z.A. Ráliš (Ch. 17): Department of Traumatic & Orthopaedic Surgery, Welsh National School of Medicine, Royal Infirmary, Cardiff CF2 1SZ, Wales.

G.D. Rooker (Ch. 18): Nuffield Orthopaedic Centre, Headington, Oxford OX3 7LD, England.

C.T. Rubin (Ch. 13): Department of Anatomy, School of Veterinary Science, Park Row, Bristol, England.

B.B. Seedhom (Ch. 1, 25): Rheumatism Research Unit, University of Leeds, England.

J.S. Shah (Ch. 21): University of Bristol, H.H. Wills Physics Laboratory, Bristol BS8 1TL, England.

N.J. Sheppard (Ch. 28): Materials Handling Research Unit, Institute of Industrial & Environmental Health and Safety, University of Surrey, Guildford GU2 5XH, England.

Ian A.F. Stokes (Ch. 5, 11): Oxford Orthopaedic Engineering Centre, Nuffield Orthopaedic Centre, Oxford OX3 7LD, England; Present address: University of Vermont, Department of Orthopaedic Surgery, Given Building, Burlington, VT 05405, USA.

D.A. Stubbs (Ch. 28): Materials Handling Research Unit, Institute of Industrial & Environmental Health and Safety, University of Surrey, Guildford GY2 5XH, Surrey, England.

T. Takeda (Ch. 25): Keio Medical School, Department of Orthopaedic Surgery, Keio University, Tokyo, Japan.

R. Van Audekercke (Ch. 15): Katholieke Universiteit Leuven, I.C.O.B.I. — Biomechanics Section, Celestijnenlaan 200A, B-3030 Heverlee, Belgium.

J. Vandecasteele (Ch. 15): Katholieke Universiteit Leuven, I.C.O.B.I. — Biomechanics Section, Celestijnenlaan 200A, B-3030 Heverlee, Belgium.

G. Van de Perre (Ch. 15): Katholieke Universiteit Leuven, I.C.O.B.I. — Biomechanics Section, Celestijnenlaan 200A, B-3030 Heverlee, Belgium.

W. Waugh (Ch. 23): Department of Orthopaedic and Accident Surgery, Queen's Medical Centre, Nottingham, England.

M.W. Whittle (Ch. 10, 11): Oxford Orthopaedic Engineering Centre, Nuffield Orthopaedic Centre, Headington, Oxford OX3 7LD, England.

V. Wright (Ch. 6, 25): Rheumatism Research Unit, School of Medicine, University of Leeds, Leeds 2, England.

A. Young (Ch. 20): Oxford Rehabilitation Research Unit, Nuffield Orthopaedic Centre, Headington, Oxford, England.

Index